MACHINE SHOP
TRAINING COURSE

MACHINE SHOP
TRAINING COURSE

VOLUME I

A Comprehensive Treatise on Machine Shop Practice Including Fundamental Principles; Methods of Adjusting and Using Different Types of Machine Tools, with Typical Examples of Work; Measuring Instruments and Gages; Cutting Screw Threads by Different Processes; Thread Grinding; Gear Cutting; Precision Toolmaking Methods; Typical Shop Problems with Solutions; and Miscellaneous Facts Relating to the Art of Machine Construction.

BY

FRANKLIN D. JONES

INDUSTRIAL PRESS INC.

200 MADISON AVENUE, NEW YORK 10016

Fifth Edition
18 20 19

CONTENTS OF VOLUME 1

The "MACHINE SHOP TRAINING COURSE" consists of two volumes. Contents of Volume 2 will be found on the page following.

CONTENTS OF VOLUME 2

Principles Underlying All Metal-Cutting Operations

This treatise deals with principles, tools and processes which are utilized in all types of machine shops or machine-building plants. The information is largely fundamental in character, and the various tools and processes described are applicable in making many different classes of machines and other mechanical products. While machine building, in a broad sense, embraces every craft and process from the making of patterns, castings, forgings, stampings, etc., to the exact procedure in finishing and assembling of parts, this course of instruction applies principally to the work of the machine shop because of the general demand for such information and its usefulness in vocational schools and in the industrial training departments of manufacturing plants. The applications of different types of machine tools are explained, and there are many other subjects which are closely allied to the metal-cutting operations performed on these tools.

In building any machine, what, in general, is the work of the machine shop?

If the work of the machine shop is merely summarized in a few words, the building of any machine consists principally in making each part of that machine to the required shape and to the required size, by utilizing practical economical methods. The assembling of these parts is, of course, the final job. In producing the individual parts, certain principles underlying the metal-cutting and other operations may be applied to machine-building practice in general and regardless of the particular type of machine.

In assembling these parts, the exact procedure naturally varies according to the design of the machine; consequently, in treatises on machine-building practice, a great deal of useful information can be given about the machines, tools, methods, and principles employed in producing the individual parts; but it is impracticable to explain just how parts must be assembled, simply because the assembling procedure varies for each type of machine—and the number of different types is endless.

Now, in order to obtain a clear understanding of the fundamental principles in machine building, suppose we begin by placing a typical machine upon the dissecting table. If a rather complicated machine is selected, it may be impressive when seen at work and appear to be very complicated. But assume that it is taken apart and each detail examined; then the various shafts, gears, levers, etc., when viewed separately, are not complicated. This illustrates an important fact regarding both the design and construction of a machine—namely, that it is a step-by-step process, and building machines consists chiefly in learning how to make the shafts, pins, screws, levers, gears, or other parts which, when assembled, form the complete machine. Most machines and other mechanical devices consist largely of these comparatively simple individual parts. The production of most machine parts is not especially difficult, when certain fundamental principles are understood. The job, however, generally is not one of mere production by any possible method. For example, whenever any part can be produced by more than one method, which frequently is the case, then the selection of an approved method usually requires a broad knowledge of machine shop processes.

What shapes are the most common for machine parts?

Finished surfaces of cylindrical form are more prevalent than any other, although flat surfaces are also very common; hence, many metal-cutting processes are for the purpose of producing either cylindrical or flat surfaces. The machines used for cylindrical or flat shapes may be, and often are, utilized also for forming the various irregular or special shapes required on many machine parts. Because of the prevalence of cylindrical and flat surfaces, the student of manufacturing practice should learn first about the machines and methods employed to produce these surfaces. The cylindrical surfaces may be external as on shafts, pins, etc., or they may be internal as in holes and cylinders. Any one part may, of course, have cylindrical sections of different diameters and lengths and include flat ends or shoulders and frequently there is a threaded part or possibly some finished surface that is not circular in cross-section.

The prevalence of cylindrical surfaces on machine parts explains why lathes or machines belonging to the lathe family are found in all machine shops. It is important to understand the various uses of the lathe because many of the operations are the same fundamentally as those performed on other types of machine tools. The machines used for producing flat surfaces represent another very important group.

What are the general methods of forming cylindrical and flat surfaces?

External cylindrical surfaces usually are machined (1) by turning; (2) by grinding or by grinding after turning. The turning may be done in some type of lathe such as engine lathe, bench lathe if the parts are small, or in a turret lathe. The boring mill, the automatic screw machine, or some other type of "automatic" may also be used. (The application of these machines will be explained later.)

Internal cylindrical surfaces in the form of holes cut from solid metal are formed by drilling which may be followed by boring, reaming or grinding to secure greater accuracy and smoothness of finish. If the operation is that of machining or truing the inner surfaces of ring-shaped castings or forgings, this is done by boring unless the holes are small enough to be finished more readily by using a reamer designed for work of this kind. Internal grinding may follow boring or even a reaming operation in order to secure greater accuracy.

Flat surfaces may be formed by milling, planing, grinding and broaching. Whenever more than one method or type of machine is applicable to a given class of work, the type selected usually depends either upon the quantity of parts to be turned, upon the size or shape, or upon both of these factors and possibly certain others. This question of selecting the right type of machine, particularly when more than one type *might* be used, is a very important one and will be considered more fully later. All of the metal-cutting operations referred to are performed on machines which are known as "machine tools."

What is the meaning of the term "machine tool" and does it apply to all metal-cutting machines?

The general term "machine tool" is applied to various classes of power-driven metal-cutting machines such as are used in machine shops. There are, however, certain types of machines used in machine-building practice which, strictly speaking, may not be classed as machine tools. There have been a number of attempts to define a machine tool so as to leave no doubt as to the intended meaning or as to the type of machine belonging under this general classification. For example, machine tools have been defined as machines which, when taken as a group, will reproduce themselves. This definition has the disadvantage of being general rather than specific, and as a secondary definition the following has been suggested: "A machine tool is any metal-working tool the waste from which is in the form of chips." This definition is specific and can easily be applied to any particular machine, although it does not include every type of machine used in machine building. It is not necessary to define a metal "chip," but it may be advisable to recall that a grinding machine produces chips, even though small. This chip classification method includes all metal-cutting machinery the action of which is a progressive cutting away of surplus stock—a gradual reduction in size until the finished dimensions are reached—but excludes sheet-metal working machinery and metal-forming and forging machines. A press, when used for piercing sheet metal, has very little in common with a lathe, a milling machine, or a planer. They are all metal-cutting machines, but here the similarity ceases. When a press is used for forming, it has nothing in common with lathes, etc., other than the fact that they are all metal-*working* machines, as are also power hammers, bulldozers, swaging machines, etc.

What are the chief functions of a machine tool?

Most machine tools perform some metal-cutting operation, although there are exceptions if we include in the machine tool classification those machines that form parts by the application of pressure, blows or by an abrading process which may not always be a cutting operation. In general, the function of a machine tool, such as the lathe, planer milling machine, drilling machine, broaching machine, etc., is to hold both the work and a cutting tool (or tools) and move them relative to each other to obtain the proper cutting action and at an economical speed. Machine tools, generally speaking, serve four main purposes: (1) They hold the work or part to be cut; (2) they hold the cutting tool or tools; (3) they impart to the cutting tool or work, or to both tool and work, whatever motion is required for cutting or forming the part; (4) they are arranged ordinarily for regulating the cutting speed and also the feeding movement between the tool and work. The work-holding device generally is a separate attachment, and in many cases it is designed especially for holding a given class of work. These special work-holding chucks or fixtures constitute a very important part of shop equipment, especially where duplicate parts are produced in large quantities, thus making it essential to place an unfinished part quickly and accurately in the working position and release it readily when the machining operation is completed.

What operations are utilized in all machine shop practice?

Practically all machine parts require more or less cutting and finishing in some type of machine to obtain the required form and size. Machine parts may be cast or forged to the approximate shape required, or they may be produced directly from bars of steel, brass, or some other material. Even when castings or forgings are used, some "machining" generally is required. (The word "machining" is used frequently in connection with machine shop practice and it means cutting away metal with some type of power-driven "machine tool" to obtain a required shape, dimension, and finish.)

In the production of machine parts of various shapes

and sizes, the type of machine and cutting tool used depends upon the nature of the metal-cutting operation, the character of the work, and possibly other factors such as the number of parts required and degree of accuracy that is essential. In machining a part to obtain a certain size, form, or degree of finish, the operation may consist of turning, boring, drilling, planing, milling, grinding, broaching, or some other operation, and two or more of these operations often are required. The edged tools used for these various metal-cutting operations include quite a wide range of shapes and may appear to have nothing in common; but metal-cutting tools in general conform to certain fundamental principles in so far as the cutting action is concerned. These principles will first be illustrated and described as applied to certain common metal-cutting operations. Later their application to different types of machine tools will be shown.

Upon what general principle is the art of metal cutting based?

The cutting of metals, as applied under practical conditions, is based upon the principle that an edged tool will "cut" or shear off metals, provided (1) the tool is harder than the metal; (2) the tool is so shaped that its edge can be effective in cutting or shearing off the metal; (3) the tool is strong or rigid enough to resist the cutting pressure but keen enough to sever the metal; (4) and provided there is movement of the tool relative to the material, or vice versa, so as to make cutting action possible.

Most metal cutting is done by means of steel tools. In modern shop practice, however, certain special cutting materials which are even harder and more durable than hardened steel are also used as described later. When steel tools are used, they are hardened (or hardened and then tempered to make them tougher and less brittle by some sacrifice of hardness). Any of these hard tools will cut unhardened steel and other metals such as cast iron, brass, aluminum alloys, etc. But it is essential to have the cutting end of the tool so formed or shaped that it will cut efficiently and at the same time be durable enough to cut for a reasonable length of time before sharpening is required.

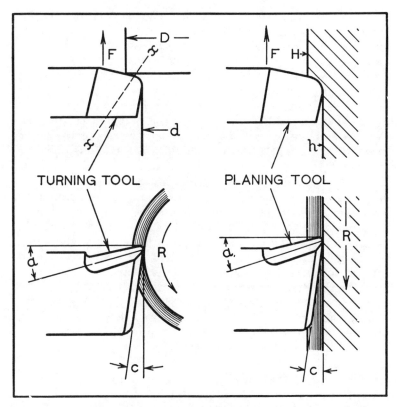

Fig. 1. Diagrams Illustrating Fundamental Principles Relating to the Cutting of Metals

How is the metal-cutting principle applied in turning a cylindrical surface?

The diagram at the left in Fig. 1 illustrates how metal is cut by turning, as in a lathe. The turning tool is held rigidly in some form of holder. The part to be turned rotates in direction R and the tool feeds along continuously in direction F, parallel to the axis of the part being turned; consequently, the part is reduced from some diameter D to some other diameter d, depending upon the requirements in each case. The upper surface of the tool against which the chip bears as it is being severed usually is ground to

some "rake" angle a to make the edge keener and lessen
cutting resistance. (There are exceptions to this rule as
explained later in the section on Single-Point Tool Forms
and Tool Grinding.) This top or chip-bearing surface generally slopes away from that part or section of the cutting
edge which normally does the cutting; hence, usually there
is both backward and side slope or a back rake angle and
a side rake angle. (The angle a of the diagram is intended
to represent the combined back and side angles or the angle
in some plane x-x.) If this inclination a is excessive, the
tool point will be weakened; on the other hand, if there is
no inclination, the tool will still remove metal, but not as
effectively as a tool with rake, especially in cutting iron
and steel. Below the cutting edge, some clearance angle c
is essential so that this end or side surface of the tool will
not rub against the work and prevent the cutting edge from
entering it freely, particularly when the tool is adjusted
inward for taking a deeper cut. This clearance is not confined to the end alone but is also required along the side
as far back as the cutting edge extends. The factors governing the amount of the rake angle a, clearance angle c,
and the general shape of the cutting edge will be considered
in connection with tool grinding.

In planing a flat surface, how is the metal-cutting principle applied?

A comparison of the turning-tool diagram, Fig. 1, with
the planing tool at the right, will show that planing a flat
surface is similar in principle to turning a cylindrical surface, the chief difference being that a straight-line movement is required for planing and a rotary or circular motion
for turning. (The planing tool, when planing a horizontal
surface, is held in a vertical position. It is shown in a horizontal position to obtain a more direct comparison with the
turning tool.) The planing tool is held stationary while cutting and the part to be planed is given a straight-line motion
R during the cutting stroke, followed by an intermittent
lateral tool-feeding movement in direction F during the
return or non-cutting stroke. (If a shaper, which is a small
type of planing machine, is used, this order is reversed, the
tool moving while the work remains stationary.) As the

tool moves laterally prior to each cutting stroke, successive strokes reduce the surface of the work from H to h, the amount depending upon the requirements.

In planing, as in turning, the surface of the tool against which the chip bears usually slopes backward or has a certain rake angle a to reduce the cutting resistance. Some clearance angle c back of the cutting edge is necessary to permit this edge to cut freely. If either angle a or c is excessive, the point of the tool will be weakened and it may not be strong enough to resist the enormous pressure required in cutting iron or steel. This is true of turning, planing and other classes of metal-cutting tools. The shapes and angles of planing tools are dealt with in the section on Single-Point Tool Forms and Tool Grinding.

In forming a surface by milling, how is the metal-cutting principle applied?

The milling cutter represented by the upper diagram, Fig. 2, has equally spaced teeth around its circumference so that as many cuts are taken per cutter revolution as there are teeth, the cutting action being continuous. The cutter is rotated by the spindle of the milling machine and the part to be milled is given a feeding movement generally in direction F or against the cutter rotation R. (Sometimes the feeding movement is in the opposite direction or with rotation R as explained in the section on Milling Flat, Curved, and Irregular Surfaces.) As the work feeds past the revolving cutter, the surface H is reduced to some height h, as may be required.

The milled surface will be flat if the cutter is cylindrical, but, frequently, cutters of other forms are used as explained later in the section on Milling. The chip-bearing surfaces of the milling cutter teeth may have some rake angle a to lessen cutting resistance and they must have enough clearance c to permit free cutting action. Thus we see that each tooth depends for its cutting action upon a clearance angle and usually a rake angle also, the same as with turning and planing tools. (The actual clearance angle c applies to a narrow top edge on each tooth as indicated by the enlarged view of one tooth. Normally, the cutter is sharpened by grinding this narrow edge or "land" as it is called.)

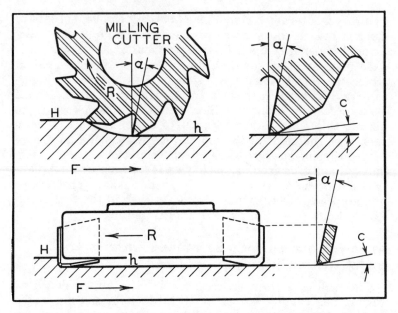

Fig. 2. Principles Involved in Cutting Metals by the Milling Process

The lower diagram, Fig. 2, illustrates the action of a face milling cutter. This general type of cutter is designed especially for milling flat surfaces. To simplify the diagram, a cutter is shown with two cutting blades only. In actual practice, however, there would be a number of blades equally spaced around the circumference of the cutter body to obtain more continuous cutting action. As the cutter rotates in direction R, the work feeds past it as indicated by arrow F so that each blade, as it sweeps around, reduces the surface from some height H to h. The feeding movement of the work is not always in a straight line but may be rotary. This, however, does not affect the operating principle. Each blade is held in a cutter body at an angle as indicated by the detail view at the right. This inclined position gives each blade a certain rake angle a. The lower end of each blade also has a clearance angle c. The face milling cutter is another illustration of the fact that metal-cutting operations with different types and designs of tools are all based upon the same fundamental principles.

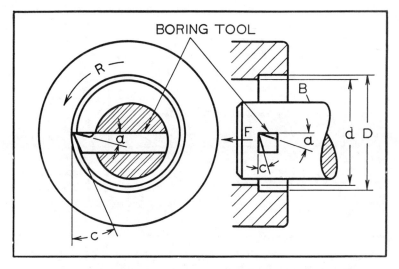

Fig. 3. Cutting Action when Enlarging or "Boring" a Hole

Is boring similar in principle to turning?

The machining of internal cylindrical surfaces, especially when a single tool or cutter is used, is called "boring." Boring may be described as internal turning. The diagram, Fig. 3, illustrates the process. The part to be bored rotates in direction R while the boring tool, with its top surface located in approximately the same plane as the center of the hole, feeds in direction F, or parallel to the axis of the hole for cylindrical boring. As the tool advances, it increases the diameter of the hole or bore from d to D. The cutting tool, as applied to iron or steel, normally would have some slope or rake a on the chip bearing surface and clearance c is essential. Note that there is both backward and side slope or rake, and, also, clearance at both the extreme end and along the leading side or below all of the cutting edge. A somewhat greater clearance angle may be required for boring than for turning, especially if the hole is small, but the cutting action, in each case, is based upon the same fundamental principle. A boring tool of the general type shown by the diagram is merely a small turning tool supported by a bar B which is rigidly supported at its outer

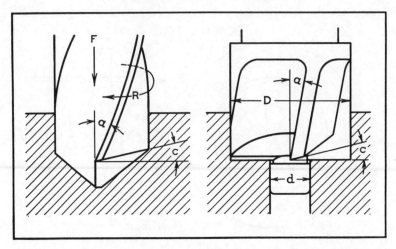

Fig. 4. (Left Diagram) Cutting End of Twist Drill. (Right Diagram)
Counterbore for Enlarging Part of a Previously Drilled Hole

end and is long enough to permit boring a hole as deeply
as may be required.

How is the metal-cutting principle applied in drilling a hole?

When a hole is drilled by using a twist drill, the cutting
point or end is ground to provide a certain amount of clearance c (left diagram, Fig. 4) back of each cutting edge and
extending along the entire length of the two edges. The
twisting or helical-shaped flute or groove through which the
chips pass also provides rake angle a above each cutting
edge, and, as will be seen, this rake or backward slope is
away from the cutting edge and is applied to the chip-
bearing surface as in the case of the other tools referred to.
It will be understood that the drilling of a hole is done
either by feeding a rotating drill in direction F and into
stationary work, as when using a drilling machine, or by
rotating the work itself instead of the drill as, for example, when drilling in a lathe or turret lathe.

The diagram at the right of Fig. 4 illustrates a counterbore. This is a tool for enlarging part of a hole from some
diameter d to D. A pilot or extension fits into the smaller

hole and insures cutting the enlarged part concentric with
it. Again we have on the counterbore, clearance angles c
at the lower end of each cutting tooth and rake angles a.
While the counterbore and the twist drill are unlike a milling cutter or turning tool in appearance, all of these tools
conform to the same fundamental principles.

In broaching, how is the metal cutting principle applied?

A broaching tool (see diagrams, Fig. 5) has a series of
teeth so arranged that they cut the metal when the broach
is given a straight-line movement, as indicated by arrow R.
(In some cases the work is moved instead of the broach,
as explained in the section on broaching, but the operating
principle is the same.) The broach cuts away the metal
because its teeth progressively increase in height, as shown
on an exaggerated scale by the lower diagram. Thus, cutting action is distributed over a series of teeth and each
tooth takes a light cut.

Any one tooth is similar to a planing tool, and the cutting of metal, in broaching, is based upon the same fundamental principles as in planing, turning, or milling. The
rake angle a, as in the case of other metal-cutting tools,
improves the cutting action. The top or land of each tooth
also has a clearance or relief angle c with the exception of
a very narrow part of the land which has no relief whatever. This lack of clearance or relief on broach teeth may
seem to be opposed to the general principle that relief is
an essential requirement. In this respect the broach is an
exception, but this straight part of the land may be less
than 1/32 inch wide and it does not interfere with the cutting action in the case of the broach because each tooth
only removes a very small amount of metal and a broach
is never adjusted inward or sunk deeper into the metal
while cutting, like the other metal-cutting tools.

The diagrams show that the broach, so far as its cutting
action is concerned, is the same in principle as the turning
tool, planing tool, milling cutter, and other metal-cutting
tools. Thus it will be seen that there is nothing mysterious
or complicated about the tool shapes required for cutting
metals, particularly if we are merely concerned with the

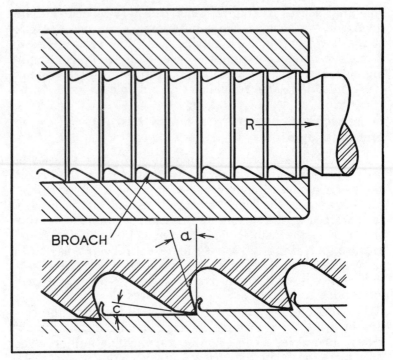

Fig. 5. Diagrams Illustrating Cutting Action of a Broaching Tool

fundamental requirements. In actual shop practice, however, it is essential to use tools which vary more or less in shape to suit different cutting conditions. The different factors to be taken into account will be referred to later in connection with tool grinding.

Why are so many different types and sizes of machine tools required?

There are many different types and sizes of machine tools, partly because machines of this class are used on an endless variety of parts, ranging from pins or screws that are so small that their weight is scarcely perceptible when held in the hand, to castings or forgings weighing many tons. Machine tools also vary in design for the reason that some are intended for general use and may be applied in different ways, whereas others are more special in their application and may be limited to the production of a single class of work. A type that might be suitable or preferable for producing a small number of duplicate parts might not be applicable when these same parts are required in large quantities.

There are three main reasons why different types of tools are used. These are: (1) Variations in the shapes of the surfaces to be machined; (2) variations in the sizes of different parts; (3) variations in the number of parts needed in a given time or the required rate of production; (4) varying degrees of accuracy required in producing different types and grades of machines or other mechanical devices. In producing the different parts of any machine or other mechanical device, one important step in the process is to make all of these parts sufficiently accurate to function properly. Another essential requirement consists in utilizing, in each case, that tool or method which is the most economical. If this is not done, the finished product may cost so much to manufacture that there will be little or no demand for it. The automotive and many other large industries are the direct result of manufacturing so economically that the product can be sold at a price which makes a big market possible.

Is the quickest method of producing machine parts always the most economical?

No, in some cases a slower method results in a lower production cost. The variety of machine tools now in use is very extensive, and as different types can often be employed for the same kind of work, the selection of the best and most efficient machine is often a rather difficult problem. To illustrate, there are many different types and designs of turning machines, such as the ordinary engine lathe, the hand-operated turret lathe, the semi-automatic turning machine, and the fully automatic type, which, after it is "set up" and started, is entirely independent; hence, when a certain part must be turned, someone must decide what kind of machine should be used, assuming that it would be possible to employ several different machines. The answer to this question usually depends principally upon the number of parts that must be turned.

For example, a certain casting might be turned in a lathe, which could also be turned in some form of automatic or semi-automatic turning machine much more quickly. It does not necessarily follow, however, that the automatic is the most economical machine to use, because the lathe is designed for general work and the part referred to could doubtless be turned with the regular lathe equipment, whereas the automatic machine might require expensive special tools and it would also need to be carefully adjusted to adapt it to any given job. Therefore, if only a few parts were needed, the lathe might be the best tool to use, but if a large number were required, the automatic or semi-automatic machine would doubtless be preferable, because the saving in time effected by the latter type would more than offset the extra expense for tool equipment and setting the machine. It is also necessary, in connection with some work, to consider the degree of accuracy required, as well as the rate of production, and it is because of these varying conditions that work of the same general class is often done in machines of different types, in order to secure the most efficient or satisfactory results.

Lathes and Their Principal Mechanical Features

Lathes of the class used by machinists for producing miscellaneous machine and tool parts are adapted to a great many operations, such as turning circular work, boring holes, cutting screw threads, and for many other classes of work. The extent or variety of these operations depends somewhat upon the type of lathe, and its auxiliary equipment. The development of the lathe as a machine tool for turning metals began with the invention of the slide-rest by means of which the turning tool could be guided mechanically. Prior to the invention of the slide-rest, the tools were clamped in a fixed position. The combination of the slide-rest with a lead-screw and change-gears for screw cutting was another very important step in the development of the lathe. After the invention of these fundamental parts, the lathe was applicable to a much wider range of work, and its further development was very rapid.

What are the chief functions of a lathe?

A lathe is designed to serve several main purposes: It is arranged to hold the work or part to be turned and rotate it at a suitable speed and it is provided with means of holding the turning or other tool. The tool may be adjusted by hand either to locate it in the working position or for certain turning operations which can be performed to better advantage by hand manipulation. Provision is also made for feeding the tool mechanically or by power at a suitable rate according to the character of the turning, boring, or other operation. For cutting screw threads, the lathe is provided with means of traversing the threading tool at whatever rate per work revolution is required for cutting a given pitch or number of threads per inch. Just how the

17

lathe is used for various typical operations will be described and illustrated later. These typical examples will illustrate different methods of holding the part to be turned, various adjustments of the lathe, and the applications of different types of tools.

What are the principal mechanical features of a lathe?

A lathe has five main features: These are (1) a horizontal bed *B* (see Fig. 1) with accurate ways *W* or guiding surfaces to insure proper alignment of the different parts; (2) a *headstock H* which is permanently secured to the bed at its left-hand end and contains the main work-driving spindle and means of regulating its speed; (3) a *tailstock T* at the right which has a conical work-supporting center (like the headstock) and is adjustable along the bed either to suit the length of the work or to remove the tailstock from the operating position when its work-supporting center is not in use; (4) a tool-supporting *carriage C* mounted upon the bed and movable along it either by hand or power as in traversing a turning tool; (5) a mechanism at the headstock end (illustrated and described later) for regulating the amount that the tool advances during each revolution of the work as in turning or thread-cutting.

The main shaft or spindle of the headstock rotates the work which may be held either between the conical centers in the headstock and tailstock, in a chuck mounted on the end of the headstock spindle, or on a faceplate which may be used instead of a chuck, as shown later by examples.

On the carriage there is a *cross-slide S* which can be moved at right angles to the lathe bed either by hand or power, and many lathes have a *compound slide* consisting of a main cross-slide *S* and an upper tool-holding slide *A* which can be swiveled in a horizontal plane to different angular positions. The tool that does the turning or boring is clamped to the upper slide in a suitable post *P* or holder and it can be moved with relation to the work either by traversing the carriage along the bed or by moving one of the slides. Ordinarily, the carriage and slide, or slides, are adjusted by hand to bring the tool in the proper position for turning to the required diameter and then the

Fig. 1. View of a Lathe from the Operating Position

power-driven or automatic feed (operating in a desired direction) is engaged. The cross-slide also has a power-driven feeding movement for such operations as facing broad flat surfaces. These *general* features are found on all engine lathes.

What type of lathe is used in all machine shops?

The type that is found in all shops is known either as a "lathe" or as an "engine lathe," the word "engine" as used in this connection merely meaning a machine. These terms designate the particular type of lathe which is used for miscellaneous classes of work such as turning, boring and thread-cutting, especially when only one or a small number of duplicate parts are required. In using a lathe of this type, many classes of work require considerable hand manipulation of the lathe. For example, the feeding movements of the tool frequently are controlled by hand in conjunction with more or less use of the power feed, particularly when the surfaces to be machined are not long enough to warrant using the power feeding movements.

In conjunction with the name "lathe" or "engine lathe,"

other names are often used to further indicate the design of the machine. For instance, most engine lathes which are driven by a belt operating on a cone-pulley have back-gears for doubling the range of speeds. When a lathe has double back-gears, instead of the ordinary single back-gears, it is often referred to as a "double back-geared engine lathe." There is also the "triple back-geared lathe," and the "geared-head" type which is now used extensively. With this type, the headstock is equipped with gearing by means of which the necessary speed changes may be obtained. The name may also indicate the kind of screw-cutting mechanism on the lathe. For instance, lathes having gears which are changed for cutting threads of different pitch are sometimes known as *plain* or *standard* engine lathes, whereas those having a gear-box by means of which the necessary gear combinations may be obtained by simply shifting two or three levers are usually known as the "quick change-gear" type. This latter type is very generally used at the present time.

How are the various members of the lathe family classified?

As lathes in general are used for a great variety of opera-tions, naturally there are various classes which differ more or less and also many different designs and sizes. The vari-ous types are usually classified, either with respect to some characteristic constructional feature, or with reference to the general class of work for which the lathe was designed.

The ordinary lathe or "engine lathe" has been described. The *tool-room* or *toolmakers' lathe* is so classified because of the general class of work for which the lathe is designed. It is similar in appearance to an ordinary engine lathe, but has extra attachments and is assumed to be exceptionally accurate. Other types of lathes which have some distinguish-ing characteristic are: The *turret lathe*, which is so named because tools for performing successive operations are held in a revolvable turret; the *bench lathe*, which is so small that it is mounted on a bench, and intended for small work usually requiring considerable accuracy; the *precision lathe*, which is usually a bench type that is capable of very accu-rate work and is more expensive than an ordinary bench *lathe*; the *gap lathe*, which has a removable section in the bed in front of the faceplate to provide a space or gap and thus increase the "swing" or maximum diameter that may be revolved; the *extension gap lathe*, which has a double form of bed, the upper section of which may be extended in order to form a gap for increasing the swing, and also the distance between the centers; the *crankshaft lathe*, which is especially arranged for turning crankshafts; the *wheel lathe*, which is a large design intended especially for turning locomotive driving wheels; the *axle lathe*, which is a powerful design for turning car axles; the *speed lathe*, which is without back-gears and is used for rotating parts rapidly for polishing, hand turning, or filing; the *chucking lathe*, which is especially adapted for parts that must be held in a chuck while being operated upon; the *manufacturing lathe* equipped with front and rear tool blocks and other features for turning duplicate parts rapidly; and the *automatic lathe*, which is also designed for the rapid production of duplicate parts.

How is the size of a lathe determined?

The size of a lathe, according to the practice in the United States, is based upon the "swing" or the maximum diameter that can be rotated over the ways of the bed. The nominal sizes listed by lathe manufacturers, however, ordinarily do not represent the maximum swing, but a diameter which is somewhat less. For instance, a lathe which is listed as a 24-inch size may actually swing 24½ or 25 inches. The variations between the nominal and actual sizes range from about ½ or ¾ inch up to 2 inches or more in some cases. According to the English practice, the size of a lathe is defined by the height of the centers above the top of the bed.

What is the meaning of the term "quick-change-gear" as applied to a lathe?

In cutting a screw thread, the distance which the carriage and threading tool moves, for every revolution of the work, equals the lead of the thread, as shown later in the section on cutting screw threads. Originally, all lathes were equipped with "change-gears" or with an assortment of gears which were changed by hand for obtaining whatever ratio is required for cutting a given number of threads per inch. The quick change-gear type of lathe (the type shown in Figs. 2, 3 and 4) has the gearing incorporated in the design and so arranged that it is unnecessary to remove gears at the headstock end of the machine and replace them with different sizes for cutting threads in the ordinary range of leads. For cutting threads of different lead, the gear ratios are changed merely by shifting control levers to the positions indicated by an index-plate attached to the gear-box. This same mechanism is also used for varying the feeding movement when turning. The arrangement of these quick change-gear mechanisms varies somewhat on lathes of different make (as illustrated later), but the general principle of operation is the same.

Why is the speed of a lathe adjusted or regulated?

In turning metals, the speed of the surface being turned should be fast enough to avoid wasting time but not so fast that the tool will become dull too quickly. The allowable speed depends upon the hardness or other tool-dulling properties of the metal being turned; upon the hardness of the tool itself or its capacity for resisting the wear resulting from the metal-cutting operation; upon the use, in many cases, of a suitable cooling compound or cutting fluid, which, by flowing onto the cutting end of the tool, prevents excessive heating and lubricates, more or less, the chip-bearing surface of the tool. These and other important factors which affect allowable cutting speeds will be considered more fully in the section on cutting speeds.

This term "cutting speed" means the *surface* speed of whatever part is being turned; hence, it is evident that the number of revolutions per minute (R.P.M.) of the lathe spindle, required for a given surface speed, depends upon the diameter of the work. For example, if a shaft is 5 inches in diameter, its speed in R.P.M. must be double that of a 10-inch shaft to obtain the same surface speed in feet per minute. In order to regulate the surface speed to suit any material or turning operation, lathes are equipped with some form of mechanism to permit changing readily the speeds over a wide range. This range may extend from, say, 15 or 20 R.P.M. or lower to 400 R.P.M., or higher. The most economical cutting speed may be difficult to determine accurately, but even a beginner in lathe work should attempt to run the lathe at speeds which conform to good practice. This explains why the subject of cutting speeds (and also feeds which are closely related to speeds) is dealt with in a separate section.

Many geared-head lathes are driven by motors. The motor may be mounted on the headstock or at some place below it. The geared-head design makes it possible to attach a motor directly to the lathe, so that the drive forms a compact unit and overhead countershafts or belts are not required.

How is the speed of a lathe regulated to suit the turning operation?

The exact method of regulating lathe-spindle speeds varies more or less with different designs of lathe headstocks. If the headstock is designed to obtain all speed changes by means of gears enclosed within it, the speeds are changed merely by shifting the positions of the controlling levers. A plate or chart attached to the headstock shows the position for each lever for obtaining any speed, in revolutions per minute, within the range of the lathe. By changing these levers, the drive from the motor, or other source of power, to the headstock spindle, is through gear combinations of different ratios. The arrangement of the speed-controlling levers varies somewhat on lathes of different design, especially if made by different manufacturers.

Speed Regulation with Headstock, Fig. 2.—The sliding gears for obtaining different spindle speeds are controlled by the speed change levers S and T. Lever S is used to obtain the four finer gradations of speeds, and lever T for the wider gradation of speeds. The speed plate P shows the positions of the levers for obtaining the various spindle speeds which range from 30 to 525 R.P.M. The changing of speeds while the lathe is running is not recommended. The handwheel W is used to turn the gears slowly when changing speeds so that they will readily mesh with one another.

Fig. 2. Headstock and Quick-change Mechanism of
an Engine Lathe

Fig. 3. Another Design of Headstock and Quick-change Mechanism
for a Lathe

Speed Regulation with Headstock, Fig. 3.—The headstock shown in Fig. 3 is equipped with two pairs of levers S and T. The instruction plate located between them shows the available speeds and the location of each lever for obtaining a given speed. The main driving clutch should be released by means of levers U or W (Figs. 3 and 11) and the spindle stopped before attempting to change spindle speeds.

Speed Regulation with Headstock, Fig. 4.—The American direct-reading shift for speed changes is controlled by the two levers S and T (see also detail view of speed plate, Fig. 5). The positions of the two levers indicate directly the spindle speed in R.P.M. that will be obtained. The top lever (S) has three positions indicating the slow or blue speed range, the intermediate or red range, or the fast or black range. The lower lever (T) has nine positions, each of which is designated on the speed plate by a circle. Each circle contains three spindle speeds, one being in the slow or blue range, one in the red or intermediate range, and

Fig. 4. A Third Design of Headstock and Quick-change Mechanism; see also Fig. 5.

one in the black or fast range. The position and color of
the top lever S shows which one of these three speeds will
be obtained for any given position of the lower lever T.
Fig. 5 shows the lever set for a speed of 615 R.P.M. because
the knob of lever T is over the circle containing 615 and
lever S is over the fast or black speed range. If the top
lever S should be moved to the intermediate position without changing the position of lever T, then an intermediate
speed of 144 R.P.M. would be obtained. If the top lever S
should be moved to the extreme left or over the slow position without changing lever T, the speed of 34 R.P.M. in

Fig. 5. Detail View of Direct-reading Speed Controlling Levers and
Speed Plate of Headstock Shown in Fig. 4

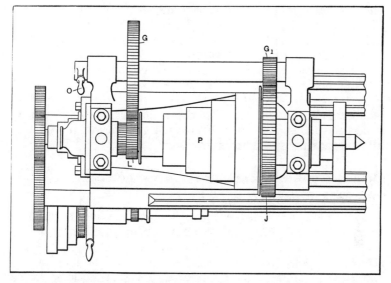

Fig. 6. Plan View of Lathe Headstock Showing Back-gears

the slow range would be obtained. If lever T were placed in the central position or perpendicular to the speed plate, then the speed would either be 28, 122, or 525 R.P.M. (depending upon the position of lever S) as shown at the bottom of the speed plate where the central position figures are located.

How are speed changes obtained with a cone-pulley type of headstock?

The speed changes with a belt-driven cone-pulley type of lathe are obtained by placing the driving belt on different steps of cone-pulley P (see diagram, Fig. 6) and also by the use of back-gears. The cone-pulley can be connected with the spindle or be disengaged from it by means of a bolt or locking pin. When the cone-pulley is locked to the gear J and spindle, five speeds may be obtained with the particular headstock shown, simply by shifting the driving belt to different steps of the cone. When a slower speed is required than can be obtained with the belt on the largest step of the cone, the latter is disconnected from the spindle, and the back-gears G and G_1 are moved forward into mesh by handle O; the drive is then from cone-pulley P and gear L to gear G, and from gear G_1 to the large gear J on the spindle. When driving through the back-gears, five more speed changes are obtained by shifting the position of the driving belt, as before. The fastest speed with the back-gears in mesh is somewhat slower than the slowest speed when driving direct or with the back-gears out of mesh; hence, with this particular headstock, a series of ten gradually increasing speeds is obtained.

How are double back-gears arranged and why are they used?

Some belt-driven lathes have double back-gears, so that two ranges of speed may be obtained in addition to those secured by shifting the belt on the cone-pulley. For instance, if there are four steps on the cone-pulley, twelve changes of speed would be available if the lathe were equipped with double back-gears. These gears may be used merely to increase the number of speed changes, or the primary object of including double back-gears in the design of a lathe may be to increase the driving power without sacrificing, appreciably, the number of speed changes, by reducing the number of steps on the cone-pulley and increasing their width, so that a much wider driving belt may be used. There are two general types of double back gearing; namely, one having sliding gears and the other, friction clutches. With either type, there are two "cone-pinions" at the left of the cone-pulley, and provision is made for rotating the back-gear shaft at two different speeds.

The diagram A, Fig. 7, shows the sliding type of double back-gear. The cone-pinions are at a and b, and the sliding gears at c and d. One speed is obtained when gears a and c are in mesh, and another speed when gears b and d are in mesh. Diagram B represents the double back-gears of the friction clutch type. Instead of sliding the gears e and f, either of these gears may be made the driven gear by means of friction clutches which are operated by a lever usually located in front of the headstock, so that it can easily be reached by the operator. This lever serves to slide collar g which, in turn, connects with the clutches. By using double

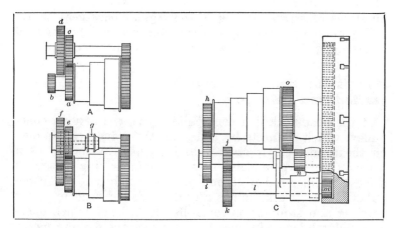

Fig. 7. Diagrams Illustrating Double and Triple Back-gearing

back-gears, nine speed changes may be obtained with the headstock, which is only one less than the total number obtained with a five-step cone and single back-gears.

How are speed changes obtained with triple-geared headstocks?

The type of gearing for lathe headstocks which has two back-gear shafts, one of which carries a pinion that may be engaged directly with an internal gear on the faceplate, is commonly known as *triple gearing*. This term, however, as used by different lathe manufacturers, is not applied to the same arrangement of gearing, and does not invariably mean that the number of speeds may be tripled. The diagram *C*, Fig. 7, illustrates a common arrangement of triple gearing. When the triple gearing is engaged, as indicated by the illustration, the drive is through gears *h* and *i* to the regular back-gear shaft, and then through gears *j* and *k* to shaft *l*, which carries at its end a pinion *m*. This pinion meshes with a large internal gear on the faceplate. To disengage the triple gearing, shaft *l* is shifted endwise in order to withdraw pinion *m* from the faceplate gear, and at the same time disengage gear *k* from gear *j;* this movement of shaft *l* also shifts pinion *n* into line with gear *o*. It will be understood that, with any of the back-gear combinations illustrated in Fig. 7, the regular back-gear shafts are mounted eccentrically so that the gears may be engaged or disengaged with those which rotate with the cone-pulley.

How is the headstock spindle started and stopped?

If the headstock is a cone-pulley type, the driving cone-pulley, which connects by belt with the driven cone-pulley on the headstock, is started and stopped by means of a belt-shifting lever which shifts the main driving belt from a loose or idler pulley to one that is attached to the cone-pulley shaft. If a lathe has a geared type of headstock, the starting and stopping is controlled by a lever which operates a clutch located somewhere between the driving motor or pulley, and the gearing in the headstock through which speed changes are obtained. The headstock shown in Fig. 3 has a double-end multiple-disk clutch. This may be operated either by lever *U* or by lever *W*, Fig. 11, which usually is in the most convenient position for the operator. Movement of lever *U* to the right or an upward movement of lever *W* will engage the clutch. Reverse movements will release it, and, if continued, a brake is applied for stopping the lathe quickly either for measuring the part being turned or for some other reason.

The headstock shown in Fig. 2 is controlled by the switch *U* which starts, stops, and reverses the lathe. When the handle is vertical, it is in the neutral or off position; turning it to the right starts the lathe running forward, and turning it to the left reverses the direction of rotation.

With the lathe shown in Fig. 4 (the American Tool Works Co.), starting, stopping and braking the headstock spindle are controlled either by the clutch and brake levers *U*, Fig. 4, or a similar lever *U*, Fig. 12, located by the lathe carriage.

Why is the power-driven feeding movement of a turning or other tool varied?

The term "feed" as applied to a lathe indicates the distance that the tool moves during each revolution of the work. There are two ways of expressing the rate of feed. One is to give the actual tool movement per work revolution in thousandths of an inch. For example, the range of feeds may be given as 0.002 to 0.125 inch. This is the usual method. Another way of indicating a feed range is to give the number of cuts per inch or the number of ridges that would be left by a pointed tool after turning a length of one inch. For example, the feed range might be given as 8 to 400.

In connection with turning and other lathe operations, the feed is regulated to suit the kind of material, depth of cut, and in some cases the finish desired. The exact arrangement of feed-changing mechanisms varies more or less on lathes of different makes, but determining the necessary adjustments is a simple matter. The mechanism for obtaining changes of feed may also be used for traversing the tool in thread cutting. This movement for thread cutting is like a feeding movement, except that the amount per spindle revolution conforms to the pitch of the thread being cut (or to the lead if the thread is a multiple type). As a general rule, the movements per spindle revolution are greater for thread cutting than for feeding the tool in ordinary turning. For example, if the range of feeds per inch is, say, 12 to 256, the range for thread cutting may be from 3 to 64 threads per inch; hence, the coarsest feed is 1/12 inch and the coarsest thread lead four times as great or 1/3 inch. All of the feeding movements in this case are reduced one-fourth by the gearing on the carriage or apron through which the feeding movements are transmitted.

How is the rate of tool feeding movement changed?

While the design of feed-control mechanisms of lathes varies more or less on different makes, lathes are equipped with index charts or instruction plates which are attached to the housing of the quick-change gear mechanism and show clearly just how to set this mechanism for obtaining any rate of feed within the available range. A typical plate is shown in Fig. 8. (This instruction plate is located at *A* in Fig. 9.) The available range of feeds per work revolution are listed on the lower part of the plate under the heading "Automatic Feeds Through Friction Clutch." The rate of feed is controlled by shifting

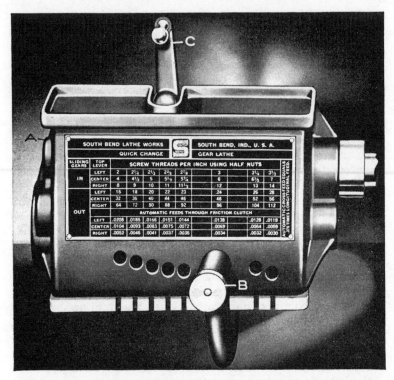

Fig. 8. Quick-change Mechanism with Index-plate Showing Threads
per Inch and Range of Feeds Obtainable

Fig. 9. Headstock and Carriage of a Motor-driven Lathe

the levers B and C, and also a sliding gear which is moved to the in or out positions by a knob (not shown) located at the left-hand end of the lathe.

Suppose the feed mechanism is to be set to feed the tool about 0.015 or 1/64 inch per work revolution. Then the tumbler lever B is engaged with that hole which is directly under the column containing 0.0151. The top lever C is moved to the left-hand position as indicated by the term "Left" on the plate opposite the row of feed movements containing 0.0151. The sliding gear at the end of the lathe is placed in the "Out" position for all feeding movements as indicated at the left-hand end of the index chart. This out position is also used for cutting half of the screw threads per inch shown on the plate, and the "In" position is required for cutting the other half.

Changing Rate of Feed with Quick-Change Mechanism, Fig. 10.—With the mechanism shown in Figs. 10 and 4, lever 2 is shifted to that one of its eight positions which

Fig. 10. Detail View of another Design of Quick-change Mechanism for a Lathe

is directly beneath the vertical row containing the rate of
feed desired. Lever 1 is placed either in its A, B, or C position, and lever 3 in its D or E position as indicated by the
combination of two letters at the right of the horizontal
row containing the selected rate of feed. For example, to
obtain a feeding movement of .011 inch per work revolution, lever 1 is placed in the C position and lever 3 in its D
position as indicated by the letters CD opposite the horizontal row containing the figure .011. The threads per inch
(and equivalent lead in inches) are, of course, given in
conjunction with the feeding movements, and lever 4 is
placed either in the "Feeds" or "Threads" position as
required.

Changing Rate of Feed with Quick-Change Mechanism,
Fig. 3.—To obtain a certain rate of feed with the quick-
change mechanism shown in Fig. 3, proceed as follows:
Find on instruction plate A the desired amount of feed
movement per revolution. Then place ratio lever C in either
the upper or lower notches as indicated. (When this lever
is in the middle notch, it is in neutral and the gear trains
are disconnected.) At the right of the instruction plate,
there is a vertical row of letters. Place lever D in the hole
marked with whatever letter is in line with the row of
figures containing the feed rate selected. Next, engage the
plunger of rocker lever B directly below the vertical column
of figures containing the rate of feed selected. Finally,
engage the plunger of lever E in the hole designated "Feed"
for turning or boring operations. (This plunger is engaged
with a hole marked "Thread" when the lathe is being used
for thread cutting.)

What is the apron of a lathe and how is the carriage or cross-slide operated by hand?

The front part of a lathe carriage, which contains the
controlling wheels and levers, is known as the "apron."
The aprons of most lathes are quite similar in their general
arrangement. There is a handwheel as at H, Figs. 11 and 12,
for moving the carriage along the bed. This is used in shifting the position of the carriage along the bed. Some handwheels have a knob in the center (see Fig. 11) which can
be pulled out to disengage the wheel, thus eliminating the

effects of its momentum in thread cutting. The smaller handwheel L is used for moving the cross-slide in or out. Handwheel M is for operating the tool-rest slide. The cross-feed screws of many lathes are equipped with dials graduated for quickly adjusting the tool a predetermined amount in turning, boring, or thread cutting. These graduations indicate 0.001 inch on the diameter of the work.

How are the power-driven feeding movements controlled?

After the feed mechanism is set for whatever rate of feed is desired, the engagement or disengagement of either the longitudinal or cross-feeds is controlled by knobs or levers located on the apron of the carriage.

Control Mechanism of Lathe Carriage, Fig. 9.—The direction of all power-driven feeding movements is controlled by the feed reverse lever R at the left-hand end of the headstock, Fig. 9. This lever has three positions. When the lever is in the upward position, the feeding movements are in one direction; and when it is in the downward position, these movements are reversed. The central position is neutral, the power feeds then being disconnected.

Knob J on the carriage controls the engagement or disengagement of a friction clutch for operating either the power-driven longitudinal feed (movement of the carriage along the bed) or the power-driven cross-feed. This knob is turned to the right to engage the clutch, and to the left to disengage it. When the clutch is engaged and lever K is in the upward position, the carriage moves along the bed (longitudinal feed) in a direction determined by the position of reverse lever R. When lever K is in the downward position, the cross-feed is engaged. The central position of lever K is neutral. It must be in this neutral position before lever G can be operated for engaging the half-nuts with the lead-screw. Such engagement of lever G is used only for thread cutting.

Control Mechanism of Lathe Carriage, Fig. 11.—On the lathe apron and carriage shown in Fig. 11, the power-driven feeding movements are controlled by levers R, J, and K. When lever R is in its lowest position, the carriage travels by power toward the headstock, and, by swinging this lever

Fig. 11. Apron and Carriage of a Lathe

to its highest position, the direction is reversed. The central or neutral position disengages all feeding movement. The power feed for the carriage or the longitudinal feed is engaged by pulling up lever J and the feeding movement is either toward or away from the headstock, depending upon the position of the forward and reverse lever R. Lever G for engaging the lead-screw nut is interlocked with lever J to prevent accidental engagement of both lead-screw and feed rod at the same time. The cross-slide power feed is engaged by pulling up lever K. This movement will then be either toward the front or rear, depending upon the position of lever R. To discontinue either the carriage or cross-feed, merely push down lever J or K.

Control Mechanism of Lathe Carriage, Fig. 12. — The longitudinal power feed is controlled by lever J, and lever K controls the power cross-feed. The direction of either the longitudinal or cross-feeding movements is determined by the position of lever R. The half-nuts for screw thread

Fig. 12. Apron and Carriage of Another Lathe

cutting are engaged with the lead-screw by lever *G*, but only after the reverse lever *R* is in its neutral position. When the carriage is to be traversed rapidly along the bed by power, this movement is controlled by lever *W*. The direction in which this lever is moved indicates the direction of the carriage travel. The cross-slide is adjusted with handwheel *L* and the upper slide with handwheel *M*.

What types of attachments are used on lathes for controlling the dimensions of turned parts?

In addition to the graduated collars for controlling cross-feed adjustments and diameters, lathes are often equipped with stops for obtaining precise movements of the carriage in facing shoulders or for similar operations.

Micrometer Stop.—A simple form of micrometer stop is illustrated in Fig. 13. This is clamped to the bed on either side of the tool carriage. If this stop is used in conjunction

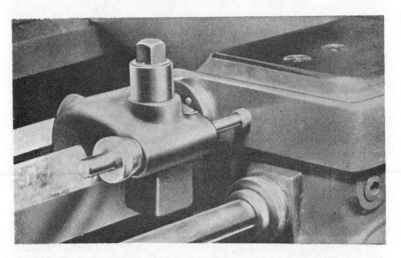

Fig. 13. Carriage Stop with Micrometer Adjustment

with the power carriage feed, the stop-collar on the stop and reverse rod, should be set to automatically disengage the feeding movements just before the carriage comes into contact with the micrometer stop. The carriage is then moved by hand up to this stop. This device is very handy in spacing grooves in shafts or in facing shoulders.

Spacing Attachment.—Fig. 14 illustrates a carriage-spacing attachment. In using it, the micrometer head and dial indicator are set to the zero position, and an adjustable measuring contact is clamped in position for the first shoulder or groove. Then the micrometer is extended by adding the necessary end measures for the required spacing. The zero readings of the dial indicator show when the carriage has reached the precise point required.

Length and Diameter Dials.—Fig. 15 shows the length and diameter measuring dials on a certain lathe. The direct length reading dial is located back of the carriage handwheel. The dial has two sections and it is graduated both in inches (1/2-inch markings) and in fractions of an inch (1/64-inch markings). One complete revolution of the outer dial indicates a carriage movement of 1 inch and a complete turn of the inner dial represents a movement of 24 inches. In using the dial, the turning tool is first set for

Fig. 14. Carriage Spacing Attachment. After the Attachment is Set
for a Given Measurement, Zero Readings of the Dial
Indicator at the Left shows when the Carriage
has reached the Position Required

Fig. 15. Direct Length-reading and Diameter Dials. One Dial Indicates
Movements of Carriage along the Bed and the Other Dial
is for Diameter Readings

the diameter to be turned and in the starting position. The dial that will give the desired length is then turned until the zero mark is under the pointer. The length of the cut can then be read directly from the dial. This length-reading dial is also used in setting length feed-stops when duplicate parts are to be turned.

The cross-feed screw also has a duplex type of dial for diameter readings. The outer dial is graduated in thousandths, and one complete turn equals a movement of 0.2 inch. The inner dial has 1/32-inch markings, and one complete turn equals a cross-slide movement of 3 inches. In using this dial, the tool is first set to just graze the work. The dial is then turned until the zero mark is directly under the pointer. Subtract the diameter to be turned from the diameter of the stock and feed the tool in one-half the difference.

Why should a lathe bed be level in both lengthwise and crosswise directions?

The beds of modern lathes are rigid, but, nevertheless, they may be sprung or twisted enough to seriously affect the accuracy of turned parts, by bolting the legs tightly to an uneven floor or foundation. When a lathe is installed, hard-wood wedges or metal shims may be used to compensate for uneven places in setting the bed level. It is important to use a precision level and not an ordinary carpenter's level or a machinist's combination-square level. The bed should be tested in a lengthwise direction and also crosswise at each end, using the flat surfaces of the bed. In cross-leveling, the level may be placed on size blocks or accurate parallel strips which are in contact with the flat surfaces. The lag screws or bolts for holding the lathe to the floor foundation should only be tight enough to prevent the lathe from "walking" or shifting.

When are bench lathes used in preference to engine lathes?

The bench lathe is similar in its general arrangement to an engine lathe, but the bench type is especially designed for the smaller classes of work, and frequently it is applied to very precise delicate operations which could not be performed advantageously, if at all, on an engine lathe. The bench lathe is used for turning, facing, boring, etc., like the larger engine lathe. The variety of work that comes within the usual range of the bench lathe is large, because this type of lathe is used widely both for the interchangeable manufacture of small parts and for fine precision tool and instrument work. This general application of bench lathes has resulted in the development of many tools and attachments for adapting such lathes to different requirements. Although the term "lathe" ordinarily implies turning operations, bench lathes with their attachments are commonly used for many other operations, such as grinding, milling, etc. Some of these attachments are intended primarily to permit handling a larger variety of operations, whereas others are designed more especially for the rapid production of duplicate parts, as, for example, when the arrangement is such that a succession of tools may be applied rapidly for finishing duplicate parts on a quantity basis. Bench lathes are not only used throughout the machine-building and tool-making industries, but also for all kinds of model and instrument making, as well as for experimental work generally.

The work for which bench lathes are commonly used may be divided into several general classes. One of these includes precision work requiring an accurate machine that may readily be set up, and speed of manipulation which can only be obtained with the bench lathe. Then there is the modern application of bench lathes in interchangeable manufacture, as applied to both small and large quantities, with production rates often comparing favorably with less accurate methods. A third group includes precision work on parts requiring such a variety of operations that bench lathes, with their provision for rapidly changing tools and attachments, provide the only practical method. Finally, we have the use of the bench lathe for producing small parts that might be machined either on turret lathes or automatic screw machines were it not for the extreme degree of precision necessary.

Turning Cylindrical Parts in Lathe

Lathes are used for machining both external and internal surfaces. Either of these metal-cutting operations might be classed as turning, but, according to the general usage of the term, external surfaces are "turned" and internal surfaces in holes or recesses are "bored." Each of these metal-cutting operations is similar in principle, as previously explained, but the terms turning and boring are useful in that they indicate the general character of the operation in each case. The turning of cylindrical parts is a very common operation and is based upon certain principles that are also applied in turning with other types of machine tools; hence, it is important to understand, first, how a lathe is used for cylindrical turning.

In turning a part held between the centers what is the general procedure?

When the lathe is used for cylindrical turning, the work is usually held between the lathe centers (see Fig. 1), especially if the part is comparatively long like a rod or shaft. The first step in this operation is to form conically-shaped center-holes in each end of the piece. These centers are necessary to keep the work in place and they serve as bearing surfaces. Methods of forming these center-holes will be explained later.

After the work is centered, a driving dog is clamped to one end, after which the piece is placed between the centers of the lathe. The dog usually has a projecting end or "tail," as it is commonly called, which enters a slot in the faceplate and drives or rotates the work. The tailstock center, after being oiled, should be set up just tight enough to eliminate all play, without interfering with a free rotary movement of the work. When the center is properly adjusted, the tailstock spindle containing the center is locked.

The tool is usually clamped about square with the work, for turning, and with the cutting end a little above the center. Before beginning to turn, an outside caliper should be set to the finished diameter of the work unless a gage is to be used instead of the adjustable caliper. These fixed gages, sometimes called "snap" gages, are accurately made to different sizes, and are particularly useful when a number of pieces have to be turned to exactly the same size. A micrometer may also be used.

The adjustments of the carriage along the bed and the in or out adjustments of the tool-holding slide, especially when beginning a cut, usually are made with the left hand, leaving the right hand free for calipering, as the illustration shows. The turning tool is started at the right-hand end of the work ordinarily, and a short length is turned first by hand feeding. When the caliper shows that the

Fig. 1. An Example of Cylindrical Turning—Operator's Left Hand is on Knob Controlling Power Feed

diameter is slightly greater than the finished size (to allow for a light finishing cut, either in the lathe or grinding machine), the power feed for the carriage is engaged; the tool then moves along the work. Evidently, if the tool movement is along a line, parallel with the axis of the work, the diameter will be the same at all points, and a true cylindrical piece will be turned. On the other hand, if the axis is inclined one way or the other, the work will be made tapering; in fact, the tailstock center can be adjusted laterally for turning tapers, but, for straight turning, both centers must be in alignment with the carriage travel.

In centering parts for turning, how are the shaft centers located?

There are a number of different methods of forming center-holes in the ends of parts that have to be turned while held between lathe centers. A common method of centering by hand is first to locate a central point on the end and then drill and ream the center-hole by using the lathe itself. Hermaphrodite dividers are useful for finding the center, as illustrated at A, Fig. 2, but, if the work is fairly round, a center-square B is preferable. A line is scribed across the end and then another line at right angles to the first by changing the position of the square; the intersection of these two lines will be the center, which should be marked by striking a pointed punch C with a hammer. If a cup or bell center-punch D is available, it will not be necessary to first make center-lines, as the conical part shown locates the punch in a central position. This style of punch should only be used on work which is fairly round. After small centers have been formed in both ends, their position can be tested by placing the work between the lathe centers and rotating it rapidly by drawing the hand quickly across it. By holding a piece of chalk close to the work as it spins around, a mark will be made on the "high" side if the centers are not accurate; the centers are then shifted toward these marks. If the work is close to the finished diameter, the centers should be located quite accurately in order that the entire surface of the work will be turned true when it is reduced to the finished size.

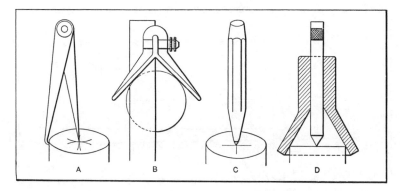

Fig. 2. Methods of Locating Shaft Center Preparatory to Drilling and Countersinking Holes to Receive Lathe Centers

How are the center holes formed in the ends of shafts to be turned?

One method of enlarging and finish-forming these center-holes is as follows: The shank of a drill chuck is inserted in the headstock spindle, and a combination center drill and countersink (see Fig. 3) is gripped by the chuck jaws and set to run true. The center is then drilled and reamed at one end by pressing the work against the revolving drill with the tailstock spindle, which is fed out by hand. The piece is then reversed for drilling the opposite end. The work may be kept from revolving while the centers are being drilled and reamed, by attaching a dog to it close to the tailstock end and then adjusting the cross-slide until the dog rests upon the slide. From the foregoing, it will be seen that the small centers made by a center-punch merely serve as a starting point for the drill and also as a support for the outer end of the work while the first hole is being drilled; these small centers are not required if a centering machine is used, as mentioned later.

The form of center-hole produced by a combination drill and countersink is shown by the lower left-hand diagram, Fig. 4. A small straight hole *a* in the bottom prevents the point of the lathe center from coming in contact with the work and insures a good bearing on the conical surface *c*. The standard angle for lathe centers is 60 degrees, as the

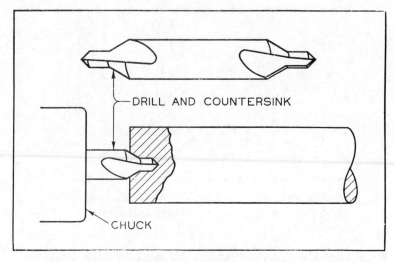

Fig. 3. Combination Drill and Countersink and Its Application in
Centering Parts for Turning

illustration shows, and the tapering part of all center-holes
should be made to this angle.

It is bad practice to form centers by the use of a center-
punch only. If there is no better tool, the end of the punch
should have a 60-degree taper. Sometimes centers are made
with punches that are too blunt, producing a shallow center,
such as the one shown by the upper left-hand diagram,

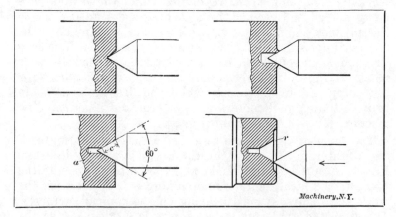

Fig. 4. Centers of Incorrect and Correct Form

Fig. 4. In this case all the bearing is on the point of the lathe center, which is the worst possible place for it. Another way is to simply drill a straight hole as shown in the upper view to the right; this is also bad practice. The lower right-hand diagram shows a form of center which is often found in the ends of lathe arbors, the mouth of the center being rounded at r, and the arbor end recessed as shown. The rounded corner prevents the point of the lathe center from catching when it is moved rapidly towards work which is not being held quite centrally (as shown by the illustration), and the end is recessed to protect the center against bruises. Stock that is bent should always be straightened before the centers are drilled and reamed. If the work is first centered and then straightened, the center will wear unevenly and the surfaces last turned will not be concentric with those which were finished first.

Many shops have a special machine for forming centers because with such a machine the operation can be performed quickly. In one type of centering machine which is common, the work is gripped in a chuck that automatically locates it in a central position so that it is not necessary to lay out the end before drilling. The spindle which holds the drill and countersink is advanced by a hand lever. The duplex type of machine is equipped with two centering heads so that both ends may be centered without reversing the position of the stock.

What types of work-drivers or dogs are in general use?

Dogs are made in a great variety of designs, some of which are more or less special in their application. A few of the typical forms are shown in Fig. 5. One of the most commonly used types is illustrated at A. The work is gripped by a set-screw and the bent end or "tail," as it is commonly called, engages a slot in the lathe faceplate and is rotated by the latter. Some drivers intended for large work have two clamping screws, as shown at B. Another double-screw type is shown at C, which differs from the previous design in that the driving end is straight instead of being bent. When using this straight form, a driving stud or bolt is attached to the lathe faceplate. The dog shown at D is

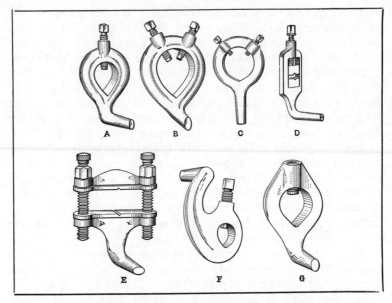

Fig. 5. Types of Dogs or Drivers Commonly Used in Connection with Lathe Work

called a "die-dog," because of its similarity to a thread-cutting die. The work is gripped between two blocks instead of being acted upon directly by the clamping screw. The clamp dog shown at *E* is so named because the work is held by clamp screws instead of by set-screws, as the illustration indicates.

Frequently it is necessary to place a dog on the threaded end of a piece of work. When the ordinary form of dog is used, the threads on the work are usually protected by wrapping a strip of copper about them. There are special dogs for threaded work which are tapped out to different standard thread sizes and are screwed onto the threaded end; the hub of the dog may be split and be tightened with a clamping bolt, or it may be left solid, in which case it is screwed against a nut or shoulder.

Every machinist who has operated a lathe realizes the danger incident to the use of the ordinary lathe dog with its unguarded set-screw which tends to catch in the clothing, especially when filing. Many dogs have been designed

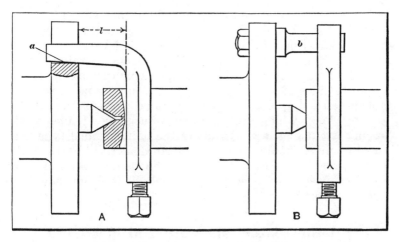

Fig. 6. (A) Dog that is too Short for Faceplate
(B) Straight Driving Dog

to eliminate this danger; two of these safety types are illustrated at F and G. The dog shown at F has a driving end which is curved around in such a way that it provides a guard in front of the set-screw or on the leading side, as determined by the direction of rotation. As may be seen, however, the set-screw is accessible for loosening or tightening. The safety dog shown at G is similar to the ordinary form, but differs from the latter in having a square socket set-screw which is always flush with the screw hub or below it. A special form of wrench having a square end is used for loosening and tightening the set-screw.

Why is inaccurate work sometimes caused by improper application of a driver or dog?

Work that is turned between centers is sometimes driven by a dog which is so short for the faceplate that the bent driving end bears against the bottom of the faceplate slot, as shown at A, Fig. 6. If the dog is nearly the right length, it may allow the headstock center to enter the center in the work part way, with the result that the turned surface is not true with the centers. When a driving dog of this type is used, care should be taken to see that it moves freely in the faceplate slot and does not bind against the bottom. By using a straight dog (B) all danger from this source is eliminated. The straight dog, however, is sometimes used to avoid the leverage l of a bent dog, as this leverage tends to spring a flexible part when a cut is taken. Straight dogs are also made with two driving ends which engage pins on opposite sides of the faceplate. This double type is preferable because it applies the power required for turning evenly to the work, which still further reduces the tendency to spring it out of shape. In using the double-ended type the driving pins should be adjusted so that each bears with equal pressure against the dog. The double-ended driver is often used for large work, especially if deep roughing cuts are necessary.

When lathe centers are worn and inaccurate, how are the conical points trued?

The lathe centers should receive careful attention especially when accurate work must be turned. If the headstock center does not run true as it revolves with the work, a round cross-section may be turned, but if the position of the driving dog with reference to the faceplate is changed, the turned surface then will not run true because it is not true with the work centers. Furthermore, if it is necessary to reverse the work for finishing the driving end, the last part turned will be eccentric to the first. To avoid such errors, the lathe centers should be kept true as it is often necessary to change the part being turned "end for end" for finishing, and any eccentricity between the different surfaces would, in many cases, spoil the work.

Some lathes are equipped with hardened centers in both the head- and tail-stock and others have only one hardened center which is in the tailstock. The object in having a soft or unhardened headstock center is to permit its being trued by turning (see diagram A, Fig. 7), but as a soft center is quite easily bruised and requires truing oftener than one that is hard, it is better to have both centers hardened. A motor driven grinder may be used for truing these hardened centers. The grinder is held in the regular toolpost (see diagram B) and the compound rest is set to an angle of 30 degrees with the axis of the headstock spindle. The grinding wheel is traversed across the conical surface

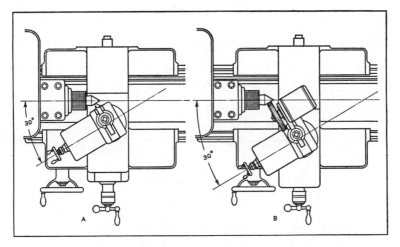

Fig. 7. (A) Re-turning Worn Lathe Center. (B) Truing
Worn Center by Grinding

of the center by moving the slide of the compound rest.
As the grinding proceeds, the wheel is fed inward slightly
by manipulating the cross-slide. As the wheel spindle is
30 degrees from the axis of the lathe spindle, the lathe center is not only ground true but to an included angle of
60 degrees, which is the standard angle for lathe centers.
The tailstock center is ground by inserting it in the spindle
in place of the headstock center. Before a center is replaced
in its spindle, the hole should be perfectly clean, as even a
small particle of dirt may affect the alignment. The center
in the headstock is usually referred to as the "live center,"
because it turns around when the lathe is in use; and the
center in the tailstock, as the "dead center," because it
remains stationary.

Before turning a cylindrical part, how is the alignment of the lathe centers tested?

When a rod or shaft must be turned cylindrical or to the
same diameter throughout its entire length, it is good practice to test the alignment of the centers before inserting
the work. The position of the tailstock center for cylindrical
turning may be indicated by the alignment of graduation

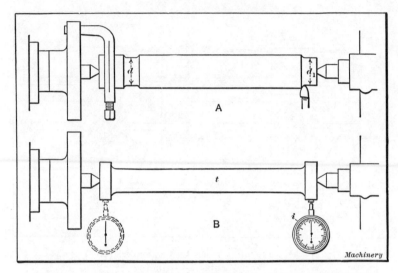

Fig. 8. Two Methods of Aligning Centers for Cylindrical Turning

marks on the base, but, if accuracy is necessary, the relative position of the two centers should be determined in a more positive way. A very simple and convenient method of testing the alignment is shown at A in Fig. 8. The work is first turned for a short distance, near the headstock end, as shown, and the tool is left as set for this cut; then the tailstock center is withdrawn and the work is moved sufficiently to permit running the tool back to the tailstock end without changing its original setting. A short cut is then taken at this end and the diameters d and d_1 are carefully compared. In case there is any variation, the tailstock center is adjusted laterally, other trial cuts are taken, and the test repeated.

Another method is illustrated at B, which requires the use of a test-bar t. This bar should have accurately made centers and the ends finished to exactly the same diameter. The lathe centers are aligned by placing the bar between them and then testing the position of the ends. This can be done by comparing each end with a tool held in the toolpost and moved from one to the other by shifting the carriage, but a better method is to clamp a test indicator i in the toolpost and bring it in contact with first one end of the bar and then the other. If the dial does not register

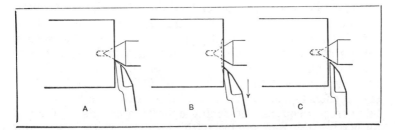

Fig. 9. Facing End with Side Tool

the same at each end, it shows that the lathe centers are not in line. Even when centers are correctly set, lathes that have been in use a long time do not always turn cylindrical or straight, because, if the ways that guide the carriage are worn unevenly, the tool as it moves along does not remain in the same plane, and this causes a variation in the diameter of the part being turned.

What is a facing operation?

When the end of a shaft or shoulder, or the side of any flange or disk-shaped part, is turned to obtain a flat surface, this is commonly known as *facing*. The ends of a cylindrical part should be faced before turning the cylindrical surface. The facing or "side tool" has a straight cutting edge with clearance below the edge and rake on the top or chip-bearing surface. The tool should be set with the cutting edge slightly inclined from a right-angle position, the point being slightly in advance so that it will first come into contact with the work. The cutting edge should also be about the same height as the center of the work. The tool is moved in until the point is in the position shown at *A*, Fig. 9. The tool point is then fed against the end until a light chip is turned off, and then it is moved outward (as indicated by the arrow at *B*), the carriage remaining stationary. As the movement of the tool point is guided by the cross-slide which is at right angles with the axis of the work, the end will be faced square. For short turning operations of this kind, the power feeds ordinarily are not used as they are intended for comparatively long cuts. If it were necessary to remove much metal from the end, a number of cuts would be taken across it.

After taking a cut as described, the surface, if left rough by the tool point, should be made smooth by a finishing cut. If the tool is set almost square, as at C, a smooth finish can be obtained; the cut should be light and the outward feed uniform. The work is next reversed in the centers and the driving dog placed on the end just finished; the other end is then faced. If the end of the work does not need to be perfectly square, the facing operation can be performed by setting the tool square with the axis of the work, and then feeding it sidewise, thus removing a chip equal to the width of one side. Evidently this method is confined to comparatively small diameters, and the squareness of the turned end will be determined by the position of the cutting edge of the tool.

What is the general procedure in facing large flat surfaces?

When it is necessary to face the side of a flange, shoulder or any comparatively large surface, regular turning tools generally are used. Diagram A, Fig. 10, shows a roughing cut on the side of a disk-shaped part. The tool is fed inward by means of the cross-slide; and this roughing cut, especially in turning cast iron, might be followed by a finishing cut with a broad straight-edged tool, as illustrated at B. The use of a wide tool having a carefully ground straight edge makes it possible to use a coarse feed, and, at the same time, secure a smooth flat surface. At the right-hand side of the carriage there is a locking screw which is used to lock the carriage to the lathe bed when taking facing cuts. (This screw is at L, Fig. 13.) Don't forget to release this screw when the facing operation is completed.

Ordinarily, facing operations with turning tools are performed by feeding the tool inward or toward the center in some cases, however, it is preferable to feed outward as illustrated by diagram C, especially if the shape of the work is such that an outward feeding movement is more convenient. The tool used for feeding outward as at C is similar to tool A, excepting that the cutting edge is on the opposite side.

Most turning operations require either a lengthwise feeding movement, as for cylindrical turning, or a crosswise

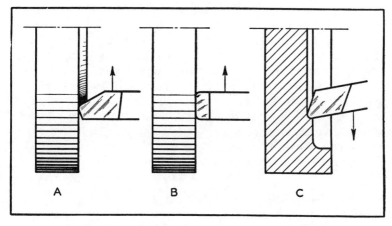

Fig. 10. Facing Flat Surfaces by Feeding the Tool Radially

movement, as for facing. In some cases, however, this feeding movement is neither lengthwise nor crosswise but at an angle in order to turn surfaces of any required angle or taper. This method of turning will be described in the next section or chapter.

Under what conditions are roughing and finishing cuts taken?

In turning, and also in connection with certain other machining operations, there are two classes of cuts, known as *roughing* and *finishing* cuts. Roughing cuts are for reducing the work as quickly as possible almost to the required size, whereas finishing cuts, as the name implies, are intended to leave the part comparatively smooth and usually to some definite size. When the rough stock is only a little larger than the finished diameter, a single cut is sufficient, but, if there is considerable metal to turn away, one or more deep roughing cuts are taken, and, finally, a light cut for finishing. Ordinarily the roughing cut would be deep enough to leave the work about 1/16 or, perhaps, 1/8 inch above the finished size.

When there is considerable metal to remove and a number of roughing cuts have to be taken, the depth of each cut and the feed of the tool are governed largely by the pulling power of the lathe and the strength of the work to withstand the strain of a heavy cut. The depth of roughing cuts often has to be reduced considerably, because the part being turned is so flexible that a heavy cut would spring the work and cause the tool to gouge in. Just as few cuts as possible should be taken in order to save time. The speed of the work should also be as fast as the conditions will allow for the same reason, but as there are many things which govern the speed, the feed of the tool, and the depth of the cut, these important points are referred to in a section dealing with this general subject.

In what position is a turning tool held relative to the work?

For cylindrical turning the tool usually is held about square with the work unless there is an advantage in locating it at an angle. The cutting end should be as high as the lathe centers or a little higher and the unsupported overhang should be reduced as far as possible. If the turning tool is clamped so that the cutting end extends too far from the supporting block, the downward spring of the tool, owing to the thrust of the cut, sometimes results in spoiled work, especially when an attempt is made to turn close to the finished size by taking a heavy roughing cut. Suppose the end of a cylindrical part is first reduced for a short distance by taking several trial cuts until the diameter is slightly above the finished size and the power feed is then engaged; when the tool begins to take the full depth of the cut, the point of the tool, which ordinarily would be set a little above the center, tends to spring downward into the work, and, if there were considerable springing action, the part would probably be turned below the finished size, the increased reduction beginning at the point where the full cut started. This springing action, as far as the tool is concerned, can be practically eliminated by locating the tool so that the distance between the tool-block and cutting end, or the "overhang," is as short as possible. Even though the tool has little overhang it may tilt downward, because the tool-slide is loose on its ways, and, for this reason, the slide should have a snug adjustment that will permit an easy movement without unnecessary play. The tool-slides of

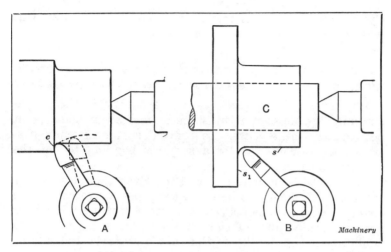

Fig. 11. (A) The Way in which Tool is Sometimes Displaced by Thrust of Cut, when Set at an Angle. (B) Tool Set for Finishing Both Cylindrical and Radial Surfaces

all lathes are provided with gibs which can be adjusted by screws to compensate for wear, or to secure a more rigid bearing.

When roughing cuts are to be taken, the tool should be located so that any change in its position which might be caused by the pressure of the cut will not spoil the work. This point is illustrated at A in Fig. 11, which shows the end of a rod that has been reduced by taking a number of trial cuts, until it is close to the finished size. If the power feed is then engaged with the tool clamped in an oblique position, as shown, when the full cut is ecountered at c, the tool may be shifted backward by the lateral thrust of the cut, as indicated by the dotted lines. The point will then begin turning smaller than the finished size and the work will be spoiled. To prevent any change of position, it is good practice, especially when taking heavy roughing cuts, to clamp the tool square with the surface being turned, or at right angles to its direction of movement. Occasionally, however, there is a decided advantage in having the tool set at an angle. For example, if it is held about as shown at B, when turning the flanged casting C, the surfaces s and s_1 can be finished without changing the position of the tool.

Cylindrical and radial surfaces are often turned in this way in order to avoid shifting the tool.

In turning a slender rod or shaft how is it prevented from springing or bending due to cutting pressure?

Whenever it is necessary to turn a part which is so slender and flexible that it must be supported at some point between the lathe centers to prevent springing (and possibly spoiled work due to a sudden "hogging in" of the turning tool), an attachment known as a "steadyrest" or "center-rest" is used (see Fig. 12). Even though a rod or shaft is stiff enough to be turned without a steadyrest, the latter may be used to prevent deflection or to permit taking heavier cuts because of this auxiliary support. If there is doubt about the rigidity of the part, a steadyrest should be used, as a general rule.

A steadyrest is composed of a frame usually containing three jaws. These jaws merely form a three-point bearing and they can be adjusted in or out radially by turning the

Fig. 12. Typical Application of Steadyrest which Provides an Intermediate Support for Slender Shafts

screws shown. The frame is hinged on one side, thus allowing the upper half to be swung back for inserting or removing the work. The base of the frame has V-grooves in it
that fit the ways of the lathe bed. When the steadyrest is in
use, it is secured to the bed by a clamp, and the jaws are
set in against the work, thus supporting or steadying it
during the turning operation. The steadyrest must be
located at a point where it will not interfere with the turning tool. In some cases it may require shifting to another
position after turning one section. Before applying a
steadyrest, it may be necessary to turn a true surface a
little wider than the jaws to provide a bearing for them.
This should be done very carefully to prevent the work
from mounting the tool. A sharp-pointed tool should be
used and very light cuts taken if the work is flexible. The
steadyrest is next clamped to the lathe bed opposite the
turned surface, and the jaws are adjusted in against this
surface, thus forming a bearing. Care should be taken not
to set up the jaws too tightly, as the work should turn
freely, but without play. That part against which the jaws
bear should be kept well oiled, and if the surface is finished
it should be protected by placing a strip of abrasive cloth
beneath the jaw with the abrasive side out; a strip of belt
leather is also used for this purpose, the object in each case
being to prevent the jaws from scratching and marring the
finished surface, as they tend to do, especially if at all
rough.

Sometimes it is desirable to apply a steadyrest to a surface that does not run true and one which is not to be
turned or cannot be turned without danger of excessive
bending; in such a case a device called a "cat-head" is used.
This is simply a sleeve which is placed over the untrue surface to serve as a bearing for the steadyrest. The sleeve
is made to run true by adjusting four supporting set-screws
at each end, and the jaws of the steadyrest are set against
it, thus supporting the work.

When is a follow-rest used for supporting slender rods or shafts?

A follow-rest is used when it is desirable to have a support which is close to the turning tool and follows it. The

follow-rest differs from the steadyrest in that it is attached to and travels with the lathe carriage. One design, illustrated in Fig. 13, has two adjustable jaws which are located opposite the turning tool, thus providing support where it is most needed. Another design (not shown) has a single notched jaw that is adjustable vertically and horizontally.

In using a follow-rest for turning, a cut is started at the end and when the length of this turned part is slightly longer than the width of the follow-rest jaws, the latter are adjusted to this turned part. The tool is then fed across the shaft, which cannot spring away from the cut because of the supporting jaws. Some follow-rests have, instead of jaws, a bushing bored to fit the diameter being turned, different bushings being used for different diameters. The bushing forms a bearing for the work and holds it rigidly. Follow-rests of this general type are commonly used for turning long shafts.

If a turned surface is finished by filing, how is this done?

In a modern manufacturing practice many cylindrical parts are first reduced to nearly the required size by turning in some form of lathe, and then they are ground to the finished dimension. After a part has been hardened, grinding is the only practicable method of truing it. On the other hand, unhardened pieces can be finished by other means, but grinding is preferable for most cylindrical work, because it enables parts to be finished accurately to a given diameter in less time than would be required by any other known method. Turned parts, especially in the smaller shops, are often finished by filing and polishing with abrasive cloth, especially if great accuracy is not essential.

In filing a turned surface the work is rotated considerably faster than for turning, and the entire surface is filed by using a flat, single-cut file. The file is passed across the work and advanced sidewise after each forward stroke, until the entire surface is finished. The file should be kept in contact with the work continually, but on the return stroke the pressure should be relieved. The movement of the file during the forward or cutting stroke should be much slower than when filing in a vise. By moving the file slowly, the work can make a number of revolutions for each stroke, which tends to keep it round, as practically the same amount of metal is removed from the entire circumference. On the other hand, short rapid strokes tend to produce flat spots, or at least an irreguar surface, especially if the work can only make part of a revolution for each cutting stroke. The pressure on the file during the forward stroke should also be kept as nearly uniform as possible.

It is very difficult to file a part smooth and at the same time to keep it round and cylindrical, and the more filing that has to be done, the greater the chance of error. For this reason, the amount left for filing should be very small; in fact, the metal removed by filing should be just enough to take out the tool marks and give a smooth finish. Very often a satisfactory finish can be obtained with a turning tool, and filing is not necessary at all. The file generally used for lathe work is a "single-cut bastard" of "mill" section, having a length of from 12 to 14 inches.

Fig. 13. A Follow-rest is Attached to the Carriage and Follows the Tool in order to Support a Slender Part

Sometimes particles of metal collect between the teeth of a file and make deep scratches as the file is passed across the work. When this occurs, the teeth should be cleaned by using a wire brush or a file card, which is drawn across the file in the direction of the teeth. This forming of tiny particles between the teeth is known as "pinning" and it can sometimes be avoided by rubbing chalk on the file. Filing is not only done to obtain a smooth finish, but also to reduce the work to an exact diameter, as a very slight reduction can be made in this way. If a polish is desired, this can be obtained by holding a piece of abrasive cloth tightly around the work as it revolves, a fine finish being obtained by using the finer grades. Work requiring great accuracy should be finished by grinding. This usually is a separate operation. (The general subject of grinding is included in volume 2.)

What are mandrels and why are they used?

Many parts such as bushings, small pulleys, etc., have holes which must be concentric with an outer surface. The general procedure is to finish the hole first. The part is then placed on a tight-fitting "mandrel" which has centers and serves to support the work while the outer surface is being turned. To illustrate, assume that bushing, Fig. 14, has finished hole through the center, and it is desired to turn the outside cylindrical and concentric with the hole. This could be done by forcing a tightly-fitted mandrel M, having accurately-centered ends, into the bushing and inserting the mandrel and work between the lathe centers h and h_1 as shown. Evidently, if the mandrel runs true on its centers, the hole in the bushing will also run true and the outside can be turned the same as though the mandrel and bushing were a solid piece. From this it will be seen that a mandrel simply forms a temporary support for parts that are reamed or bored and therefore cannot be centered.

Another example of work that would be turned on a mandrel is shown by the lower illustration, Fig. 14. This is a small cast-iron wheel having a finished hole through the hub, and the outer surface and sides of the rim are to be turned true with this hole. In this case, the casting would also be held by pressing a mandrel through the hub, as shown. This method, however, would only apply to comparatively small wheels because it would be difficult, if not impossible, to prevent a large wheel from turning on the mandrel in taking a cut, and even if it could be driven, large work could be done to better advantage on another type of machine. (The vertical boring mill, which is dealt with in another section, is used extensively for turning large wheels.) When turning the outside of the rim, a straight tool similar to that shown at t should be used, but for facing or turning the sides, it might be better, if not necessary, to use tools having bent ends as shown by the dotted lines; in fact, turning tools of various kinds are made with the ends bent to the right or left, as this enables them to be used on surfaces that could not be reached very well with a straight tool. If a comparatively large pulley is mounted near the end of the mandrel, it can be driven directly by pins attached to the faceplate and engaging the

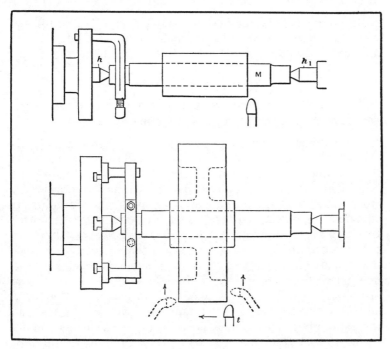

Fig. 14. (Upper Diagram) Bushing Mounted on Arbor for Turning
(Lower Diagram) Turning Pulley Held on an Arbor

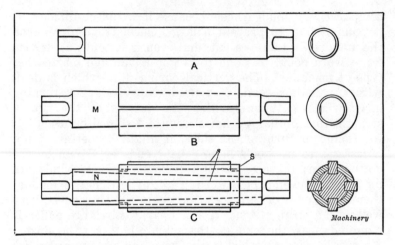

Fig. 15. Different Types of Lathe Mandrels

pulley arms. This method of driving is often employed when the diameter to be turned is large and the hole for the mandrel is so small that there will not be sufficient friction for driving.

What is the difference between a mandrel and an arbor and what types of mandrels are used?

The names *arbor* and *mandrel* are often used inter-changeably to designate a shaft or spindle that is employed for holding bored parts while turning the outside surfaces in a lathe. Tools of this class are known as "mandrels" by most small-tool manufacturers, whereas the spindles or supports for milling cutters, saws, etc., are called "arbors." In many machine shops and tool-rooms, however, the term arbor is commonly used to indicate a tool or shaft for hold-ing parts while turning, although some forms of work-holding devices are known as mandrels even by those who ordinarily use the name arbor. There are two general classes of work-supporting mandrels: the solid type and the expanding type. The solid type (*A*, Fig. 15) is usually made of tool steel and the body is ground to a standard size. The ends are somewhat reduced and flat spots are milled, as shown, to give the clamping screw of the dog a good grip. The body of the mandrel is usually tapered about 0.006 inch per foot. This taper makes it easier to insert the mandrel in a close-fitting hole, and it also permits slight variations in the diameter of different holes. As to hardening, the practice at the present time among manufacturers is to harden mandrels all over, but for extremely accurate work, one having hardened ends and a soft body is considered superior by some who believe that there is less tendency of distortion from internal stresses. Hardened mandrels are "seasoned" before finish-grinding to relieve these internal stresses.

Why are expanding mandrels used?

In shops where a great variety of work is being done and there are many odd-sized holes, some form of expanding mandrel can be used to advantage. The form shown at B, Fig. 15, instead of being solid, consists of a tapering inner mandrel M on which is placed a split bushing that can be expanded, within certain limits, by driving in the tapering member. The advantage of this type is that a comparatively small stock of mandrels is required, as different-sized bushings can be used. This type can also be fitted to holes of odd sizes, whereas a solid mandrel must be provided for each different size hole, unless the variation is very slight. Another form of expanding mandrel is shown at C. This type has a straight body in which four tapering grooves are cut lengthwise, as shown, and there is a sleeve containing four slots that are located to correspond with the tapering grooves. Strips s are fitted into these slots, and, as the body of the arbor is driven in, the strips are moved outward as they ascend the tapering grooves. By having different sets of these strips of various heights, one arbor of this type can be made to cover quite a range of sizes. It is not suited, however, to thin work, as the pressure, being concentrated in four places, would spring a flexible part out of shape.

The cone mandrel shown at A, in Fig. 16, is convenient for holding parts having comparatively large holes, as it can be adjusted for quite a range of diameters. The work is gripped between the two cones c and c_1 which are forced together by nut n. The cones are prevented from turning upon the arbor by keys. This style of arbor should not be

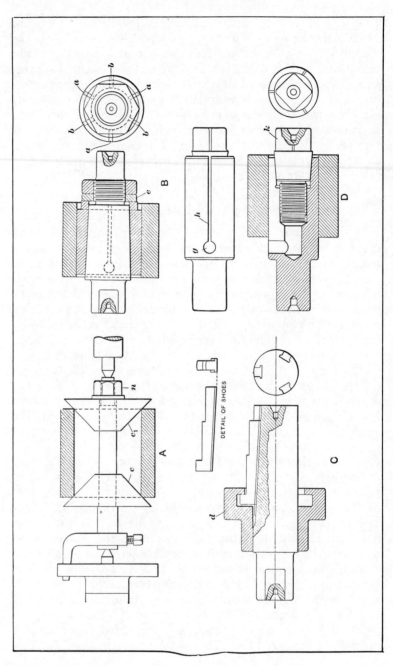

Fig. 16. (A) Cone Arbor. (B) Split-sleeve Expansion Arbor. (C) Sliding-shoe Arbor. (D) Arbor Expanded by Taper Plug

used for accurate work. The mandrel shown at B has a split sleeve which is expanded by a nut. This does away with the necessity of using the mandrel or arbor press to expand the sleeve. The collar e is interposed between the nut and the split bushing. This bushing is saw-cut at a from one end and at b from the other, thus allowing a fairly uniform expansion along its entire periphery. In this connection, it is well to note that the ends of the saw-cuts should be left tied together until after the sleeve has been hardened and ground; they can then readily be cut apart with a thin grinding wheel.

The mandrel shown at C consists of a body in which are milled tapered slots. The shoes (also shown in detail) have a narrow rib running along each side and this rib engages with the grooves in the sides of the slots, thus preventing the shoes from falling out. The collar d controls the action of the shoes and is ground to a sliding fit on the cylindrical portion of the arbor. It may be noted that the shoes have two shoulders, thus increasing the range of the arbor. By providing shoes of various diameters, the range can be increased considerably. This type of expanding mandrel has a wide range, but it is expensive to make, as compared with the more commonly used types. The mandrel illustrated at D might be called a solid expanding type. Three holes g are drilled 120 degrees apart and the saw-cuts h are milled as shown. The special screw k is tapered and threaded in the body. The end of this screw is squared and contains the center. When made as shown, this mandrel is not recommended for precision work. The expansion takes place at one end only and the center in the end of the screw may not remain true, even assuming that it was true originally.

What is the best method of inserting or removing a solid mandrel?

The best method of inserting a mandrel of the solid type in a hole is by using a press designed for that purpose, but if such a press is not available and it is necessary to drive the arbor in, a "soft" hammer, made of copper, lead, or other soft material, should be used to protect the centered end of the arbor. In either case, the arbor should not be forced in too tightly, for, if it fits properly, this will not be necessary in order to hold the work securely. The work might be easily broken by attempting to force the arbor in as far and as tightly as possible. In using an arbor or mandrel press, the work is placed on the base with the hole in a vertical position, and the arbor (which should be oiled slightly) is forced down into it by the press ram.

Some shops are equipped with power-driven mandrel or arbor presses. This type is particularly desirable for large work, owing to the greater pressure required for inserting mandrels that are comparatively large in diameter.

If one surface is eccentric to another, how is the eccentric surface turned?

Castings or forgings having two or more cylindrical surfaces eccentric to each other may be machined by a variety of methods. The most suitable method for any particular case depends upon a number of factors. The number of pieces to be machined is an important factor, in that it has an influence on the permissible tool expense. It is apparent that a high tool cost might not be expedient in the case of a small number of pieces; whereas, if a large number were to be machined, the cost of tooling and fixtures might be of little importance provided substantial gains in production were to be made by some improved method of handling.

When one cylindrical surface must be turned eccentric to another in an engine lathe, as when turning the eccentric of a steam engine, an arbor having two sets of centers is commonly used, as shown in Fig. 17. The distance x between the centers must equal one-half the total "throw" or stroke of the eccentric. The hub of the eccentric is turned upon the centers $a-a$, and the eccentric surface, upon the offset centers, as indicated by the illustration. Sometimes eccentrics are turned while held upon special fixtures attached to the faceplate.

Under what conditions are adjustable eccentric turning fixtures used?

The adjustable type of fixture is used when the amount of eccentricity or "throw" varies on different parts. Many different kinds of special chucks and fixtures have been de-

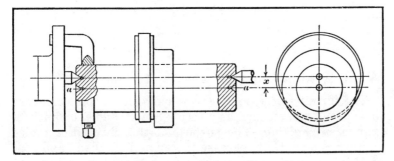

Fig. 17. Special Arbor for Turning Eccentrics

signed to provide the necessary adjustments for eccentric turning. In Fig. 18 is shown a fixture that can be adjusted to vary the amount of eccentricity of the part being turned. It consists essentially of a faceplate A, attached to the lathe spindle, and a plate B which is secured to the faceplate by means of a dovetail joint. The sliding member can be offset so that work which has been centered on and clamped to its face can be turned to any degree of eccentricity C within the capacity of the fixture. The plate B is provided with T-slots to receive the clamping bolts.

Fig. 19 shows a lathe equipped with adjustable fixtures for turning single-throw crankshafts of the type used extensively on textile machinery. Each end of the crankshaft is held in an adjustable slide. These slides are moved later-

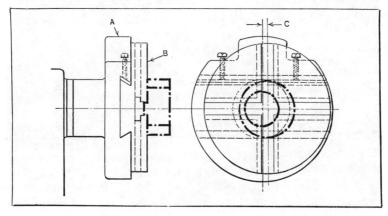

Fig. 18. Adjustable Faceplate for Eccentric Turning and Boring

ally by graduated adjusting screws to suit the throw of the crankshaft to be turned. A special and very rigid type of tool-holder is used.

What is knurling and why is it done?

The forming of a series of fine ridges upon the periphery of a circular part, such as a screw-head, handle, or knob, is known as *knurling*. The purpose of this checked or milled surface is usually to increase the grip of the hand and thus facilitate rotating the knurled part, although knurling may be done merely to produce an ornamental effect. The handles of gages and other tools are often knurled, and the round thumb-screws used on instruments, etc., usually have knurled edges. The knurling may consist of small closely-spaced ridges which are either at an angle to the axis of the circular surface or parallel with it, like the milled edge of a coin. A great many knurled surfaces, such as

Fig. 19. Reed-Prentice Lathe Equipped for Crankshaft Turning

are found on gage handles, thumb-screw heads, etc., are formed of small diamond-shaped projections produced by using two knurls having diagonal teeth inclining in opposite directions. This is known as *diamond* or *cross knurling*.

A knurling tool has a hardened disk or a set of disks mounted in a holder; when knurling, one or two of these disks (the number depending upon the type of knurling tool used) are pressed against the unhardened work, and rotate with it, thus reproducing upon the work the knurling which has been formed upon the periphery of the knurl itself. Knurling is done in the lathe either by a hand-controlled tool or by a tool which is held in the toolpost the same as for turning. The former method is known as *hand* knurling, and the latter, as *machine* knurling.

What types of lathe knurling tools are used?

Knurling tools include a number of different types and designs. An adjustable knurling tool is shown at *A*, Fig. 20. This tool has three knurls which operate on different sides of the work and thus support it so that the tool may be applied to flexible parts. Diameters up to about ¾ inch may be knurled, the adjustment being effected by screwing the handle in or out. The handle is hollow and contains an extra set of three knurls. Another hand knurling tool is illustrated at *B*. When using this type of tool, the inner or knurling end is supported upon some form of rest, such as a T-rest, and, in this way, a leverage is obtained for pressing the knurl against the under side of the work by forcing the outer end of the handle downward. A tool of this kind is used for knurling the narrow edges of screw-heads, etc., which do not require a traversing movement of the tool, such as is necessary when knurling a surface that is wider than the knurl. It is adjustable and will hold knurls of any width up to ½ inch. Ordinarily, a set of knurls is provided with a holder of this kind; these knurls vary as to width, form, and pattern. For instance, some knurls have a flat edge and produce straight lines upon the work, the pattern being similar to the milled edge of a coin. Other knurls are made concave in order to fit the rounding edge of a screw-head, whereas others have fancy patterns in order to produce ornamental effects.

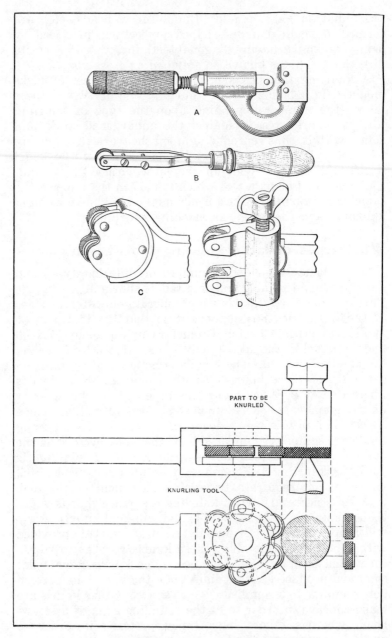

Fig. 20. Different Types of Knurling Tools

The knurling end of a tool which is adapted to lathe work is shown at *C*. This tool produces cross or diamond knurling, which is one of the patterns or designs in common use. The shank of the tool is held in the toolpost like a turning tool. The rocking holder which carries the two knurls fits into a tongued circular seat in the shank. The holder is thus free to swivel when brought into contact with the work so that both of the rolls bear on the metal with an even pressure. If it were not for this self-centering feature, one of the knurls would press deeper into the work than the other, thus producing an irregular pattern.

Another design of self-centering knurling tool for the lathe is shown at *D*. The knurls are held by adjustable arms which may be moved toward or away from each other for varying the distance between the knurls. These arms remain parallel and are adjusted by a right- and left-hand screw that is turned by the thumb-nut shown. The knurl-holder proper is connected to the shank of the tool by a rocking joint so that the knurls bear evenly upon the work.

The knurling tool shown by the diagram at the bottom of Fig. 20 has three pairs of knurls which are mounted in a revolving holder that not only serves to locate any pair of knurls in the working position, but also permits the knurls to bear against the surface with an equal pressure. Concave knurls are sometimes used for knurling rounded edges on screw heads, etc.

How is the lathe used in knurling?

The diagram at the bottom of Fig. 20 illustrates how a lathe knurling tool is used. The two knurls in use have teeth or ridges that incline to the right on one knurl and to the left on the opposite knurl, as shown by the end view. When these two knurls are pressed against the work as the latter revolves, one knurl forms a series of left-hand ridges and the other knurl, right-hand ridges, which cross and form the diamond-shaped knurling which is generally used. If the surface to be knurled is wider than the knurls, the power feed of the lathe should be engaged and the knurling tool is traversed back and forth until the diamond-shaped projections are well formed. To prevent forming a double set of projections, feed the knurl in with considerable pressure at the start, then partially relieve the pressure before engaging the power feed.

The speed of the lathe should be very slow for knurling. Before beginning to knurl, adjust the lathe carriage until about one-third or one-half the width of the knurl is in contact with the surface to be knurled; then, with the work revolving, feed the cross-slide and knurl inward until well-formed knurling is obtained. It may be desirable at this point to feed the knurl in to the full depth, especially if the knurling is fine; but usually knurling is done by several passages of the knurl across the work and by feeding it inward before each passage until the full depth is obtained. The longitudinal feeding movement of the lathe carriage is used for knurling. When the leading edge of the knurl has passed the left-hand face or edge of the knurled part, the carriage feed is reversed. This reversal should occur while the knurl is still in contact with the work. For knurling steel, oil should be used; lard oil will give good results. Cast iron should be knurled dry. While knurling, keep the surface free from any minute loose particles or chips, as these will mar the surface.

The knurls commonly used for lathe work have spiral teeth and ordinarily there are three classes, known as coarse, medium, and fine. The medium pitch is generally used. The teeth of coarse knurls have a spiral angle of 36 degrees and the pitch of the knurled cut (measured parallel to the axis of the work) should be about 8 per inch. For medium knurls, the spiral angle is $29\frac{1}{2}$ degrees and the pitch, measured as before, is 12 per inch. For fine knurls, the spiral angle is $25\frac{3}{4}$ degrees and the pitch 20 per inch. The knurls should be about $\frac{3}{4}$ inch in diameter and $\frac{3}{8}$ inch wide. When made to these dimensions, coarse knurls have 34 teeth; medium, 50 teeth; and fine knurls, 80 teeth.

Why are the turned surfaces of some bearings finished by burnishing with hardened rollers?

Finishing turned surfaces by burnishing with a hardened roller (or rollers) is done in some shops to obtain a dense, smooth, wear-resistant surface, but many burnished surfaces are not wear-resistant and flake off. While grinding is the common method of finishing turned surfaces requiring smoothness and accuracy, burnishing has been applied in finishing many locomotive and car journals, crankpins, piston-rods, etc. When burnishing is done in a lathe, the rolling tool may be held in the toolpost or it may be held in a special holder at the rear of the cross-slide to permit burnishing without removing the turning tool from the regular tool-holder. The roller may be made of Stellite or of a good grade of high-speed tool steel hardened and ground. The roller may be traversed by the regular power feed of the carriage. The regular burnishing machines used for car axles are equipped with front and rear rollers to equalize the thrust or pressure of rolling. By setting the front roller at a slight angle, a self-feeding action is obtained so that the use of a feed-screw is unnecessary. The surface to be burnished should be turned true and with tool marks or ridges practically eliminated. Since burnishing merely flattens the minute ridges, the surface will be of poor quality, especially if the ridges are so large that they spread out under the pressure of the roller, thus forming flakes which are liable to break off when the bearing or other part is in use.

Taper Turning in Lathe and Taper Attachments

Many machine parts, tool shanks, arbor shanks, etc., have tapering surfaces. Taper fits are desirable for certain classes of machine parts because the taper insures a tight fit and the parts are readily assembled or separated. Many arbors, twist drills, milling cutters, and other tools have taper shanks which fit into taper holes in machine spindles. The taper fitting centers or aligns the tool and drives it more or less through frictional resistance. Because of these numerous applications, lathes are frequently used for taper turning and boring.

How is a lathe arranged for taper turning by adjustment of tailstock?

If the part to be turned is held between the centers, one method of turning a taper (on a lathe not equipped with a taper attachment) is to set the tailstock center out of alignment with the headstock center. When both of these centers are in line, the movement of the tool is parallel to the axis of the work and, consequently, a cylindrical surface is produced; but if the tailstock is set out of alignment, as shown in Fig. 1, the work will then be turned tapering as the tool is traversed from a to b, because the axis x-x is at an angle with the movement of the tool. The amount of taper or the difference between the diameters at the ends for a given length will depend upon how much center h_1 is set over from the central position. To adjust the tailstock, the clamp nuts are first loosened and then the upper part is shifted sidewise by turning a screw provided for this purpose.

How is the amount of tailstock offset determined for turning a given taper?

There are various methods of determining how much to adjust the tailstock laterally for obtaining a given amount

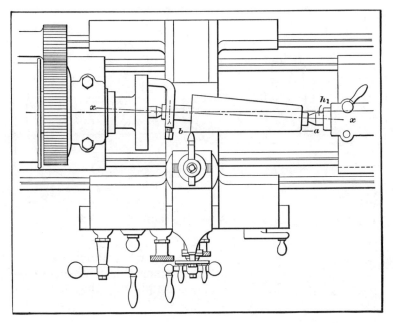

Fig. 1. Taper Turning by the Offset-center Method on Lathe not Equipped with Taper Attachment

of taper. A simple and practical method is to turn small sections at the beginning and end of the tapering part, making the diameters equal to the diameters at the largest and smallest part of the taper. The work is then set by these turned-down grooves or sections by using a caliper tool. This tool, Fig. 2, has a pointer p that is free to swing about a pivot r which should be set to about the same height as the center of the work. The tailstock center should be adjusted laterally until pointer p, as it is swung vertically, barely touches the large and small diameters previously turned. The travel of the carriage and turning tool will then be parallel to a line representing the taper required.

When there are a number of tapered pieces to be turned to the same taper, the adjustment of the tailstock center will have to be changed unless the total length of each piece and the depth of the center holes are the same in each case. It should be mentioned that on work of this kind, especially if great accuracy is required, the final finish is

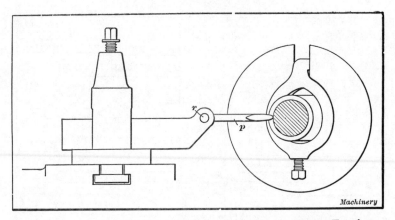

Fig. 2. Caliper Tool Used in Adjusting Tailstock for Taper Turning

often obtained by grinding in a regular grinding machine, instead of by filing in the lathe. When this method is employed, a lathe is used merely to rough-turn the part close to size.

Is it practicable to calculate the amount of tailstock offset for taper turning?

The amount that the tailstock center should be set over for turning a given amount of taper can easily be estimated, but it should be remembered that the estimated amount of offset is not absolutely correct, and is only intended to locate the center approximately.

If Taper Extends Full Length of Work.—If the taper extends along the entire length of the part to be turned, the tailstock is offset from its central position an amount equal to one-half the difference between the large and small end diameters.

Example.—A part 10 inches long is tapered throughout its length. The small end diameter is 1½ inches and the large end diameter is 2 inches. Determine the tailstock offset.

$$\text{Offset} = \frac{2 - 1\frac{1}{2}}{2} = \frac{1}{2} \times \frac{1}{2} = \frac{1}{4} \text{ inch}$$

If Taper per Foot is Given.—If the taper is given in inches per foot, divide the total length of the work, in inches, by 12 and multiply quotient by one-half the required taper per foot to find the amount of tailstock offset.

Example.—A taper plug has a total length of 7½ inches and the taper per foot is ¾ inch. Determine the tailstock offset.

$$\text{Offset} = \frac{7.5}{12} \times \frac{0.75}{2} = 0.234 \text{ or } \frac{15}{64} \text{ inch.}$$

If Diameters and Lengths Are Given.—Divide total length of the work, in inches, by the length of the tapered section and multiply quotient by one-half the difference between the large and small end diameters of the tapered section.

Example.—A shaft having a total length of 10 inches is tapered at one end. The length of the taper is 4 inches, the small diameter is 1⅜ inches, and the large diameter 1⅝ inches. Determine the offset.

$$\text{Offset} = \frac{10}{4} \times \frac{1\frac{5}{8} - 1\frac{3}{8}}{2} = 0.3125 \text{ or } \frac{5}{16} \text{ inch}$$

If Total or Included Angle of Taper is Given.—Find in a table of trigonometric functions the tangent of *one-half* of the given angle (angle as measured from the center line). Multiply this tangent by the total length of the work to obtain the tailstock offset.

Example.—A shaft 10 inches long has a taper section 5 inches long. The included angle of the taper is 5 degrees. Determine the offset.

$$\text{Tangent of } 2\frac{1}{2} \text{ degrees is } 0.04366$$

$$\text{Offset} = 0.04366 \times 10 = 0.4366 \text{ or } \frac{7}{16} \text{ inch}$$

Why is a taper attachment preferable for taper turning?

Turning tapers by setting over the tailstock center has some objectionable features. When the lathe centers are not in alignment, as when set for taper turning, they bear unevenly in the work centers because the axis of the work is at an angle with them; this causes the work centers to

wear unevenly and results in inaccuracy. The adjustment of the tailstock center must also be changed for turning duplicate tapers, unless the length of each piece and the depth of the center holes are the same. To overcome these objections, many lathes are equipped with a device especially designed for turning tapers. This is known as a taper attachment. It permits the lathe centers to be kept in alignment for taper turning, the same as for cylindrical turning, and enables more accurate work to be done. Taper attachments are not only used for taper turning and boring, but for taper thread cutting. The section, however, deals only with taper turning. For information on taper thread cutting, see Cutting Screw Threads in the Lathe.

What is the general function of a taper attachment and how does it operate?

When a taper attachment is used for taper turning (see Fig. 3), the tailstock center remains in its central position the same as for cylindrical turning. The general function of the taper attachment is to move the cross-slide and cutting tool laterally while the carriage moves longitudinally or in a lengthwise direction. The rate or extent of the lateral movement for a given lengthwise movement determines the amount of taper. Taper attachments are so designed that this amount can be varied from zero up to a maximum large enough to include most taper-turning and boring operations. The taper attachment does not interfere with straight or cylindrical turning and boring and it is a permanent part of the lathe and is always in position ready for use, after proper adjustment. A taper part is turned practically the same as a cylindrical part; that is, the power feed is used and, as the carriage moves along the bed, the cross-slide and tool are gradually moved laterally by the taper attachment.

Main Features of a Taper Attachment.—All taper attachments operate on the same general principle, but they differ more or less in construction. All taper attachments have a bar *A* (see Figs. 3 to 5 inclusive) which can be swiveled in a horizontal plane about a central pivot and in either direction. The angle to which this bar is set determines the angle of the taper. Graduations at the end of the bar show the position required for obtaining a given taper per foot or angle in degrees. A sliding block or shoe B moves along bar A which is held stationary when the attachment is in use. Shoe B is connected in some manner with the cross-slide, thus causing this slide to move as the carriage feeds along the bed. This movement will be outward if the small end of the taper is adjacent to the tailstock. All taper attachments have these main features, but there is more or less difference in regard to the connection between the sliding shoe and the cross-slide or in the method of transmitting the cross movement to this slide.

Plain Type of Cross-feed Screw.—On some lathes the cross-feed screw (connecting with the lower or main slide) is fixed in its bearings against endwise movement. When this is the case, the nut connecting the main cross-feed screw with the slide must be disconnected from the slide in order to permit it to move laterally as shoe B moves

Fig. 3. Example of Taper Turning with Taper Attachment. Amount of Taper Depends Upon Angular Position of Bar A

along bar *A*. (This may be done by removing a bolt which fastens the nut to the slide when the taper attachment is not in use.) The connection between the sliding shoe and cross-slide is by means of a direct-connecting link or yoke; hence, the cross-feed nut must be disconnected to permit movement of the cross-slide. If there is an upper tool-slide, this can be used for adjusting the tool in or out when taking successive cuts. If the lathe does not have a compound slide, then the plain type of attachment is quite inconvenient so far as tool adjustments are concerned.

Telescopic Type of Cross-feed Screw.—This type is so designed that the main cross-feed screw can be moved axially along with the cross-slide when the taper attachment is in use. This axial movement is made possible by a splined or telescopic connection with the feed screw handle at the front. With this arrangement, the feed screw moves in or out of this telescopic connection when the cross-slide is moved in or out by the taper attachment; consequently, the cross-feed screw nut does not need to be disconnected from the cross-slide and this main feed screw can also be used for adjusting the tool in or out. This is a convenient feature, especially if the lathe does not have a compound slide.

Operation of Taper Attachment, Fig. 3.—The exact method of arranging an attachment for use in turning or boring varies somewhat with different designs. In using the attachment shown in Fig. 3, first, loosen bolts or nuts *D* and set the guide bar *A* to the given angle or taper per foot as shown by the graduations. Next, tighten bolts *D* and attach an arm (not shown) to the lathe bed, thus holding guide bar *A* stationary. The sliding shoe *B* connects directly with the cross-slide by a yoke which is clamped to the shoe by means of a lever *E*.

Operation of Taper Attachment, Fig. 4.—In using this attachment, bar *A* is set either to the required taper per foot or to a given angle in degrees as determined by graduations at the ends of the bar. The nuts *D* are used to clamp the bar securely in the required position. Arm *C* is clamped to the lathe bed by tightening nuts *F* so that bar *A* is held stationary. Nut *G* is loosened to permit draw-bar *H* to slide freely through arm *C*. When the attachment is not in use, nut *G* is tightened so that the auxiliary draw-bar *H* will insure a smooth easy movement of arm *C* along the bed without any cramping tendency. The taper bar *A* may be adjusted to the exact position required by means of the knurled knob *J*. This attachment has the telescopic type of cross-feed screw. It has a maximum capacity of 6 inches taper per foot. The attachment contains twenty-four permanently sealed anti-friction bearings to reduce frictional loads, especially in turning or boring exceptionally steep tapers.

Operation of Taper Attachment, Fig. 5.—This taper attachment is mounted at the rear of the bed upon a finished pad having a T-slot and extending the full length of the bed. When the attachment is in use, it is moved along the bed and securely clamped opposite the operating position. The taper bar *A* has a slot which is engaged by the taper

Fig. 4. Rear View of Another Taper Attachment. Bar A is set
Either to Required Taper per Foot or to Given Angle in Degrees

bar shoe *B*. As this shoe moves along the slot, it transmits motion to the cross-slide through the cross-feed screw. When the attachment is to be used, the cross-feed screw sleeve at the rear of the carriage is unlocked and connected by bolts with the taper bar shoe. The angular position of bar *A* is indicated either by degree graduations up to an included angle of 20 degrees or by tapers per foot up to 4 inches. After the taper bar is unlocked, it is adjusted by turning knob *J* and is then reclamped. Before taking a cut, the carriage with the tool in position should be moved along the full length of the work to make sure that the taper bar shoe does not run out of the slot in the taper bar.

The function of stop-rod *F* is to eliminate all backlash so that a cut may be taken in either direction without any lagging of the tool at the points of reversal. When cuts in both directions are desirable, the stop-rod is clamped to the

Fig. 5. A Third Design of Taper Attachment—View is from
Front of Carriage

taper bar shoe by nut *C*. The jam nuts *D* are also adjusted so as to make contact with either side of plate *E* attached to the cross-slide, thus making a positive connection between the cross-slide and the taper bar shoe. When this stop-rod is in use, the upper or tool-rest slide can be used in adjusting the tool in or out; or the lower or cross-slide can be used by adjusting one of the jam nuts *D*, positioning the cross-slide until plate *E* is in contact with this jam nut, and then adjusting the other jam nut *D* against the plate *E*. When the taper attachment is not in use, be sure to loosen nut *C* before using the power cross-feed.

Combination or Dual Type of Taper Attachment.—Some taper attachments are so designed that the connection between the sliding shoe at the rear and the cross-slide may be either (1) through the cross-feed screw, or (2) through a yoke or bar connecting directly with the cross-slide. In other words, the taper attachment may be arranged to transmit motion to the cross-slide by either of these two methods. An attachment of this type requires a telescopic connection for the cross-feed screw. When motion is transmitted from the sliding shoe to the cross-slide through the cross-feed screw, then the cross-feed screw and cross-slide move laterally together. The yoke attached to the cross-slide also moves laterally at the same time. With this arrangement, the main cross-slide can be adjusted in or out by merely turning the cross-slide handle at the front. When such adjustments are made, the cross-slide and yoke move relative to the cross-feed screw. Such relative movement, however, is not possible when the yoke is clamped to the sliding shoe. The taper attachment may be used with the yoke unclamped, when taking finishing cuts or in cutting taper screw threads. For heavier cuts, the yoke is clamped to the shoe, thus providing a more rigid connection and transferring the strain of the cutting from the cross-feed screw to the yoke connecting with the cross-slide. With this arrangement, the clamp must be loosened if an adjustment of the main or lower slide is required. Ordinarily, such adjustments are unnecessary because changes for regulating the depth of cut may be made with the compound rest or upper slide. The following rules may prove useful in connection with taper turning operations.

If end diameters and length of taper are given, how is angle of taper attachment determined?

The problem is to determine the angle as measured from the center line—that is, one-half the included or total angle.

Rule.—To obtain the tangent of the required angle, divide one-half the difference between the diameters of the large and small ends of the tapered section by the length of the tapered section.

Example.—Total length of part is 10 inches; length of tapered portion is 4 inches; diameter at small end of taper is 2 inches; diameter at large end of tapered section is $3\frac{1}{8}$ inches. To what angle should slide of taper attachment be set?

$$\text{Tangent of angle} = \frac{0.5 \times (3\frac{1}{8} - 2)}{4} = 0.1406$$

A table of trigonometric functions shows that 0.1406 is the tangent of 8 degrees, practically. This is one-half of the included angle of the taper and the taper attachment slide is set to this angle.

If end diameters and length of taper are given, how is equivalent taper per foot determined?

If taper-per-foot graduations are to be used in setting a taper attachment but the taper per foot is not given, proceed as follows:

Rule.—Divide difference between diameters of large and small ends of tapered section by length of this section; then multiply quotient by 12.

Example.—Total length of part is 10 inches; length of tapered portion is 4 inches; diameter at small end is 2 inches; diameter at large end of tapered section is $3\frac{1}{8}$ inches. To what taper-per-foot graduation should the taper attachment be set?

$$\text{Taper per foot} = \frac{3\frac{1}{8} - 2}{4} \times 12 = 3\frac{3}{8} \text{ inches per foot}$$

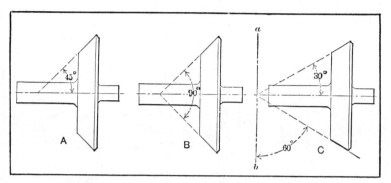

Fig. 6. Example of Taper Work Turned by Using Compound Rest

When is the compound rest used for taper turning?

The compound rest is used for turning steep tapers or angles. The amount of taper that can be turned by setting over the tailstock center and by the taper attachment is limited, as the centers can only be offset a certain distance, and the slide of the taper attachment cannot be swiveled beyond a certain position. For steep tapers, the upper tool-slide E is swiveled to the required angle and used as indicated in Fig. 7, which shows a plan view of a slide set for turning the valve V. The base of the tool-slide is graduated in degrees and the position of these graduations shows to what angle the slide is set. Suppose the seat of valve V is to be turned to an angle of 45 degrees with the axis or center, as shown on the drawing at A, Fig. 6. To set the tool-slide, nuts on either side, which hold it rigidly to the lower slide, are first loosened and the slide is then turned until the 45-degree graduation is exactly opposite the zero line; the slide is then tightened in this position. In this particular instance the tool-slide is set to the same angle given on the drawing, but this is not always the case. If the draftsman had given the included angle of 90 degrees, as shown at B, which would be another way of expressing it, the setting of the slide would, of course, be the same as before, or to 45 degrees, but the number of degrees marked on the drawing does not correspond with the angle to which the slide must be set. As another illustration, suppose the valve were to be turned to an angle of 30 degrees with the

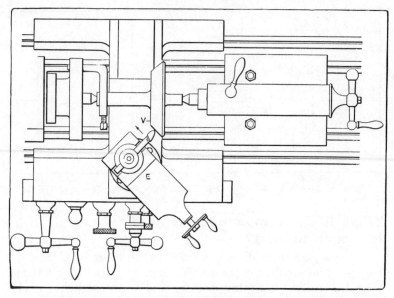

Fig. 7. Plan View Showing Method of Turning a Taper with the Compound Rest

axis as shown at *C.* In this case the slide would not be set to 30 degrees but to 60 degrees, because in order to turn the work to an angle of 30 degrees, the slide must be 60 degrees from its zero position, as shown. From this it will be seen that the number of degrees marked on the drawing does not necessarily correspond to the angle to which the slide must be set, as the graduations on the rest show the number of degrees that it is moved from its zero position, which corresponds to the line *a–b.* The angle to which the slide should be set can be found, when the drawing is marked as at *A* or *C,* by subtracting the angle given from 90 degrees. When the included angle is given, as at *B,* subtract one-half the included angle from 90 degrees to obtain the required setting. The lathe centers are set in line the same as for straight turning, as otherwise the angle will be incorrect.

Is it practicable to turn a tapering part by combining the longitudinal and cross-feeds?

This method is practicable and it has been applied to a certain class of lathes made by a well-known manufacturer.

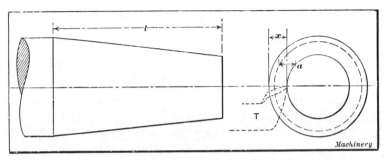

Fig. 8. Tool Point Should be in Same Horizontal Plane as Axis of Work for Taper Turning

This geared taper turning mechanism is designed to turn tapers within a certain range of diameters on any length of work up to the full center distance capacity of the lathe. The taper is produced by the simultaneous functioning of the longitudinal and cross feeding mechanisms, the various degrees of taper being determined by the relation of the length of carriage travel to the rate of cross-feed of the tool-slide. The cross-feed rate is controlled by a series of change-gears in the apron. The taper turning mechanism is operated through the feed-rod and the regular apron gearing.

Why is the position of the tool important in taper turning?

The cutting edge of the tool for turning tapers should be at the same height as the center or axis of the work, whether a taper attachment is used or not. The importance of this will be apparent by referring to Fig. 8. To turn the taper shown, the tool T would be moved back a distance x (assuming that an attachment is used) while traversing the length l. In order to illustrate the principle, assume that the tool could be placed as high as point a, the setting of the attachment remaining as before; then the tool would again move back a distance x, while traversing a distance l, but the large end would be undersized (as shown by the dotted line) if the diameters of the small ends were the same in each case. Of course, if the tool point were only slightly above or below the center, the resulting error would also be small. The tool can easily be set central by comparing the height of the cutting edge at the point of the tool with one of the lathe centers before placing the work in the lathe.

Why have certain tapers been standardized and what are the common standards?

Tapering tool shanks, tapering holes in machine tool spindles for receiving these shanks, and other tapering parts are used so extensively that standard tapers are required to insure interchangeability for tapers the same as for screw threads. Certain types of small tools and machine parts, such as twist drills, end mills, arbors, lathe centers, etc., are provided with taper shanks which fit into spindles or sockets of corresponding taper, thus providing not only accurate alignment between the tool or other part and its supporting member, but also more or less frictional resistance for driving the tool. There are several standards for "self-holding" tapers, but the Morse, the Brown & Sharpe and the Jarno are the standards most widely used by American manufacturers.

The name *self-holding* has been applied to the smaller tapers—like the Morse and the Brown & Sharpe—because, where the angle of the taper is only 2 or 3 degrees, the shank of a tool is so firmly seated in its socket that there is considerable frictional resistance to any force tending to turn or rotate the tool relative to the socket. The term "self-holding" is used to distinguish relatively small tapers from the larger or *self-releasing* type. A milling machine spindle having a taper of 3½ inches per foot is an example of a self-releasing taper. The included angle in this case is over 16 degrees and the tool or arbor requires a positive locking device to prevent slipping, but the shank may be released or removed more readily than one having a smaller taper of the self-holding type.

Morse Taper.—The taper for different numbers of Morse tapers is slightly different, but it is approximately ⅝ inch per foot in most cases. The actual tapers, accurate to four decimal places, range from 0.5986 to 0.6315 inch per foot. Morse taper shanks are used on a variety of tools, and exclusively on the shanks of twist drills.

Brown & Sharpe Taper.—This standard taper is used for taper shanks on tools such as end mills and reamers, the

Rules for Finding Taper per Foot and Other Important Dimensions

Given	To Find	Rule
The taper per foot.	The taper per inch.	Divide the taper per foot by 12.
The taper per inch.	The taper per foot.	Multiply the taper per inch by 12.
End diameters and length of taper in inches.	The taper per foot.	Subtract small diameter from large; divide by length of taper, and multiply quotient by 12.
Large diameter and length of taper in inches and taper per foot.	Diameter at small end in inches.	Divide taper per foot by 12; multiply by length of taper, and subtract result from large diameter.
Small diameter and length of taper in inches, and taper per foot.	Diameter at large end in inches.	Divide taper per foot by 12; multiply by length of taper, and add result to small diameter.
The taper per foot and two diameters in inches.	Distance between two given diameters in inches.	Subtract small diameter from large; divide remainder by taper per foot, and multiply quotient by 12.
The taper per foot.	Amount of taper in a certain length given in inches.	Divide taper per foot by 12; multiply by given length of tapered part.

taper being approximately ½ inch per foot for all sizes except for taper No. 10, where the taper is 0.5161 inch per foot. Brown & Sharpe taper sockets are used for many arbors, collets, and machine tool spindles, especially milling machines and grinding machines. In many cases there are a number of different lengths of sockets corresponding to the same number of taper; all these tapers, however, are of the same diameter at the small end.

Jarno Taper.—The Jarno taper is based on such simple formulas that practically no calculations are required when the number of taper is known. The taper per foot of all Jarno taper sizes is 0.600 inch on the diameter. The diameter at the large end is as many eighths, the diameter at the small end is as many tenths, and the length as many half inches as are indicated by the number of the taper. For example, a No. 7 Jarno taper is 7/8 inch in diameter at the large end; 7/10, or 0.700 inch at the small end; and 7/2, or 3½ inches long; hence, the large and small end diameters,

or the length of a taper of given number, can be determined
by the following simple rules:

$$\text{Diameter at large end} = \frac{\text{No. of taper}}{8}$$

$$\text{Diameter at small end} = \frac{\text{No. of taper}}{10}$$

$$\text{Length of taper in inches} = \frac{\text{No. of taper}}{2}$$

American Standard Machine Tapers. — A self-holding
series of machine tapers for small tools and machine tool
elements was approved by the American Standards Association in 1937 and revised in 1953. This taper series consists of
twenty-two sizes. The three smaller sizes are taken from the
Brown & Sharpe tapers, Nos. 1, 2 and 3. These are followed
by eight sizes taken from the Morse Series, Nos. 1, 2, 3, 4, 4½,
5, 6, and 7. The American Standard continues with eleven
larger sizes, all having a taper of ¾ inch per foot. These
eleven sizes have the following large-end diameters: 2, 2.5,
3, 3.5, 4, 4.5, 5, 6, 8, 10, and 12 inches.

Taper Pins.—The American and British standards for
steel taper pins specify a taper of ¼ inch per foot.

Use of Chucks and Faceplates
Drilling and Boring in Lathe

Chucks of various designs and types are used on different classes of machine tools, either for holding a part while it is being operated upon or for holding some form of cutting tool. The chucks that are used on lathes and other types of turning machines hold and rotate the work, whereas the chucks of drilling machines hold and rotate drills, counter- bores, and other tools. Chucks vary greatly both in regard to their size and design. Some are of special construction and are intended for a limited class of work or for holding one particular part, although most work-holding devices of the latter class are known as jigs or fixtures, rather than chucks. The term "chuck," as applied in the machine shop, usually means a device which not only holds but rotates either the work or a cutting tool, although there are excep- tions as, for instance, in the case of planer chucks which are attached to the planer table and travel with it. Most work- holding devices which are classified as chucks, excepting magnetic chucks, have gripping jaws that are adjustable in order to adapt the chuck for holding parts or tools of different sizes. These jaws are operated either by screws by a combination of screws, or a spiral scroll and gearing, by compressed air, or by the engagement of conical surfaces which serve to move the chuck jaws radially by a wedging action. The magnetic chucks do not require jaws, as the work is held by magnetic force instead of by mechanical means.

When are chucks used to hold parts for turning or other operations?

Many disk- or ring-shaped parts that are turned in the lathe cannot be held between the lathe centers like shafts and other similar pieces, and it is often necessary to hold them in a chuck which is placed on the lathe spindle. The work is gripped by the chuck jaws which can be moved in

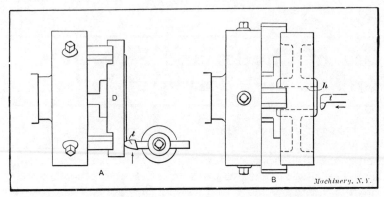

Fig. 1.   (A) Radial Facing.   (B) Boring a Pulley Held in Chuck

or out to accommodate various diameters. The diagram *A*, Fig. 1, shows a disk held in a chuck for facing the side by feeding tool *t* inward or radially. Another example of chuck work is shown at *B*. In this case, a cast-iron pulley is to have a true hole *h* bored through the hub. The casting should be set true by the rim instead of by the rough-cored hole in the hub. After a casting or other part has been set true by the most important surface, all other surfaces which require machining should be tested to make sure that they all can be finished to the proper size. The hole is bored by tool *t* as the carriage moves along the bed. The power feed would be used ordinarily.

Work that is held in a chuck is sometimes sprung out of shape by the pressure of the chuck jaws so that, when the part is bored or turned, the finished surfaces are untrue after the jaws are released and the work has resumed its normal shape. This applies more particularly to frail parts, such as rings, thin cylindrical parts, etc. Occasionally, the distortion can be prevented by so locating the work with relation to the chuck jaws that the latter bear against a rigid part. Special end-clamping chucks are sometimes used for holding bushings and similar parts, especially for grinding operations requiring accuracy.

What classes of chucks are used on lathes?

There are three classes of chucks ordinarily used on the engine lathe, known as the independent, universal, and com-

Fig. 2. Lathe Having Four-jaw Independent Chuck on the Spindle

bination types. The *independent chuck* (Fig. 2) is so named because each jaw can be adjusted in or out independently of the others by turning the jaw screws with a wrench. The jaws are reversible, to adapt them either to outside or inside chucking. In outside chucking, the jaws grip the outer surface of the work as shown in Fig. 2. When the jaws are reversed, it is possible to grip inner surfaces of fairly small diameters. The jaws of the *universal chuck* all move together and keep the same distance from the center, and they can be adjusted by turning any one of the screws, whereas, with the independent type, the chuck wrench must be applied to each jaw screw. The *combination chuck*, as the name implies, may be changed to operate either as an independent or universal type. The advantage of the universal chuck is that round and other parts of a uniform shape are located in a central position for turning without any adjustment. The independent type is, however, preferable in some respects, as it is usually stronger and adapted for holding odd-shaped pieces, because each jaw can be set to any required position. The *collet chuck* is another class which is commonly applied to tool-room lathes, turret lathes, bench lathes, etc., usually for holding rods or bar stock

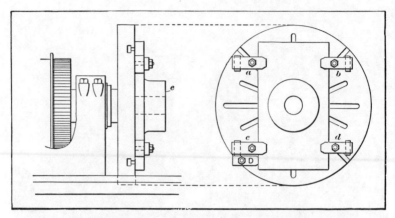

Fig. 3. Casting Clamped to Faceplate for Turning and Boring

which is inserted through the hollow spindle of the machine, so that the end projecting beyond the chuck may be operated upon. The collet type of chuck consists of a split sleeve or collet which has a tapering or conical end that fits into a seat of corresponding taper so that a lengthwise movement of the collet causes a contraction or expansion of the gripping surfaces. The collet type of chuck is the most convenient form for gripping pieces that are long in relation to their diameter, such as bar stock, etc. Some collet chucks are closed by a backward pull and others by a forward push, the movement for closing depending upon the inclination of the taper.

What classes of work are attached to the lathe faceplate?

Some castings or forgings are so shaped that they cannot conveniently be held in a chuck, and work of this kind is often clamped to a faceplate. Most lathes have two faceplates: One of small diameter is used principally for driving work turned between centers, and a large one is used for holding heavy or irregularly shaped pieces; either of these can be attached to the spindle, and the large faceplate has a number of slots through which clamping bolts can be inserted. An example of faceplate work is shown in Fig. 3 This is a rectangular-shaped casting having a round boss or projection, the end e of which is to be turned parallel with the finished back face of the casting. A rough cored hole through the center of the boss also is to be bored true. To perform this operation in the lathe, clamp the finished surface of the casting directly against the faceplate by bolts and clamps *a, b, c,* and *d,* as shown; the work would then be turned in the same way as if it were held in a chuck. By holding the casting in this way, face *e* will be finished parallel with the back surface, because the latter is clamped directly against the true-running surface of the faceplate. If a casting of this shape were small enough it could also be held in the jaws of an independent chuck, but, if the surface *e* needs to be exactly parallel with the back face, it is better to clamp the work to the faceplate.

The proper way to clamp a piece to the faceplate depends largely upon its shape and the location of the surface to be machined, but in any case it is necessary to hold it securely to prevent any shifting after a cut is started. Sometimes castings can be held by inserting bolts through previously drilled holes. If the hole to be bored is larger than the central hole in the faceplate, the casting should be clamped against parallel pieces, and not directly against the faceplate, to provide clearance for the tool when it reaches the inner end of the hole and prevent it from cutting the faceplate. The parallel pieces should be of the same thickness and be located near the clamps, in order to prevent springing the casting.

Driver for Faceplate Work.—When deep roughing cuts have to be taken, especially on large diameters, it is well to bolt a piece to the faceplate and against one side of the casting, as at *D,* to act as a driver and prevent the work from shifting. A faceplate driver is always placed to the rear, as determined by the direction of rotation, because the work tends to shift backward when a cut is being taken. If the surface which is clamped against the faceplate is finished, as in this case, the work will be less likely to shift if a piece of paper is placed between it and the faceplate.

What classes of work are held on an angle-plate attached to the faceplate?

An angle-plate is used in conjunction with a faceplate for holding elbows or other parts which cannot be clamped

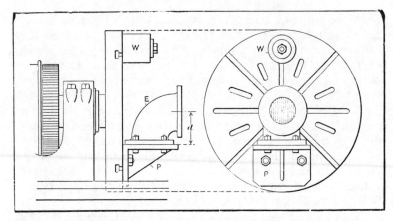

Fig. 4.   Cast Elbow Held on Angle-plate Attached to Faceplate

against a vertical surface.   Fig. 4 illustrates how an angle-plate is used for holding a cast-iron elbow E, the two flanges of which are to be faced true and square with each other. The shape of this casting is such that it would be very difficult to clamp it directly to the faceplate, but it is easily held on an angle-plate P, which is bolted to the faceplate.   The two surfaces of this angle-plate are square with each other so that, when one flange of the elbow is finished and bolted against the angle-plate, the other will be faced square. When setting up an angle-plate for work of this kind, the distance from its work-holding side to the center of the faceplate is made equal to the distance d between the center of one flange and the face of the other, so that the flange to be faced will run about true when bolted in place.

Counterbalance on Faceplate.—As the angle-plate and work are almost entirely on one side of the faceplate, a weight W is attached to the opposite side for counterbalancing.   Very often weights are also needed to counterbalance offset parts that are bolted directly to the faceplate. The necessity of counterbalancing depends somewhat upon the speed to be used for turning.   If the surface to be machined is small in diameter so that the lathe can be run quite rapidly, any unbalanced part should always be counterbalanced.

Clamping Work to Detached Faceplate.—Sometimes it is rather difficult to hold heavy pieces against the vertical surface of the faceplate while applying the clamps, and occasionally the faceplate is removed and placed in a horizontal position on the bench; the work can then be located approximately, and, after it is clamped, the faceplate is placed on the lathe spindle by the assistance of a hoist.

Faceplate Chuck Jaws.—Special faceplate jaws can often be used to advantage for holding work on large faceplates. Three or four of these jaws are bolted to the faceplate which is converted into a kind of independent chuck. These faceplate jaws are especially useful for holding irregularly shaped parts, as the different jaws can be located in any position.

How are faceplates and chucks attached to the spindle of a lathe?

The ends or "noses" of the spindles of most lathes are threaded and faceplates and chucks have threaded holes which fit the spindle screw thread accurately. Before mounting a faceplate or chuck on the spindle, first remove any dirt which may have accumulated either on the spindle nose thread or in threaded hole of the spindle chuck or faceplate. The thread should also be oiled slightly whenever it gets dry. In screwing a faceplate or chuck onto the spindle, it should be seated firmly against the shoulder at the inner end of the thread; but do not jam it too tightly as removal later may be difficult.

How are chucks and faceplates held on spindles conforming to the American Standard?

Some of the lathes in use at the present time have, instead of a threaded spindle end or "nose," the American standard lathe spindle nose. This standard includes four general types. It was developed primarily for turret lathes and automatic lathes but it is also applicable to engine lathes.

Type A.—The general type of standard nose designated as Type A, is designed to hold the faceplate or chuck in position by means of tapped holes and socket head capscrews. There is also a driving button on the spindle flange which engages a circular recess in the back of the chuck or faceplate.

Type B.—A second general type is so arranged that the chuck or faceplate may be held by bolts or studs passing through clearance holes in the spindle nose flange. Nuts bearing against the back of the flange hold the chuck or faceplate in position.

Type D.—The third general type is shown on an engine lathe, Fig. 5. The illustration shows the chuck in position ready for mounting. This spindle nose has six equally spaced clearance holes for receiving cam-lock studs projecting from the back of the faceplate or chuck. When the faceplate or chuck has been seated on the conical end of the spindle nose, these studs are in position to be engaged by cams which are turned, thus locking the studs and drawing the faceplate or chuck firmly back against its conical seat and the flange face. This type of nose is especially designed to save time in changing faceplates and chucks on machines requiring frequent changes or where the time element is of considerable importance. A partial turn of each of the cams releases the cam-lock studs and allows instant removal

Fig. 5. Engine Lathe Equipped with American Standard Cam-lock Spindle Nose. Six Cam-lock Studs on Chuck (Shown in Position for Mounting) are Engaged by Six Cams in Spindle Flange

of the chuck or faceplate. In mounting chucks on the spindle, the locking is also done quickly and easily by merely giving each cam a partial turn.

Type L.— A fourth type of spindle nose is provided with a long, steep taper for locating and centering chuck and face plates, with a key for driving, and with a flange nut for holding the chuck or face plate on the spindle. This type of spindle is available in five sizes and was added as an alternate standard for engine lathes, since many of this type have been used both here and abroad in the past.

Which types of American Standard spindle noses are applicable to engine lathes?

Engine lathes may be equipped either with Type D, A, or B, depending upon the service for which the lathe is intended, the size of the spindle nose, and the sizes of chucks to be used. This standard permits interchanging chucks, faceplates or other work-holding devices on different makes of engine lathes, turret and automatic lathes. The size of nose to be used on any particular lathe is determined both by the size of the hole in the spindle and by the size of the chuck or chucks which the machine requires. These standard spindle noses all have a conical projecting pilot with a taper of 3 inches per foot. The taper pilot and the flat face on the spindle insures chucks and fixtures running true within a fraction of a thousandth of an inch, even when transferred from one machine to another. The rigid mounting employed is well suited to modern high-production and high-speed requirements. The mating members are easy to clean, which facilitates keeping large faceplates running true.

Is there a standard for chucks to fit the standard spindle noses?

Yes, there is an American standard for chucks and chuck jaws. This standard includes eleven different chuck sizes ranging from 6 to 36 inches. (These nominal sizes are the same as the outside diameters excepting the 6- and 8-inch sizes which have outside diameters of 6½ and 8¼ inches.) There are also three classes of standard chucks. The medi-

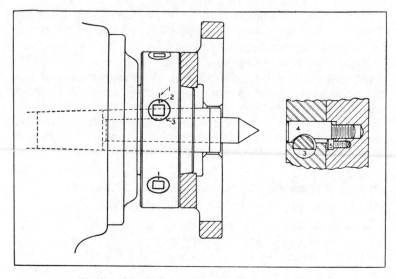

Fig. 6. Cam-lock Type of Lathe Spindle Nose

um-duty chucks of Class 1 are for application to engine lathes or other turning machines where the service is not severe and the chucks must be handled frequently. The heavy-duty tongue-and-groove jaw-type chucks of Class 2 are for application to turret lathes and other machines where the service requires heavy gripping. The heavy-duty serrated type of Class 3 is for application to those turret lathes subjected to exceptionally heavy duty.

How is a faceplate or chuck mounted on a cam-lock spindle nose?

When a lathe is equipped with a Type D spindle nose, proceed as follows in mounting faceplates or chucks: Wipe off all chips and dirt from the pilot and flange of the spindle nose and of the corresponding recess and shoulder on the faceplate or chuck, so that no chips remain that would otherwise prevent their running true. (See illustration Fig. 6, which shows the cam-lock spindle nose on a lathe.) Place the registration lines 2 on the heads of the six cam-locks so as to match the corresponding lines 1 on the outer rim of the spindle nose. Detents will hold them in these positions. Lift the faceplate or chuck up in line with the spindle, either by hand (resting it on a wooden block) or by using the sling of a crane, and push it onto the spindle nose. Tighten the cam-locks 3 by a "clockwise" turn of the wrench, pulling them up tight by hand—it is not necessary to use a hammer on the wrench. When the cam-locks are tightened, the registration lines 2 on their heads should be between the "three o'clock" and "six o'clock" positions. If any one of these does not register within this range, the mating stud 4 in the faceplate or chuck should be adjusted. (See detail view.) This is done by removing the hollow-head retaining screw 5, and by turning the stud 4 one or more complete turns to the right to shorten and to the left to lengthen. Be sure to replace the hollow-head retaining screw 5.

To remove the faceplate or chuck, reverse the operations. Unlock the cam-lock studs 3 by turning the wrench "counter-clockwise" until the registration lines 2 on the heads of the six cam-locks match the corresponding lines 1 on the flange of the spindle nose. Gently tap the faceplate or chuck with a lead hammer so as to loosen it, and then pull it away from the spindle nose.

When are lathes used for drilling holes?

The usual method of drilling holes is by using some type of drilling machine; but in some cases, a lathe is used because drilling is done in conjunction with other operations For example, if a hole is required in a part which is solid or without a drilled or cored hole, as delivered to the lathe, drilling would be necessary. Drilling usually is followed by other operations. For example, drilled holes frequently require reaming or boring after the drilling operation, to obtain a given diameter or greater accuracy. Parts which require drilling, reaming or boring usually are held in some form of chuck. Typical operations of this general character are included in this section.

What is the usual method of drilling holes in a lathe?

When a hole is to be bored from the solid, it is necessary to drill a hole before a boring tool can be used. One method of drilling in the lathe is to insert an ordinary twist drill in a holder or socket which is inserted in the tailstock spindle in place of the center. The drill is then fed through the work by feeding the tailstock spindle outward. Before beginning to drill, it is well to turn a conical spot or center for the drill point so that the latter will start true. This is often done by using a special tool having a V-shaped point like a flat drill. This tool is clamped in the toolpost with the point at the same height as the lathe centers. It is then fed against the center of the work and a conical center is turned. If the drill were not given this true starting point, it probably would enter the work more or less off center. Drills can also be started without turning a center by bring-

Fig. 7. Drilling in Lathe by Rotating the Drill and Holding Work
Against Pad Supported by Tailstock Spindle

ing the square end or butt of a tool-shank held in the toolpost in contact with the drill near the cutting end. If the point starts off center, thus causing the drill to wobble, the stationary tool-shank will gradually force or "bump" it over to the center as the point of the drill is fed inward.

In some cases, drilling is done in a lathe by rotating the drill which is held and driven by the headstock spindle. When this method is employed, the work may be held against a pad supported by the tailstock spindle as illustrated in Fig. 7. The feeding movement is obtained by advancing the tailstock spindle.

How are holes finished by reaming in a lathe?

After a hole has been bored, or drilled and bored, a reamer frequently is used for taking a light finishing cut. Reamers are especially useful when a number of duplicate parts must have holes of the same size within close limits. Reaming is applied both to cylindrical and to tapering holes. A reamer may be turned by hand for taking a very light cut. Ordinarily, however, the work is revolved slowly by power and the reamer is held stationary. Reamers having taper shanks may be held by inserting the shank in the taper bore of the tailstock spindle after removing the work-holding center; or, small reamers may be held in a drill chuck, the shank of which is held in the tailstock spindle. A third method is to support the outer end of the reamer by the tailstock center as illustrated in Fig. 8. The object in all cases is to hold the reamer in alignment with the hole to be reamed. When the center-supporting method is employed, the reamer can be kept from revolving, either by attaching a heavy dog to the end or, if the end is squared, by the use of a wrench long enough to rest against the lathe carriage. A common method is to clamp a dog to the reamer shank, and then place the tool-rest beneath it to prevent rotation. If the shank of a tool is clamped to the toolpost so that the dog rests against it, the reamer will be prevented from slipping off the center as it tends to do; with this arrangement, the carriage is gradually moved along as the tailstock spindle is fed outward. Some taper reamers are provided with stop-collars which come against the finished side of the casting when the hole has been reamed to size.

A boring and reaming operation might be performed much faster on a turret lathe than on an engine lathe. The turret lathe is designed for just such work, but, ordinarily, it would only be used for producing quite a number of duplicate parts. There are many classes of work that can be turned more quickly on machines designed for high production than on the lathe, but as more or less time is required for arranging these machines, and often special tools have to be made, the ordinary lathe is frequently indispensable. when only a few parts are needed; in addition, it is better adapted to some turning operations than any other machine.

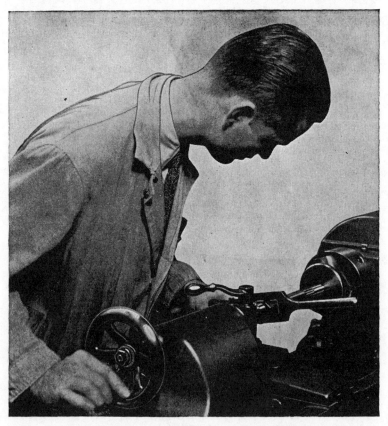

Fig. 8.   One Method of Reaming Holes in Lathe

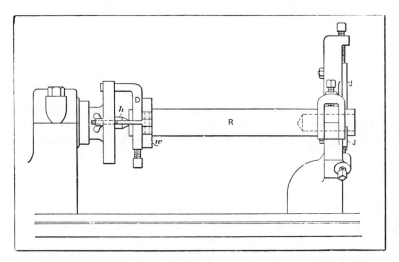

Fig. 9.   Outer End of Shaft Supported by Steadyrest while Drilling,
Boring and Reaming Hole

If a hole is to be drilled, bored or reamed in the end of a shaft, how is this end supported?

The outer end is supported by a steadyrest. The opposite end may be supported either by a chuck or by the head-stock center. If the center is used, the work should be driven by a dog equipped with some form of clamp or "hold-back" to keep the work on the center. To illustrate, the rod R, Fig. 9, is turned on the outside and a hole is to be bored in the end (as shown by dotted lines) true with the outer surface. If the centers used for turning the rod are still in the ends, as they would be ordinarily, this work can be done very accurately by the following method: The rod is first placed between the centers as for turning, with a driving dog D attached, and the steadyrest jaws J are set against it near the outer end, as shown. Before any machine work is done, means must be provided for holding the rod back against the headstock center h, because, for an operation of this kind, the outer end cannot be supported by the tailstock center; consequently, the work tends to shift to the right. One method of accomplishing this is shown in the illustration. A "hold-back" w, having a hole somewhat larger than the work, is clamped against the dog

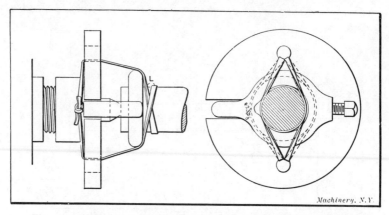

Fig. 10.   Method of Using Belt Lacing to Hold Work Against
Headstock Center while Boring Outer End

in a crosswise position, by the swinging bolts and thumb-screws shown. Another method of holding such work on a lathe center is by means of an ordinary leather belt lacing which is crossed over the driving dog and tied back of the faceplate (see Fig. 10) while the latter is screwed off a few turns. The faceplate is then screwed onto the spindle, thus tightening the lacing and drawing the work against the headstock center.

An improved form of dog for holding and driving a part when the outer end cannot be supported by the tailstock center of the lathe, has two bolts which pass through the faceplate. These bolts are supported by spiral springs at the rear of the faceplate, which give the required flexibility and permit the bolts to be so adjusted as to draw equally on both ends of the dog.

Fig. 11 illustrates another method of holding the work on the headstock center while boring the outer end. The work is held against the headstock center by a steel strap which has an opening large enough to pass over the work. This strap bears against the dog and has two threaded extension ends which are bent backward so as to pass through slots on opposite sides of the faceplate. By tightening nuts back of the faceplate, the strap is drawn up against the dog, thus holding the work securely against the headstock center.

Chuck Used in Conjunction with Steadyrest for End-Drilling and Boring.—For some end-drilling or reaming operations, the outer end is supported by the steadyrest and the other end is held and driven by a chuck. While this is a convenient arrangement, the center-supporting method (Figs. 9 and 11) usually is preferred for very accurate work to insure alignment between the hole in the end of the shaft and the outer surface which was previously turned true with the centers. If a chuck is used, the surface of the work near the chuck jaws should be tested to see if it runs true. A dial indicator should be used for this purpose if a very accurate test is essential.

How are taper holes machined in a lathe?

Taper holes may be produced in several different ways, depending upon the size of the hole, the amount of taper, and the degree of accuracy required. If the amount of

Fig. 11. Boring Hole in End of Spindle. Note Strap or Yoke
for Holding Work on Headstock Center

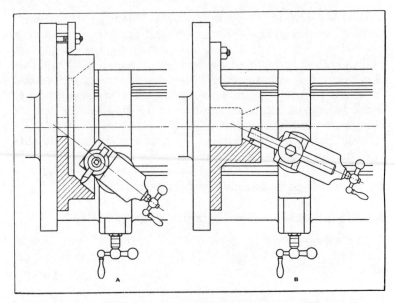

Fig. 12. Boring Taper Holes by Using Compound Rest Set
to the Angle Required

taper is small (like the Morse or Brown & Sharpe stand-ard), a drilled hole may be reamed to the required taper. A second method of producing taper holes is by boring or by boring and then reaming. The boring may be done by using the compound rest which is set to the required angle as shown by the diagrams A and B, Fig. 12. If the taper hole or opening is quite large, as shown at A, the boring may be done by using a regular turning tool. Smaller holes like the one shown at B require the use of a boring tool that is small enough to enter the hole. In clamping this tool in the toolpost, it is important to reduce the overhang as much as possible. In other words, the tool should only project beyond the toolpost far enough to permit boring the hole to the required depth.

How is the taper attachment used for boring taper holes?

The taper attachment may be used for taper boring the same as for taper turning. In boring a hole, however, the slide is set to the opposite side of the central zero mark, because the taper of a hole decreases in size during the boring operation, whereas a tapering rod or plug is smallest at the beginning of the cut, so that the tool must move outward rather than inward as it advances.

Fig. 13 shows how a taper attachment is used on a South Bend lathe when boring the hole in the end of a spindle. The taper attachment slide or bar *A* is set to the taper per foot required, as shown by the graduations. The slide is locked in position by screws *D* and arm *C* is clamped to the lathe bed by tightening the screw shown. When lever *E* is tightened, the attachment is ready for use. Taper attachments vary more or less in their general arrangement, as previously explained in the section on Taper Turning. In taper turning and boring, the angle equivalent to a given taper per foot may be required and in such cases the following rule may be used:

Rule.—If the taper per foot is given and the equivalent angle is required, divide the taper in inches per foot by 24;

Fig 13. Use of Taper Attachment for Boring Taper Hole
in End of Spindle

next find the angle corresponding to the quotient thus obtained in a table of tangents and then double this angle.

How is a lathe used for boring parts which are too large to be held in a chuck or on a faceplate?

When it is necessary to bore engine or pump cylinders, linings for cylinders, and other cylindrical parts which are too long to be held in a chuck or on a faceplate, the work must be clamped to the lathe carriage. As a rule, work of this class is done in a special boring machine, but, if such a machine is not available, it may be necessary to use a lathe. The part to be bored is held on blocks or in special fixtures attached to the lathe carriage, and the boring-bar is rotated by the lathe spindle, the necessary speed changes being obtained by the regular speed-changing mechanism of the lathe.

There are two general methods of boring: In one case a cutter head is traversed along the boring-bar by an automatic feed mechanism which forms part of the boring-bar. When such a boring-bar is used, the lathe carriage and the part being bored remain in a fixed position. With the second method, the work is attached to the carriage and bored by using a plain boring-bar mounted between the centers. The boring-bar must be provided with a cutter for small holes or a tool-head for larger diameters (preferably holding two or more tools), and the boring is done by feeding the carriage along the bed by using the regular power feed of the lathe. A symmetrically shaped casting, such as a bushing or lining, is often held upon wooden blocks bolted across the carriage. These are first cut away to form a circular seat of the required radius, by using the boring-bar and a special tool having a thin curved edge. The casting is then clamped upon these blocks by the use of straps and bolts, and, if the curved seats were cut to the correct radius, the work will be located concentric with the boring-bar. When boring by traversing the carriage along the bed, the boring-bar must be long enough to allow the part being bored to feed from one side of the cutter head to the other, the cutter head being approximately in a central location.

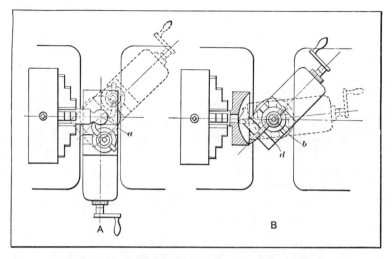

**Fig. 14. (A) Spherical Turning with Compound Rest.
(B) Concave Turning**

Can a lathe be used for turning spherical surfaces?

Occasionally it may be necessary to turn a spherical surface in the lathe. Sketch *A*, Fig. 14, shows how a small ball-shaped end can be turned on a piece held in a chuck. The lathe carriage is adjusted so that the pin around which the compound rest swivels is directly under the center *a*. The bolts which hold the swivel are slightly loosened to allow the top slide to be turned, as indicated by the dotted lines; this causes the tool point to move in an arc about center *a*, and a spherical surface is turned. Light cuts must be taken as otherwise it would be difficult to turn the slide around by hand.

Diagram *B* illustrates how a concave surface can be turned. The cross-slide is adjusted until swivel pin is in line with the lathe centers, and the carriage is moved along the bed until the horizontal distance between center *b* of the swivel, and the finished face of the work, equals the desired radius of the concave surface. The turning is then done by swinging the compound rest as indicated by the dotted lines. The slide can be turned more evenly by using the tailstock center to force it around. A projecting bar

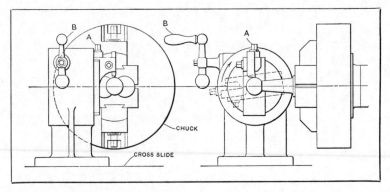

Fig. 15. One Type of Spherical Turning Attachment for Lathe

is clamped across the end of the slide at *d,* to act as a lever, and a centered bar is placed between this lever and the tailstock center; then by screwing out the tailstock spindle, the slide is turned about pivot *b.*

When spherical turning must be done repeatedly, special attachments are sometimes used. Fig. 15 shows an attachment applied to a lathe for turning the spherical ends of ball-and-socket joints. The height or radius of the cutting tool and, consequently, the diameter of the turned ball, is regulated by adjusting screw *A.* The tool is swung around in an arc, by turning handle *B* which revolves a worm meshing with an enclosed worm-wheel. As will be seen the work is held in a special chuck, owing to its irregula shape.

In connection with lathe work, special attachments an tools are often used, especially when considerable work (one class must be turned; however, if a certain part is r quired in large quantities, it is usually more economical use some semi-automatic or automatic turning machin especially designed for repetition work.

When a lathe is used for elliptical turning or boring, what method is employed?

Chucks or attachments for elliptical turning are requir in making oval dies, punches, molds, etc. A combined 1 tating and lateral motion is derived from some mechanis

in order to generate the elliptical curvature. The rotary
motion may be given to the work and the lateral motion to
the tool, but the most common arrangement consists of a
special form of chuck which is so designed that the combined motion is imparted to the work, the turning or boring
tool being held and used in the usual way. These elliptical
chucks differ more or less in their construction, but the
fundamental operating principle is the same. The chuck
is essentially a rotary compound slide, the action of which
is regulated by an adjustable eccentric ring. A design
adapted for metal turning is shown by the diagram, Fig. 16.
The faceplate P is supported by, and slides on, the dove-
tailed driving member H, which is threaded to fit the lathe
spindle. The sliding movement is imparted to the faceplate
by the cross-head C. The cross-head is a running fit on the

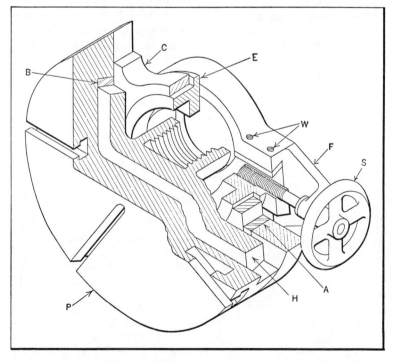

Fig. 16. A Heavy-duty Elliptic Chuck with Handwheel Adjustment
for Producing an Ellipse of the Required Proportions

eccentric ring E and slides in the transverse ways at the back of the faceplate. The eccentric is normally stationary, but is fitted to the adjusting bracket F by dovetail ways, so that it can be adjusted radially by means of the hand-wheel S. The adjusting bracket is securely bolted to the lathe headstock. The range of adjustment of the eccentric is from a central position up to the limit of its capacity, which may be several inches.

In adjusting the chuck for operation, the eccentric ring is moved off center an amount equal to half the difference between the major and minor axes of the ellipse to be generated. The ring is then clamped in this position by tightening the gib screws W. After the chuck is adjusted in this way, the machining operations are practically the same as in other turning or boring work. In designing the chuck, it is, of course, essential that the proper amount of clearance be maintained between the sliding parts; for this purpose, adjustable gibs, as shown at A and B, are provided to compensate for wear. The cross-head is made in two parts to compensate for wear between it and the eccentric ring.

Single-Point Tool Forms and Tool Grinding

The tools used on such machines as lathes, planers, shapers, boring mills, etc., commonly are referred to as "single-point" tools. As this name indicates, the tool has a single cutting edge at one end. This cutting edge may be formed on the end of a solid or one-piece tool, or the tool may consist of a holder with an inserted bit or cutter. The cutting ends of these single-point tools vary more or less in shape. These variations are to adapt the tool for a given class of metal-cutting operation; but, in some cases, the shapes vary more or less, even when the tools are intended for the same general class of work. For example, there is no standard shape or generally accepted tool form for turning cylindrical surfaces, and it may be possible to use several different forms for this and certain other classes of turning. One form, however, may be superior to the others although the difference in results is not always apparent to the casual observer. In this section, certain fundamental principles relating to tool shapes or tool grinding will be explained.

What terms are generally used to designate the different parts or surfaces of tools?

The terms and definitions relating to single-point tools vary somewhat in different plants, but the following are in general use (see diagram, Fig. 1).

Shank.—The shank is the body of the tool or that part on one end of which the cutting edge is formed. If the tool is an inserted cutter type, the shank is that part into which the cutter or bit is inserted.

Nose.—This is a general term which is sometimes used to designate the cutting end but usually it relates more particularly to the tip of the cutting end.

117

Face.—The surface against which the chips bear, as they are severed in turning or planing operations, is called the face.

Flank.—The flank is that end surface that is adjacent to the cutting edge and below it when the tool is in a horizontal position as for turning.

Base.—That surface of the tool shank which bears against the supporting tool-holder or block is the base.

Rake Angle.—The nominal rake angle is the angle between the tool face and a plane parallel to the base of the tool. Back rake angle is measured in the direction of the tool shank and side rake angle in a direction at right angles to the tool shank. The active or effective rake of a turning tool depends upon its position relative to the axis of the work as explained later.

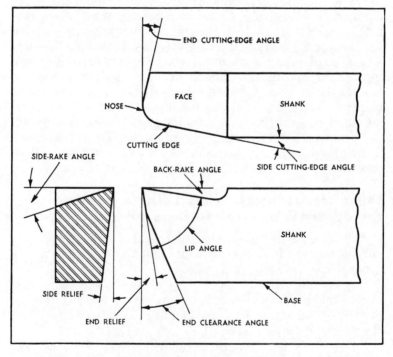

Fig. 1. Terms Commonly Applied to Different Surfaces or Sections of Turning Tools

Negative Rake.—If the inclination of the tool face is such as to give the tool less keenness than is equivalent to a rake angle of zero, the term negative rake is often used. If the face of the tool lies in a plane intersecting the axis of the work, the rake angle is zero. The face of a lathe tool having negative rake would slope *upward* from the point, relative to this plane, instead of sloping downward. Negative rake is seldom required.

Clearance Angle.—The clearance angle is the angle of the end or side surfaces which are below the cutting edge when the tool is in a horizontal position as for turning. The nominal clearance angle is measured from a plane that is perpendicular to the base of the tool shank. The effective clearance angle may be greater or less than this, depending upon the position of the tool relative to the axis of the work as explained later.

Relief Angle.—Clearance may consist of two angles (as shown by the diagram, Fig. 1) to reduce the amount of end surface and the amount of grinding required in sharpening the tool. In such cases, the angle of that surface which is adjacent to or just below the cutting edge may be called the relief angle—end relief or side relief angle, depending upon the location of the surface.

Cutting Angle.—The true cutting angle is the angle between the face of the tool and a line tangent to the machined surface at the cutting point. The true cutting angle depends upon the position of a turning tool relative to the axis of the work.

Lip Angle.—Lip angle is the angle between the tool face and the ground end surface or flank. If the tool has side and back rake, the lip angle should be measured in whatever plane it is smallest.

Ground Tool.—This term is sometimes used to designate a tool having a cutting edge that is formed on the end of a bar or shank entirely by grinding.

Forged Tool.—This term indicates that the cutting end has been forged roughly to shape on the end of a bar or shank prior to hardening and grinding.

Tipped Tool.—This term designates the type of tool having a small tip of either high-speed steel or special cutting

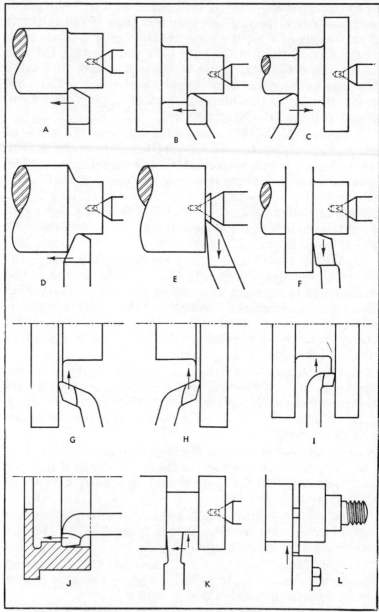

Fig. 2. Diagrams Showing Typical Applications of Different
Types of Turning Tools

material permanently fixed to the shank, as by brazing. The cutting edge is formed on this tip.

Tool Bit.—The term "bit" is commonly applied to the cutting tools which are inserted in a tool shank or holder so designed that the bit may readily be removed either for sharpening or for replacing with another form.

Nominal Size.—The size of a tool of square or rectangular section, according to the American Standard for single-point tools, is expressed by giving the width of the shank, the height of the shank, and the total tool length, in the order named. For example, the size might be ¾ × 1½ × 12 inches. This same method of designation is used for tool-bit holders, and the size of the bits is added.

How are turning tools formed to suit different classes of work?

Tools are adapted to different classes of work partly by using cutting edges of different shapes. The cutting end of the tool in some cases may also be bent at an angle or be offset to the right or left to permit locating the cutting edge in the proper working position relative to whatever surface is to be turned. In cylindrical turning, the cylindrical form produced is the result of the rotation of the work and the lengthwise feeding movement of the tool. In this case, the tool is ground or formed to cut efficiently. For certain other operations, there is close relation between the tool form and the shape of the machined surface, as shown by examples to follow. The diagrams, Figs. 2 and 3, illustrate the general relationship of the tool form to the class of work it is used for. The arrows on these diagrams indicate the direction of the tool feeding movement.

Turning Tools.—The tool shown at A, Fig. 2, is one form that is used for rough-turning or for removing metal rapidly. Tool B may also be used for rough turning; it has a bent end which is often convenient in turning close to a shoulder which might interfere with the tool holder if a straight form of tool were used. Tool C is bent in the opposite direction for the same reason. Many rough-turning tools have the leading cutting edge beveled more or less, as illustrated at D. The important principles which govern

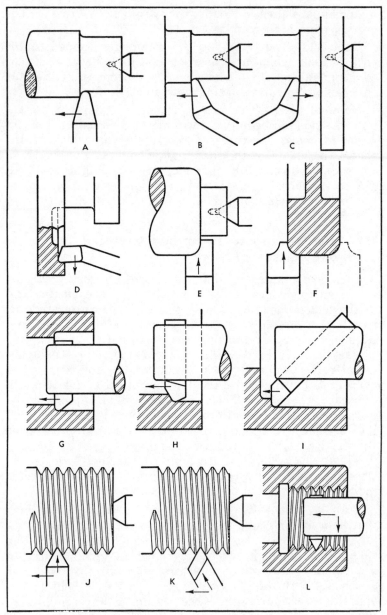

Fig. 3. Diagrams Showing Typical Applications of Different Types
of Turning Tools (Continued)

the shape or contour of the cutting edge will be explained a little later.

Facing Tools.—Frequently, it is necessary to turn or "face" the flat end of a shaft as at *E*. The side tool or facing tool shown has a cutting edge along the side and a pointed end so that there will be no interference with the work-holding center. A heavier form of side or facing tool is shown at *F*. This might be used for facing the sides of collars or shoulders. Tools *E* and *F* are also made to the opposite "hand" or with the cutting edge on the opposite side. (Whether this makes them right- or left-hand tools will be discussed later.) Tools of the general type shown at *E* and *F* are used ordinarily for light finishing cuts. For rough-facing, tools of the general shape illustrated at *G*, *H* and *I* might be used, provided these bent forms are necessary. In many cases, rough-facing can be done by using straight-shank tools like those shown at *A* and *D*, or possibly the bent forms at *B* and *C*. These diagrams are merely intended to show typical applications, and frequently a certain form of tool can be adapted to several different kinds of turning operations. For example, a tool similar to the one shown at *I*, but of opposite hand, might be used for boring as illustrated at *J*. Tool *D*, Fig. 3, has the side cutting edge on the *inner* side of the bend instead of outer side like tools *B* and *C*, Fig. 2. This reverse or hook form *D*, Fig. 3, might be preferable for some facing operations and for certain other applications.

Square Nose and Cutting-Off Tools.—For some purposes, a tool having a straight cutting edge at the end is required, as, for example, in turning a reduced section (as at *K*, Fig. 2) having square shoulders. The sides of such tools incline slightly inward to provide side clearance. For cutting off finished pieces from a bar of stock, a narrow-blade cutting-off tool is used as illustrated at *L*. Many of these tools ccnsist of a shank and an inserted cutter. This is true of various other classes of turning and boring tools. Some tools for taking finishing cuts, in conjunction with coarse feeds, have broad straight cutting edges. This type will be referred to later.

Round-Nose Tools.—Round pointed tools, similar to the one shown at *A*, Fig. 3, are commonly used for turning brass castings or any alloys that are brittle and form small chips instead of long curling chips. Round-nose tools are also used for taking finishing cuts in steel when using a fine feed. The radius of the point frequently is larger than is shown at A. Bent round-nose tools are shown at B and C, and the diagrams illustrate typical applications.

Radius Tools.—In most turning operations, the shape produced is the result of the rotary movement of the work and the feeding movement of the tool, in conjunction with more or less hand manipulation. In some cases, however. the shape produced on the work is a direct reproduction of the shape of the cutting edge on the tool. A simple example is illustrated at E, Fig. 3, which shows a radius tool. As the name indicates, this is for forming rounded corners whenever these are required. The double radius tool F is a convenient form, since it may be used for rounding both right- and left-hand corners, if desired.

Boring Tools.—One form of tool for boring, or internal turning as it might be called, is shown at G, Fig. 3. A beveled form is shown at H. If a hole is comparatively small, and, consequently, the tool-supporting bar rather light, form G is preferable because the thrust of the cut is straight back or opposite the direction of the arrow indicating the feeding movement. Tool H is a good form, especially when it is possible to use a rigid supporting bar. If the bore has a shoulder at the inner end which would strike the projecting end of the tool-holding bar, the cutter may be held in the position shown at I so that the cutting end extends beyond the end of the bar.

Thread-Cutting Tools.—The thread-cutting tool J, Fig. 3, is another example of a tool which reproduces its shape on the work. In other words, the cutting end of the tool has the same shape as the cross-sectional shape of the thread to be cut. In taking a cut, the tool is traversed from right to left (for a right-hand thread) and it is fed inward or radially for each successive cut. If a screw thread is quite coarse, it may be rough-turned by using tool K, which has one cutting edge and enough rake to make it cut easily. This tool is fed in at an angle as indicated by the upper arrow. An internal thread-cutting tool is illustrated at L. This tool is somewhat like a boring tool, except that the end is shaped to correspond with the thread to be cut. As thread cutting is a very important branch of lathe work it is dealt with in a separate section (see Cutting Screw Threads in the Lathe).

Many of the tools represented by these diagrams, Figs. 2 and 3, are used on different types of lathes or other turning machines. With a comparatively small number of tools, it is possible to turn an almost endless variety of forms. Occasionally, however, some special form of tool is needed for doing an odd job. Such a tool, for example, might have a cutting edge shaped to some special form or an end which is bent to hold the cutting edge in some unusual position.

What governs the general shape of a turning tool and the contour of its cutting edge?

The forming or grinding of single-point tools is based upon the following general principles: First, the cutting edge of the tool must have a certain shape or contour, and, in some cases, this may vary more or less as explained later. Second, the end of the tool, or the surface below the cutting edge in the case of a lathe tool, must have a certain inclination to provide clearance or relief. Third, the face of the tool, or the chip-bearing surface, is, with some exceptions, given a certain amount of inclination or rake.

Turning tools such as are used for turning cylindrical parts or for facing broad flat surfaces include shapes which vary more or less, especially if the tools are used chiefly for removing metal or for roughing cuts. These variations may be for the purpose of adapting the tool to a certain class of work, but frequently they merely represent differences of opinion or shapes based upon the experiences of different lathe operators. While there is some latitude in tool shapes that will produce satisfactory work, the approved forms do not vary much, and they are based upon certain principles which should be understood.

Some turning tools have straight cutting edges with rounded corners as at *A*, *B* and *C*, Fig. 4, whereas others have curved edges. Examples of the latter are shown at *D* and *E*. Under certain conditions, a cylindrical part might be turned with any of these tools; under other conditions, tools *A* or *B* might be preferable to tool *C* or to a curved tool of large radius like *E*.

Why is chip thickness affected by tool shape, irrespective of feed rate?

The chip thickness for a given amount of feed and the efficiency of the tool may be affected considerably by the contour of the cutting edge. When tool *A* (Fig. 4) is in use, the thickness of the chip is equal to the feeding movement per revolution. With tool *B*, the chip thickness T is somewhat less than the feeding movement due to the inclination of the cutting edge. With tool *C*, the chip thickness is further reduced for a given feeding movement because the

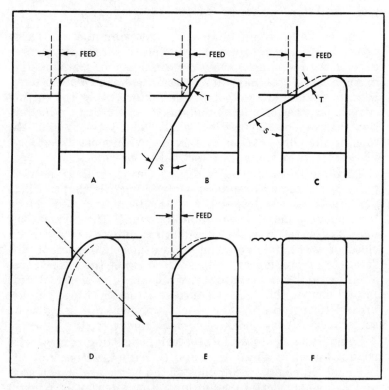

Fig. 4. Diagrams Illustrating Principles Governing General
Shape or Contour of Cutting Edge

cutting edge is more nearly parallel to the axis of the work than in the case of tool B. If the side edge angle S is 45 degrees, the chip thickness T will be seven-tenths of the chip thickness from a tool like A which has no side edge angle. If this angle is further increased to 60 degrees, or to the approximate form shown at C, the chip thickness will be only one-half that resulting from the use of tool A. Theoretically, at least, a tool of type C is capable of higher cutting speeds than tool A because for a given feeding movement per work revolution the chip is thinner; or, if the cutting speed is the same in each case, tool C can be used longer than tool A without sharpening, especially in turning tough steel. In actual practice, however, tool A or some intermediate form may be preferable to shape C. This is particularly true when turning parts that are not sufficiently rigid to withstand the lateral thrust resulting from the cutting with a tool having a large side edge angle. The thrust from tool A is largely endwise, whereas tool C exerts considerable lateral thrust which tends to bend the work; consequently, chattering may result, and this is not only destructive to the edge of the tool but may necessitate a reduction of cutting speed. A tool of the general shape shown at B, or one having a side edge angle ranging from 10 or 15 to 25 or 30 degrees, is used extensively, because it gives some reduction in chip thickness without introducing excessive lateral thrust against the work.

Cutting tools frequently have curved edges as shown at D and E. Shape D is similar in its action to B, whereas shape E is more like tool C. Experiments have shown that a cutting edge of large radius like E is capable of higher speeds than a tool like D. This is also because tool E, for a given feed, removes a thinner chip than tool D, the principle being the same as that referred to in connection with the straight-edged tools. At F is shown a tool having a flat or straight cutting edge along the end or nose. This type of tool may be used for finishing cuts whenever a rough-turned surface can be finished by using a coarse feed. The feed per revolution should be somewhat less than the width of the tool. This method is frequently employed both in turning and planing cast iron, and the same method may also be applied to steel, provided the part is sufficiently rigid to prevent the tool from gouging in.

In what direction does the tool face incline to provide "rake"?

When a lathe or other metal-cutting tool is so ground that the surface against which the chips bear, while being severed, inclines in such a way as to increase the keenness of the cutting edge, it is said to have "rake." Practically all tools for cutting steel and cast iron have rake. In general, the face of the tool should slope away from the *working part of the cutting edge*. For example, the working edge of a roughing tool *D* (Fig. 4) would be along that part of the edge marked by the dotted line. In other words, most of the work would be done by this part of the cutting edge; therefore, the top should slope back from this part of the edge or in the direction indicated by the arrow. A tool ground in this way will have both a back and a side rake.

When most of the work is done on the point or nose of the tool, as, for example, with the lathe finishing tool *F* which takes light cuts, the slope should be straight back from the front or cutting edge. This point should be remembered, because, when the top or face slopes in the right direction, less power is required for cutting. Tools for certain classes of work, such as thread tools, or those for turning brass or chilled iron, are ground flat on top, that is, without back or side slope. A thread tool is ground without rake so that its shape will be reproduced in the thread groove. Tools for cast brass cut effectively without rake.

What are the common rake angles for turning tools?

The lip angle of a tool (see Fig. 1) or its "angle of keenness" has an important bearing on the cutting action. This angle is governed by the clearance *C* and the rake *R*, Fig. 5, and as the clearance remains practically the same, it is the rake which is varied to meet different conditions. (Only back rake is shown to simplify the diagram, but roughing tools also have side rake). The amount of rake a tool should have depends upon the work for which it is intended. If, for example, a turning tool is to be used for roughing medium or soft steel, it should have a back rake of about

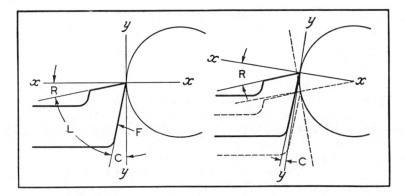

Fig. 5. Illustrations Showing How Effective Angles of Slope and Clearance Change as Tool is Raised or Lowered

8 degrees and a side rake ranging from 14 to 20 degrees, while a tool for cutting very hard steel should have a back rake of about 5 degrees and a side rake of 9 degrees. The reason for decreasing the rake and thus increasing the lip angle L for harder metals is to give the necessary increased strength to the cutting edge to prevent it from crumbling under the pressure of the cut. If a blunt tool or one having little rake angle were used for cutting very soft steel, there would be a greater chip pressure on the top and, consequently, a greater resistance to cutting, than if a keener tool had been employed; furthermore, the cutting speed would have to be lower, which is of even greater importance than the chip pressure; therefore, the lip angle, as a general rule, should be as small as possible without weakening the tool so that it cannot do the required work.

Experiments conducted by F. W. Taylor to determine the most efficient form for lathe roughing tools showed that the nearer the lip angle approached 61 degrees, the higher the cutting speed. This, however, does not apply to tools for turning cast iron, as the latter will work more efficiently with a lip angle of about 68 degrees. This is doubtless because the chip pressure, when turning cast iron, comes closer to the cutting edge which should, therefore, be more blunt to withstand the abrasive action and heat. The foregoing remarks concerning lip angles apply more particularly to tools used for roughing.

Is the rake angle practically the same for all materials?

The rake, and, consequently, the lip angles of tools, include quite a wide range and depend upon the hardness of the material to be cut and other properties which affect the cutting action. For example, in cutting chilled or very hard castings, the rake angle may range from zero to 2 or 3 degrees only. The angle is reduced in order to secure a strong well-supported cutting edge. Tools for cutting cast brass, which is brittle, are ground flat on the top or without rake. In this case, however, it is not a matter of increasing the strength of the cutting edge but rather to prevent the tool from gouging into the work, which it may do if the part being turned is at all flexible and the tool has considerable rake. On the other hand, aluminum alloys require exceptionally large rake angles. After considerable experimenting, it was found that a tool for aluminum alloys should have a back rake of about 45 degrees, a side rake of about 15 degrees, and a clearance of about 7 degrees, making the lip angle approximately 38 degrees. A tool which proved successful in machining Monel metal and nickel has a back rake of 8 degrees, a side rake of 14 degrees, and a clearance of 6 to 8 degrees. The nose of the tool has a rounded cutting edge. Other tools which have proved satisfactory for Monel metal and nickel alloys have back rake angles of from 6 to 8 degrees, and side rake angles of from 15 to 18 degrees. Tools made of cemented carbides usually have a back rake of 6 to 8 degrees, and a side rake of 8 to 12 degrees for cast iron, and 12 to 15 degrees for ordinary steel.

What clearance angle is required and is it affected by the position of the tool?

The cutting edge, to work without interference, must have clearance; that is, the flank F, Fig. 5, must be ground to a certain angle C so that it will not rub against the work and prevent the cutting edge from entering the metal. This clearance should be just enough to permit the tool to cut freely. A clearance angle of 8 or 10 degrees is about right for lathe turning tools made of steel.

A turning tool for brass or other soft metal, particularly

where considerable hand manipulation is required, could advantageously have a clearance of 12 or 14 degrees, as it would then be easier to feed the tool into the metal; but the clearance for turning tools should be just enough to permit them to cut freely. Tools made of cemented carbides usually have a clearance angle ranging from 4 to 6 degrees. Excessive clearance weakens the cutting edge and may cause it to crumble under the pressure of the cut.

Normally the back rake of a tool is measured from a line $x-x$ which is parallel to the shank, and the clearance angle, from a line $y-y$ at right angles to line $x-x$. These lines do not, however, always occupy this position with relation to the tool shank when the tool is in use. As shown to the left, the base line $x-x$ for a turning tool in use intersects with the point of the tool and center of the work, while the line $y-y$ remains at right angles to the first. It will be seen, then, that by raising the tool, as shown to the right, the *effective* clearance angle C will be diminished, whereas lowering it, as shown by the dotted lines, will have the opposite effect. Note also the changes in rake angle R.

How should a cutting-off tool be ground?

In grinding tools for cutting off finished parts from a bar or for cutting narrow grooves, there should be clearance not only at the end of the tool but also along the sides. A type of cutting-off or "parting tool" which has been used widely consists of a narrow cutting blade that is held in some form of holder (as at A and B, Fig. 6). These blades or cutters are given a slight amount of relief or clearance on each side by the manufacturers of such tools, and the blade is sharpened by grinding on the end only. The cutting edge usually is ground straight, but a slight curvature will produce chips that emerge more readily from the groove during the cutting-off operation.

The widths of these blades usually range from 3/32 inch to ¼ inch, the wider blades being used for larger diameters in order to secure the necessary rigidity. The shank or holder may be designed to hold the blade at a slight angle to provide a back rake angle of 2 or 3 degrees. The tool should be set so that the top surface is in line with the center of the work and it should be supported as rigidly as possible. Vibration of either the tool or work will cause trouble, and any chattering may indicate lack of proper support. Cutting-off tools frequently are held in an inverted position on turret lathes and screw machines and operate on the rear side of the work. This may also be done at times on an engine lathe by providing a special rear holder. When the tool is upside down or inverted, the chips are readily washed out by the cutting compound. The pressure from cutting is also downward which may be an advantage, especially when the work tends to lift or climb upon the tool when applied at the front in the usual position.

What is the general method of grinding single-point tools?

The practice varies. In some shops, tools are ground "by hand," which means that the shape depends upon the experience and judgment of different workmen. Turning and planing tools are ground in special tool-grinding machines in many shops, instead of by the workmen on an ordinary grinding wheel. When these tool grinders are used, the tools which have been sharpened by them usually are kept in a tool- or storage-room, and each workman obtains from this stock of tools as many as may be required. There are several important advantages connected with the grinding of tools by means of these special machines. In the first place, when the tools are ground in this way, it is not necessary for the workman to stop his machine and go to a grinding wheel whenever a tool needs resharpening; moreover, a machine designed especially for this class of work makes it possible to grind all the tools to standard angles of rake and clearance, which have been found to give the most efficient results. With this system of sharpening and storing the tools, a smaller stock will be required, which is another important advantage.

In grinding single-point tools for turning, planing, etc., means should be provided to maintain whatever rake and clearance angles are conducive to efficient cutting and long tool life. In many shops, tool grinding is left entirely to the judgment of the workmen; consequently, there is a wide variation of rake and clearance angles. Many tools are injured by overheating while grinding. The wheels used for tool grinding frequently are much harder than they should be. A soft free-cutting grinding wheel wears more rapidly than a hard one, but it is more economical in the long run because there is less tendency to burn tools and thus greatly reduce their life and cutting efficiency. Another practical method of preventing overheating is to reduce the wheel speed. Most grinding wheels have surface speeds of 5000 feet per minute or more. By reducing this speed, the danger of overheating or burning may be practically eliminated. The local heating and expansion which results from forcing a tool against a rapidly moving wheel, especially if a hard grade is used, not only reduces the hardness of the cutting edge but is likely to cause checking or cracking.

High-Speed Steel.—In rough grinding a forged high-speed steel tool, begin by grinding slowly. When the tool is warm, the grinding may be rapid but water should not be used while rough grinding as this tends to cause checking.

Carbide Tools.—In grinding carbide tools, traverse tool across wheel face to avoid local heating, always grind with the wheel rotating against the cutting edge and either use *generous amount* of soda solution or plain water, or grind dry. Never cool the carbide tip by quenching in water.

Why have tool-holders with inserted cutters replaced many solid or one-piece turning tools?

The cutting tools used for turning (and also for planing operations) are made in three different ways.

1. The tool may be a solid one-piece type, in which case the cutting end is forged to the approximate shape required and the entire tool is made of tool steel—usually high-speed steel.

2. According to a second method, the tool consists of a low-carbon steel shank with a small cutting tip welded or brazed to form the cutting end. This cutting tip may be made of either high-speed steel, Stellite, or a sintered carbide such as tungsten carbide or tantalum carbide. The Stellite and sintered carbides are not steel as they do not contain iron in their composition; but these special materials are very efficient since they operate at relatively high

speeds. The Stellite or sintered carbide tools always have a steel holder and an inserted tip or cutting end, because such materials are especially adapted to this construction and it would be impracticable and expensive to make the entire tool of these special cutting materials.

If high-speed steel is used, the entire tool might be made of it; however, since this steel is more expensive than low-carbon steel, it is common practice to use only a high-speed steel insert brazed to the cutting end, especially when the tool is large. Instead of using an insert, a high-speed steel end may be butt-welded to the shank.

3. A third type of construction consists of a drop-forged tool-holder or shank with an inserted tool steel cutter or bit which is held in place by a screw or some form of clamp, thus permitting the cutter to be replaced readily. This type of tool, like the second type referred to, requires much less tool steel than a solid or one-piece tool. Moreover, the expense of forging and reforging solid tools is also eliminated when tool-holders are used, since the cutters are of uniform section and are simply adjusted outwards as the ends are ground away. Another claim made for the inserted cutter is that it is more easily ground, since the cutter is held at a definite and constant angle, and there is no need of grinding more than the end surface. As the cutter is adjustable, the cutting end may readily be located in the correct position relative to the work.

Solid forged tools also possess certain advantages over cutters which are inserted in tool-holders, and they are still used extensively. The fact that the tool is formed of one solid or continuous piece is favorable to the dissipation of heat from the cutting end. In general, solid tools are undoubtedly stiffer and better able to withstand severe service than tool-holders of the same size, in which a cutter is held by some clamping device. Tool-holders have not been used as much as the solid or welded-bit types, for the heavier turning and planing operations, although at the present time tool-holders are manufactured which are rigidly constructed and adapted to heavy work. Solid tools are preferred for some classes of work, because the cutting end is more compact, the "nose" or end of the average tool-holder being wider, for the same capacity, than a solid tool, owing to the necessity of providing adequate means for holding and clamping the cutter in a tool-holder. Different makes of tool-holders, however, differ greatly in regard to compactness, as well as effectiveness of the cutter clamping device and durability of the tool.

How are high-speed steel cutting tips brazed to low-carbon steel shanks?

A reliable method which is used in a large manufacturing plant is as follows: A seat is formed in the tool shank to receive the tip. A welding compound or flux is used in welding the tip to the shank. The flux is placed on the seat of the shank and the tip is then put on top of the flux in the desired position. The tool is placed in the preheating chamber of the furnace and heated to 1550 to 1600 degrees F., allowing sufficient time for complete penetration of the heat. The tool is then removed from the preheating chamber and the tip is pressed firmly to the seat of the shank to insure a close contact between the two pieces. Then the tool is placed in the main furnace chamber and heated rapidly to a temperature of approximately 2250 to 2400 degrees F., depending upon the kind of material used for the tip and its hardening requirements. The tool is next removed from the furnace and sufficient pressure applied to the tip to force out the slag and insure perfect cohesion. The press used for this purpose should be equipped with a pivoted pressure shoe and this shoe must be preheated to prevent cracking of the tip.

The hardening is accomplished at the same time as the tipping operation when tools are tipped with low-cobalt high-speed and high-cobalt high-speed steel. Tools that cannot be ground after hardening are often heated in barium chloride or some similar salt bath. After the pressing and welding operation, the tool is cooled to room temperature under an air blast or quenched in oil.

It is advisable to maintain the oil quenching bath at a temperature of 150 to 200 degrees F. After the tipping operation, the tool should be reheated uniformly in an open furnace to a temperature of 1050 to 1150 degrees F. and allowed to cool in air. The hardened tools should have a minimum Rockwell C hardness of 63.

The cutting tip materials include tungsten high-speed steel; low-cobalt high-speed steel; high-cobalt high-speed steel; Stellite No. 3; and Stellite J-Metal. Tips are cut from bar stock according to dimensions on standard detail drawings. The material generally used for the shanks of tools tipped with the cutting materials regularly employed contains 0.50 to 0.63 per cent carbon; 0.60 to 0.90 per cent manganese; 0.04 per cent phosphorus; and 0.15 per cent silicon.

How are Carbide Tips Brazed to Steel Shanks?

The carbide tip usually is inserted into a milled recess or seat, or the tip may be brazed to the top of the shank. All surfaces to be brazed must be cleaned either by grinding lightly, by sand-blasting, or by using carbon tetrachloride. The brazing metal may be copper, naval brass such as Tobin bronze, or silver solder. A flux such as borax is used to protect the clean surfaces and prevent oxidation. Copper brazing usually is done in a furnace, although an oxy-hydrogen torch with excess hydrogen is sometimes used. An oxy-acetylene torch usually is employed for silver brazing or soldering.

One method of brazing with a torch is to first place a thin sheet material, such as copper foil, around and beneath the carbide tip, the top of which is covered with flux. The flame is applied to the under side of the tool shank, and, when the materials melt, the tip is pressed firmly into its seat with tongs or with the end of a rod. If the brazing material is in the form of wire or rod, this may be used to coat or tin the surfaces of the recess after the flux melts and runs freely. The tip is then inserted, flux is applied to the top, and the heating is continued until the coatings melt and run freely. A firm which supplies carbide tips with nickel-coated surfaces ready for silver soldering, suggests the following procedure: The tip, after coating with flux, is placed in the recess and the shank end is heated. Then a small piece of silver solder, having a melting point of 1325 degrees F., is placed on top of the tip. When this solder melts, it runs over the nickel-coated surfaces while the tip is held firmly into its seat.

In all carbide tip brazing, the brazed tool should be cooled slowly to avoid cracking due to unequal contraction between the steel and carbide. To insure slow cooling, the tool may be buried in powdered charcoal, graphite, asbestos, mica, or lime. One prominent manufacturer of carbide tools recommends the following shank steels in the order listed: (1) High-silicon steel containing approximately 0.55 carbon, 0.85 manganese, 0.30 vanadium, 2.10 silicon, 0.25 chromium, and maximum sulphur and phosphorous contents of 0.025; (2) S A E 2340 steel; (3) any low-alloy steel having 0.40 to 0.60 carbon.

What is the basis for distinguishing between right-hand and left-hand turning tools?

Unfortunately, the practice in designating right-hand and left-hand tools varies in different shops and also among tool manufacturers. According to one plan, a lathe tool is classed as "right hand" if it is adapted for cutting from the right-hand end of the work or, in facing operations, on the right-hand side of a shoulder, collar, or shaft end. Thus it will be seen that the "hand" of the tool in this case is determined with reference to the location of the surface the tool is adapted for cutting instead of considering the location of the tool's cutting edge. Another basis for determining the hand of a tool is to consider either the location of the cutting edge, the direction in which the tool moves while cutting, or both. While this may appear to be a logical method of determining the hand of a tool, the first plan referred to is applied in most shops.

Methods of designating "offset" tools also vary. It is common practice among lathe tool manufacturers to apply the term "offset" to bent cutting-off and bent turning tools. These "offset" cutting-off tools are designed for holding the cutting blade either to the right or left of the central position (see the diagrams A and B, Fig. 6). If the blade is offset to the left, as shown by diagram A, it appears logical to class this tool as left hand. However, it is common practice to designate tool A as right hand. On the contrary, a turning tool like the one at C is designated as a left-hand offset type and the one at D as right hand. It would seem as though tools A and C should be of the same hand, and also tools B and D. Evidently tool A is classed as right hand because the cutting blade is inclined to the right as seen from the shank end; however, the purpose of inclining the blade to the right is to permit locating the tool in a left-hand offset position relative to the central position normally occupied by a straight tool; therefore, tools A and C both appear to be left hand as determined by the direction of the offset or by the working position. If tool C is used for facing as at E, it is still left hand as determined by the location of the machined surface. If tool D is used as indicated by diagram F for facing a right-hand surface, it is still right hand.

While lathe tools have been referred to particularly, similar confusion exists in designating the "hand" or planer tools. The names of lathe and planer tools of similar

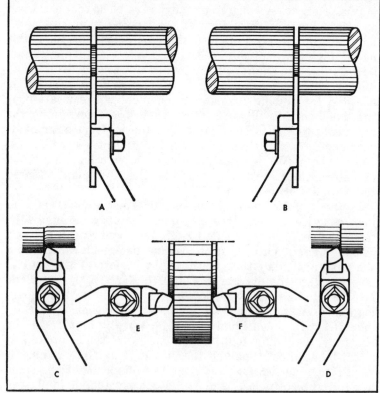

Fig. 6. Diagrams Showing Right-Hand and Left-Hand Tools

types should preferably agree as to right- and left-hand classifications.

Have the terms and definitions applying to turning and planing tools been standardized?

There is an American standard for the terms and definitions relating to "single-point" cutting tools such as are used on lathes, planers, shapers, turret lathes, boring mills, etc. This standard includes the following definitions relating to the "hand" of tools.

Straight Tool.—A straight tool has the point on the forward end of a straight shank (see diagram A, Fig. 7).

Bent Tool.—A bent tool has the point bent to the left or right (see diagrams B and C), to make its operation more convenient. These tools are called left-bent tools if the point is bent to the left as at B, when looking at the tool from the point end with the face upward and the shank pointing away, and vice versa.

Offset Tool.—An offset tool has the point at either side of, but parallel to, the shank. It is known as a right-offset tool if the point is offset to the right of the shank when looking at the tool from the point end with the face upward and the shank pointing away. Diagram D illustrates a left-offset tool. (Note that the tools illustrated in Fig. 6 are not *offset* types according to this definition. Tool A, for example, would be classed as a "left-bent cutting-off tool" and this appears to be a correct classification.)

Right-Cut Tool.—A right-cut single-point tool is one which, when viewed from the point end of the tool, with the face up, has the cutting edge on the right side, like tools A, B, and C, Fig. 7.

Left-Cut Tool.—A left-cut tool has the cutting edge on the left when looking at the point end with the face upward. (Diagram D.)

End-Cut Tool.—An end-cut single-point tool is one having its principal cutting edge on the end.

According to these definitions, as applied to right-cut and left-cut tools for lathes, a right-cut tool cuts from right to left or on the right-hand side of a shoulder in the case of a facing or side tool; and a left-cut tool from left to right

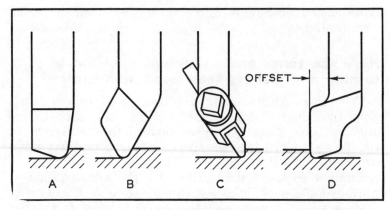

Fig. 7. (A) Straight Tool. (B) Left-Bent Tool. (C) Right-Bent Tool.
(D) Left-Offset Tool

or on the left-hand side of a shoulder or flange; hence, these definitions conform to the most prevalent American practice in designating the "hand" of lathe tools.

In grinding carbide tools, what grinding wheels and methods are employed?

The general procedure depends upon the kind of grinding operation required. If the operation is merely to re-sharpen a dull tool, a diamond wheel of fine grit ordinarily is used. If the tool is new or is a "standard design" and changes in shape are necessary, the general practice is to use vitrified silicon carbide wheels for roughing, and diamond wheels for finishing, although silicon carbide wheels of comparatively fine grain are sometimes used for finishing. A final operation commonly designated as lapping, may or may not be employed for obtaining extra-fine finish.

Wheel Speeds: — The speed of silicon carbide wheels usually is about 5000 feet per minute. The speeds of diamond wheels generally range from 5000 to 6000 feet per minute. In grinding single-point tools (excepting chip breakers) the common practice is to hold the tool by hand, press it against the wheel face and traverse it continuously across the wheel face while the tool is supported on the machine rest or table which is adjusted to the required angle. This is known as "offhand grinding" to distinguish it from the machine grinding of cutters as in regular cutter grinding practice.

Silicon Carbide Wheels:—The green colored silicon carbide wheels generally are preferred to the dark gray or gray-black variety, although the latter are sometimes used. For roughing, a grain size of 60 is very generally used. For finish grinding with silicon carbide wheels, a finer grain size of 100 or 120 is common. For under-cutting steel shanks up to the carbide tip, it may be advantageous to use an aluminum oxide wheel suitable for high speed steel grinding.

According to the standard system of marking, different grades from soft to hard are indicated by letters from A to Z. For carbide tool grinding fairly soft grades such as G, H, I and J are used. The usual grades for roughing are I or J and for finishing H, I and J. The grade should be such that a sharp free-cutting wheel will be maintained without excessive grinding pressure.

The common structure numbers for carbide tool grinding are 7 and 8. The larger cup-wheels (10 to 14 inches) may be of the porous type and be designated as 12P. The standard structure numbers range from 1 to 15 with progressively higher numbers indicating less density and more open wheel structure.

What are the advantages of diamond wheels for carbide tool grinding?

Wheels with diamond-impregnated grinding faces, are fast and cool cutting and have a very low rate of wear. They are used extensively both for resharpening and for finish grinding of carbide tools when preliminary roughing is required. Diamond wheels are also adapted for sharpening multi-tooth cutters such as milling cutters, reamers, etc., which are ground in a cutter grinding machine.

Resinoid bonded wheels are commonly used for grinding chip breakers, milling cutters, reamers or other multi-tooth cutters. They are also applicable to precision grinding of carbide dies, gages, and various external, internal and surface grinding operations. Fast, cool cutting action is characteristic of these wheels.

Metal bonded wheels are often used for offhand grinding of single-point tools especially when durability or long life and resistance to grooving of the cutting face, are considered more important than the rate of cutting.

Vitrified bonded wheels are used both for roughing of chipped or very dull tools and for ordinary resharpening and finishing. They provide rigidity for precision grinding, a porous structure for fast cool cutting, sharp cutting action and durability.

Grit Sizes:—For roughing with diamond wheels a grit size of 100 is the most common both for offhand and machine grinding. Grit sizes of 120 and 150 are frequently used in offhand grinding of single point tools (1) for resharpening, (2) for a combination roughing and finishing wheel and (3) for chip-breaker grinding. Grit sizes of 220 or 240 are used for ordinary finish grinding all types of tools (offhand and machine) and also for cylindrical, internal and surface finish grinding. Grits of 320 and 400 are used for "lapping" to obtain very fine finishes, and for hand hones. A grit of 500 is for lapping to a mirror finish of such work as carbide gages and boring or other tools for exceptionally fine finishes.

Grades:—Diamond wheels are made in several different grades to better adapt them to different classes of work. The grades vary for different types and shapes of wheels.

Should Carbide Tools be Ground Wet or Dry?

In using silicon carbide wheels, grinding should be done either absolutely dry or with enough coolant to flood the wheel and tool. Satisfactory results may be obtained either by the wet or dry method. However, dry grinding is the most prevalent usually because, in wet grinding, operators tend to use an inadequate supply of coolant to obtain better visibility of the grinding operation and avoid getting wet; hence checking or cracking in many cases is more likely to occur in wet grinding than in dry grinding.

Wet Grinding with Silicon Carbide Wheels:—One advantage commonly cited in connection with wet grinding is that an ample supply of coolant permits using wheels about one grade harder than in dry grinding thus increasing the wheel life. Plenty of coolant also prevents thermal stresses and the resulting cracks, and there is less tendency for the wheel to load. A dust exhaust system also is unnecessary.

Wet Grinding with Diamond Wheels:—In grinding with diamond wheels the general practice is to use a coolant to keep the wheel face clean and promote free cutting. The amount of coolant may vary from a small stream to a coating applied to the wheel face by a felt pad.

Coolants for Carbide Tool Grinding:—In grinding either with silicon carbide or diamond wheels a coolant that is used extensively consists of water plus a small amount either of soluble oil, sal soda, or soda ash to prevent corrosion. One prominent manufacturer recommends for silicon carbide wheels about 1 ounce of soda ash per gallon of water and for diamond wheels kerosene. The use of kerosene is quite general for diamond wheels and usually it is applied to the wheel face by a felt pad. Another coolant recommended for diamond wheels consists of 80 per cent water and 20 per cent soluble oil.

How are Carbide Tools Finished by Lapping?

Carbide tools may be finished by lapping, especially if an exceptionally fine finish is required on the work as, for example, tools used for precision boring or turning non-ferrous metals. If the finishing is done by using a diamond wheel of very fine grit (such as 240, 320 or 400), the operation is often called "lapping." A second lapping method is by means of a power-driven lapping disk charged with diamond dust, Norbide powder, or silicon carbide finishing compound. A third method is by using a hand lap or hone usually of 320 or 400 grit. In many plants, the finishes obtained with carbide tools meet requirements without a special lapping operation.

Hand Honing:—In all cases any feather edge which may be left on tools should be removed and it is good practice to bevel the edges of roughing tools at 45 degrees to leave a chamfer 0.005 to 0.010 inch wide. This is done by hand honing and the object is to prevent crumbling or flaking off at the edges when hard scale or heavy chip pressure is encountered. Hand honing of carbide tools at the machine or while tools are in use, is done frequently to defer removal for grinding. The consensus of opinion seems to be that hand honing "between grinds" is desirable *if correctly done by an experienced workman* so as not to change relief angles or round over the cutting edges. However, since hand honing by the machine operator is difficult to control and since many operators are incapable of proper honing, the preference in many plants is to avoid honing.

How is a chip breaker formed on a tool and why is it employed for some turning operations?

When carbide-tipped tools are used for turning steel, high cutting speeds are possible. When the cutting speed is 200 to 300 feet per minute or higher, long continuous chips will be formed rapidly unless this is prevented. Such long chips would occupy considerable space and are difficult to handle. They may also be a source of danger to the operator. The diagram at the left of Fig. 8 shows a common method of grinding the cutting end of a tool in order to break the chips into short pieces as they are removed. The triangular-shaded area is ground to some depth D (see section) below the top surface and so as to form a curved shoulder at the rear at some distance W back of the cutting edge. As the chip is severed, it encounters this rear shoulder and is either broken by it or deflected against the turned shoulder on the work which causes breakage. The angle A of this chip-breaking surface or deflecting shoulder, relative to the cutting edge, usually varies from 8 to 10 degrees. The depth D may vary from 1/32 to 3/32 inch, but, ordinarily, this depth need not exceed 1/16 inch. The preferable width W depends upon the nature of the turning operation. If the tool is used for heavy roughing cuts and coarse feeds, width W should be increased proportionately. The chip-breaking surface should be ground flat and not concave, as this would weaken the cutting edge.

The chip-breaking form of tool is unnecessary for operations requiring only light cuts, intermittent or broken cuts, or for a forged surface which is sufficiently uneven to prevent long chips from forming.

The diagram at the right of Fig. 8 shows a tool that is ground the same as for chip breaking, except that the de-

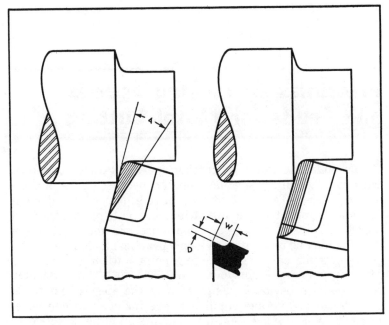

Fig. 8. Carbide-Tipped Steel-Turning Tools Ground to Insure Chip
Breaking or Chip Control

necting shoulder is parallel with the cutting edge instead of
being at an angle as at A. With this form of tool, the chips
are likely to come off in the form of short curled sections.
The triangular shape usually is employed, although the chip-
curling form sometimes is preferred.

In forming chip-breaking grooves on a carbide tool, use
a diamond wheel ⅛ to ¼ inch thick and 4 to 6 inches in
diameter. Either a universal tool and cutter grinder or a
small reciprocating surface grinder is recommended.

Principles Governing Speeds and Feeds for Metal-Cutting

The general subject of cutting speeds is difficult to deal with in a definite, specific manner because there are so many different factors that may have a decided effect upon the speed for any one operation. If cutting speed data based upon past records or experience are not available, a general idea as to what speeds are practicable doubtless will prove of some value as a starting point until more accurate information can be obtained from tests with the particular equipment to be used. That is why the speeds and feeds for typical or average conditions are included in engineering handbooks which feature machine-building practice.

Should metals be cut at the highest possible speed?

In establishing cutting speeds, the life of a tool between grindings or the time elapsing before it requires sharpening is a very important factor. To illustrate, suppose that we attempt to turn steel at such a high speed that the tool must be resharpened every 5 minutes. It is evident that such practice would require too much tool changing and sharpening and too many idle periods for the machine. On the other hand, if the speed were so slow that a tool could be used for 5 hours, this might represent the other extreme. Generally speaking, the speed should be such that a fair amount of work can be done before the tool requires regrinding. Evidently, it would not pay to grind a tool every few minutes in order to maintain a high cutting speed; neither would it be economical to use a very slow speed and waste considerable time in turning, just to save the few minutes required for grinding. Tool life, then, is a starting point for establishing cutting speeds.

146

What is a reasonable tool life or length of time before tool grinding is required?

The allowable "tool life" between grindings depends upon the cost of regrinding and resetting a tool and this varies widely for different types of tool and machine. For example, a simple lathe tool is more readily ground and replaced than a tool such as might be found on an automatic screw machine. In the case of a lathe, cutting speeds for rough turning usually are established so that the tool life will not be less than 30 or 40 minutes and not longer than 1½ hours. The period has not been standardized and opinions differ as to the most economical length of time between tool grindings. Tool life on hand screw machines usually averages about 2 hours, whereas on "automatics" the tool life may range from 6 to 8 hours, depending upon the cost of regrinding and resetting; consequently, cutting speeds and feeds often vary over a considerable range.

A common method of increasing tool life, especially on machines equipped with tools requiring considerable time for grinding and setting, is to use cutting tools which are more durable than ordinary high-speed steel. This is the reason why cobalt high-speed steels and carbide tools are used on many "automatics." These materials cost more than tools ordinarily used but this increase is more than offset by the greater productive capacity.

An operator who has charge of two or more automatics should, of course, have ample time for loading and reloading one machine while the others are running.

Why do cutting speeds vary so widely?

A cutting speed that is high enough to avoid any unnecessary waste of time in machining operations depends upon a number of different factors, any one of which may have a decided effect upon the allowable speed. These factors include the hardness of the metal (or its machinability, which does not depend upon hardness alone); the kind of steel or other material used for the cutting tool; the shape of the tool and quality of its heat-treatment, if made of steel; the area of the cut; the relation between the depth of the cut and the rate of feed; whether or not a coolant or cutting compound is used; the condition of machine, especially in regard to rigidity; the rigidity of the tool, the rigidity of the work itself, and the tool life.

It must not be inferred that these factors affect cutting speeds merely in a theoretical manner. They have a direct and decided influence, and any one of them may greatly decrease or increase the permissible cutting speed; consequently, all data pertaining to cutting speeds and feeds are intended only as a general guide. In many cases, figures which are supposed to represent average conditions are misleading, because the speed for certain conditions is far from the average. In the following paragraph, however, some figures are given on the assumption that a "half-loaf is better than none." There is only one reliable method of determining what cutting speed is consistent with reasonable tool life between grindings, and that is by actual experience and test with a given machine, tool, and material.

What are the usual speeds for cutting ordinary materials?

The figures which follow are intended merely to indicate speed ranges in a very general way. It is impossible to give figures which are at all precise, because cutting speeds are governed by so many different factors, as explained previously. (Information about the cutting tool materials referred to will be found in the section on tool steels and other metal-cutting materials in volume 2.)

High-Tungsten High-Speed Steel Tools.—With this grade of high-speed steel which is very generally used, ordinary cast iron may be cut at from 75 to 100 feet per minute, soft steel at 100 to 200 feet per minute, medium steel at 75 to 125 feet per minute, soft brass at 150 to 250 feet per minute, and hard bronze at 50 to 100 feet per minute. For a given depth of cut, a change in the feeding movement may account for the minimum and maximum figures given.

Cobalt High-Speed Steel Tools.—When using the cobalt type of high-speed steel, the speeds given for tungsten high-speed steel tools may be increased ordinarily from 20 to 30 per cent. For example, if the cutting speed with a tungsten high-speed tool is 100, it might be 120 for a low-cobalt steel tool and 130 for a high-cobalt steel.

Stellite Tools.—There are several grades of Stellite; but the speed, as compared with ordinary high-speed steel, may be increased one and one-half times or more. For turning ordinary cast iron, try speeds from 125 to 150 feet per minute; when using J-Metal, hard cast iron can be rough-turned at 60 to 90 feet per minute, and medium cast iron at 100 to 150 feet per minute.

Carbide Tools.—The speeds for carbide cutting tools may be from two to four times faster than for high-speed steel tools. Permissible speeds, however, extend over a very wide range. In turning steels with tantalum-carbide tools, the speeds may vary from 200 to 600 feet per minute or more, depending upon hardness of the steel and depth of the cut. For cast iron, try 200 to 300 feet per minute; for malleable iron, 250 to 350 feet per minute; for brass, 400 to 600 feet per minute; for aluminum alloys, 800 to 1500 feet per minute. An example of modern turning is shown in Fig. 1. The material is 0.50 carbon steel. The machine

Fig. 1. Turning 0.50 Carbon Steel with a Tantalum-carbide Tool. Cutting Speed, 390 Feet per Minute; Feed, 1/16 Inch; and Depth of Cut, ¾ Inch

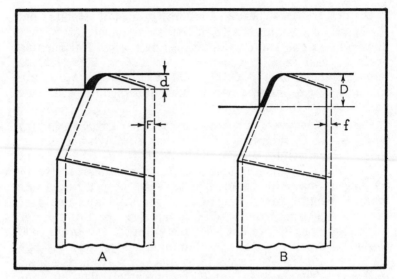

Fig. 2. Diagrams Showing Effect of Depth of Cut and Feed on Length
of Cutting Edge in Contact with Work

is a heavy-duty turret lathe with a tantalum-carbide single
cutter mounted on the cross-slide. The cutting speed is 390
feet per minute; feed, 1/16 inch per revolution, and the
depth of cut, ¾ inch.

Twist Drills.—Drilling speeds usually are given in drill
revolutions per minute for different drill diameters. These
R.P.M. speeds, however, are based upon cutting speeds in
feet per minute at the circumference of the drill, which explains why small drills are rotated at such high speeds.

Is cutting speed affected by the ratio of feed per revolution to depth of cut?

Tests have shown that a cutting speed representing a certain "tool life," does not remain constant for a given area of
cut because it is affected by the relation between the depth
of the cut and the feeding movement per work revolution.
(In all references indicating a practical cutting speed, it
should be understood that the speed is related to a reasonable length of tool life before grinding or sharpening is
required.) Tests have shown that a cut ⅛ inch deep with

1/20-inch feed can be taken at a higher speed than a cut 1/16 inch deep with 1/10-inch feed, although the area of the cut is the same in each case. When the depth of cut is doubled and the feed reduced one-half, the cutting speed usually can be increased 25 to 40 per cent. This increase is due to the fact that there is a narrower chip and twice as much cutting edge in contact with the work; consequently, the cooling area for conducting away the heat is larger. If the cutting speed is increased 25 per cent by doubling the depth of cut and reducing the feed one-half, the cubic inches of metal removed in a given time will also be increased 25 per cent. The diagrams A and B, Fig. 2, illustrate cuts of equal area. Diagram B shows how the length of cutting edge in contact with the work is increased when the depth D of cut is doubled and the feed f is reduced one-half.

Tests have demonstrated that a depth of cut equal to 8 times the feed is a desirable ratio. The depth ordinarily varies from 5 to 10 times the feed in taking roughing cuts.

In rough-turning, is one deep cut preferable to two or more shallow cuts?

As a general rule, it is preferable to take deep rather than shallow roughing cuts. For example, if the diameter of a part is to be reduced about ½ inch in roughing, we might take two ⅛-inch cuts or one ¼-inch cut. Assume that the feed is 1/32 inch for the ⅛-inch cuts and 1/64 inch for the ¼-inch cut; also, assume that the speed is increased 25 per cent for the ¼-inch cut because of the feed reduction. In such cases, the combination of a deeper cut at reduced feed but increased speed will reduce the total turning time, because when two shallow cuts are taken, the coarser allowable feed does not compensate for the speed reduction. An example will be given to illustrate this point.

Rule.—To find the time in minutes for taking a cut, divide the total length of the cut, in inches, by the revolutions per minute multiplied by the feed per revolution, in inches.

Example.—Assume that the length of a turned surface is 12 inches, the lathe speed is 100 R.P.M., the feed per work revolution 0.030 inch; then,

$$\text{Time for one cut} = \frac{12}{100 \times 0.030} = 4 \text{ minutes}$$

Assume that the example just referred to applies to a ¼-inch depth of cut and we want to determine the time for two cuts when the speed has been decreased to 80 R.P.M. (which would also decrease the surface speed 20%). Then, for double the rate of feed or 0.060 inch,

$$\text{Time for two cuts} = \frac{12}{80 \times 0.060} \times 2 = 5 \text{ min.}$$

In some cases, the work might not be rigid enough for taking a cut ¼ inch deep without considerable feed reduction. In the preceding example, if the feed were reduced to 0.024 inch per work revolution, then, with a lathe speed of 100 R.P.M., the time would equal 5 minutes.

Is the speed of a machine tool regulated to obtain a given cutting speed in feet per minute?

Cutting speeds for turning, planing and milling ordinarily are expressed in feet per minute because the number of revolutions per minute does not indicate the surface speed at the circumference or the speed at which the metal is being cut. However, the operator of a lathe, for example, does not know ordinarily what the cutting speed is in feet per minute and he is guided usually by past experience. He may know from experience with previous jobs of the same kind about what the cutting speed should be as determined by a certain adjustment of the speed-regulating mechanism and without reference either to feet per minute or revolutions per minute. In fact, the best cutting speed for a given class of work would be determined by speeding up the machine as far as practicable. The equivalent surface speed in feet per minute might then be determined for future use. If the revolutions per minute are known, the speed in feet per minute can be determined as follows:

Rule.—Multiply the revolutions per minute by the circumference of the turned surface in inches and divide by 12 to obtain the speed in feet per minute.

Example.—A part being turned is 5 inches in diameter and rotates 46 revolutions per minute; what is the cutting speed in feet per minute?

$$\text{Cutting speed} = \frac{46 \times 3.1416 \times 5}{12} = 60 \text{ feet per minute.}$$

The number of revolutions per minute equivalent to a given cutting speed can be obtained as follows:

Rule.—Multiply the cutting speed in feet per minute by 12 and divide by the circumference of the turned surface.

An instrument called a "cut-meter" is sometimes applied to a rotating part to show the cutting speed in feet per minute. This is similar to the well-known tachometer or revolution counter, but is arranged to show the cutting speed in feet per minute.

In turning, how far does the tool move per work revolution?

The tool feeding movement varies widely for different conditions. When turning soft machine steel in a lathe of medium size, the feed under ordinary conditions might vary between 1/32 and 1/16 inch per revolution. For turning soft cast iron, the feed might be increased to from 1/16 to ⅛ inch per revolution. These feeds apply to fairly deep roughing cuts. Coarser feeds might be used in many cases, especially when turning large rigid parts in a powerful lathe. The depth of a roughing cut in machine steel might vary from ⅛ to 3/8 inch, and, in cast iron, from 3/16 to ½ inch. These figures are intended simply to give a general idea of the feeds and cuts that are feasible under average conditions. Ordinarily, coarser feeds and a greater depth of cut can be used for soft cast iron than for soft steel, because cast iron offers less resistance to turning. When the turning operation is simply to remove metal, the cut should be as deep and the feed as coarse as practicable. Sometimes the cut must be comparatively light, because the work is too fragile and springy to withstand the strain of a heavy cut. The difficulty with light slender work is that a heavy cut may cause the part being turned to bend under the strain, thus causing the tool to gouge in. Steadyrests can often be used to prevent flexible parts from spring-ing, but there are many kinds of light work to which the steadyrest cannot be applied to advantage.

Is a coarse feed ever used for finishing cuts?

A coarse feed in conjunction with a broad straight-edged tool is preferable for some finishing or final cuts, especially in turning cast iron. The straight edge of the finishing tool is set parallel with the rough-turned surface and this broad edge enables a coarse feed to be taken, thus reducing the time required for the finishing cut. If a coarse feed were taken with the round tool, the turned surface would have spiral grooves in it, whereas, with the broad cutting edge, a smooth surface is obtained even though the feed is coarse. (See Fig. 3.) The amount of feed per revo-lution of the work, however, should always be less than the width of the cutting edge.

Very often broad tools cannot be used for finishing cuts, especially when turning steel, because their greater contact causes chattering and results in a rough surface. An old and worn lathe is more liable to chatter than one that is heavy and well-built, and, as the diameter of the work also makes a difference, a broad tool cannot always be used for finishing, even though, theoretically, it would be preferable. Broad flat tools and wide feeds are also used for finishing cuts on boring mills and planers.

What is meant by the "machinability" of a metal?

The term "machinability" indicates the degree of resist-ance encountered in cutting a metal. If a metal is machin-able, this implies cutting it under practical conditions or by the application of practical shop equipment. A hard metal that is machinable with a carbide tool may not be machin-able with a steel tool. Even though the steel tool will cut the metal, if it will not continue cutting a reasonable length of time before sharpening is necessary, then we have an example of machinability that is impractical. It is evident, then, that the hardness of steel does not always show whether it is machinable or not, because we must consider the kind of cutting tool to be used and also such factors

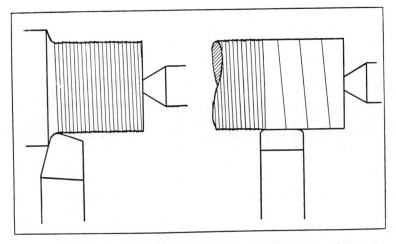

Fig. 3. Roughing Cut (at Left) and a Light Finishing Cut
(at Right) with Coarse Feed

as the cutting speed, the kind and quantity of cutting fluid if any, and the rigidity of the tool support. The maximum hardness of a machinable steel or other material, because of these variable factors, extends over a wide range which has been increased greatly since the introduction of cemented carbide tools. The maximum hardness of a machinable material under one set of conditions, for example, might not exceed 200 Brinell, and under other conditions, it might range from 400 to 500 Brinell or even higher.

Does the machinability of different metals depend only upon hardness?

In cutting steels, the allowable cutting speed for a given tool life between grindings is, as a general rule, inversely proportional to the hardness *of a given steel*. To illustrate, tests in turning an alloy steel with a high-speed steel tool showed a cutting speed of 70 feet per minute when the hardness of the steel was 180 Brinell; the cutting speed had to be reduced to about 35 feet per minute when the hardness was increased to 360 Brinell, the life between tool grindings for these tests being 20 minutes in each case. The machinability of other steels of the same hardness might vary. For example, the tests just referred to showed more or less variation in the cutting speeds for steels of the same hardness, but having different compositions or properties. Thus, while there is a constant relationship between the hardness of a steel and its tensile strength, there is not the same constant relationship between steel hardness and machinability as applied to different steels. In one test a high-speed steel turning tool lasted 20 minutes between successive grindings when cutting chromium-vanadium steel of 300 Brinell at 30 feet per minute, whereas a 3½ per cent nickel steel of the same hardness permitted a cutting speed of about 45 feet per minute for a tool life of 20 minutes. To cite another example, the cutting speed during a 20-minute interval between grinds was 170 feet per minute for nickel-chromium steel of 280 Brinell and 210 feet per minute for chromium-vanadium steel of the same hardness.

Although the allowable cutting speed of a given steel is approximately in inverse proportion to the hardness, the machinability of cast iron may not be changed by increasing the hardness and may even be improved. For example, it was found more difficult to machine a plain cast iron of about 170 Brinell than a nickel-chromium cast iron of 240 Brinell. In another case, plain iron of 160 Brinell was more difficult to machine than a cast iron of about 200 Brinell containing less silicon and 1.25 per cent nickel. As the foregoing examples show, there is no fixed relationship between the hardness and machinability of plain and alloy cast irons.

Cooling and Lubricating Fluids for Metal-Cutting Tools

Cutting fluids are used in connection with most machining operations, especially on steel, to prevent excessive friction and heat generation. Just why this is important will be explained in the next paragraph. There are various kinds of cutting fluids and also many different opinions concerning the most effective kind to use for certain operations. These differences of opinion probably are due largely to the fact that more than one kind of cutting fluid is, or appears to be, suitable for a given class of work. This section will deal with the general types of cutting fluids and what is believed to be the common practice in using them. Incidentally, cutting fluids frequently are referred to as "cutting lubricants" or as "coolants," and such terms as "cutting oils" or "cutting compounds" may also be used, especially to designate more definitely a given type of cutting fluid.

Why are metal-cutting fluids used?

There are several advantages in directing a stream of cutting fluid upon the cutting end or side of a tool, especially when cutting steel. Metal cutting generates considerable friction and heat. In turning steel, for example, the sliding of the chip across the tool face and the crimping or thickening of the chip would, unless prevented by some fluid, cause the temperature of both tool and work to rise rapidly, especially when taking heavy roughing cuts. The function of a cutting fluid is to prevent excessive friction and heating in order to permit higher cutting speeds and reduce the power required for metal cutting. This is accomplished partly by direct cooling and also by lubrication, especially of the tool face. The relative importance of direct

157

cooling and the lubricating effect varies for different jobs, and some fluids, consisting largely of water, are selected primarily for their cooling effect, whereas others containing oil, or consisting entirely of oil, are also intended to serve as lubricants.

The temperature reduction and lower power consumption resulting from varying degrees of cooling and lubrication, increases the cutting efficiency of the tool and prevents excessive dulling. Proper application of the cutting fluid permits higher cutting speeds, with increases, in turning steel, of 20 to 25 per cent and higher in some cases, assuming that from 2 to 5 gallons per minute are used. In taking heavy roughing cuts, a stream of cutting oil not only lubricates the face of a turning tool but greatly reduces the chip pressure as the chip contracts on the outer side, which is the first to encounter the cutting fluid. For certain operations, such as drilling, tapping, etc., a cutting fluid not only cools and lubricates, but carries the chips away.

When a fluid is used in machining steel, a smoother surface is obtained, but the importance of this feature varies for different classes of work. In many cases, for example, turned or milled surfaces are later finished by grinding, so that the surface left by the first operation is of little or no importance. In some cases, a cutting fluid is useful in preventing expansion of the work and, consequently, an increase in dimensions, which might result in temporary warping or inaccurate measurements. Errors from this cause might occur in grinding to a given dimension within a small tolerance. Fig. 1 shows the application of a cutting or cooling fluid in connection with a cylindrical grinding operation. (Additional information will be found in the section on Grinding Cylindrical and Tapering Parts, vol. 2.)

What are the general classes of cutting fluids?

The following general classes of cutting fluids are extensively used in modern machine shop practice.

Soluble Oils or Emulsions.—These are types of oils or paste compounds which form emulsions when mixed with water: Soluble oils are used extensively in machining both ferrous and non-ferrous metals when the cooling quality is paramount and the chip-bearing pressure is not excessive.

Care should be taken in selecting the proper soluble oil for precision grinding operations. Grinding coolants should be free from fatty materials that tend to load the wheel, thus affecting the finish on the machined part. Soluble coolants should contain rust preventive constituents to prevent corrosion.

When an emulsifying oil is mixed with water, an emulsion is formed rather than a solution, but the name "soluble oil" has been generally accepted because the oil apparently dissolves or goes into solution with the water. To obtain a mixture of oil and water, an emulsifying agent is required and soap has proved to be very effective. The emulsion formed contains an infinite number of minute and invisible oil particles which give the mixture a milky or creamy white color. The proportions of the mixture should be determined by test. If the mixture is too weak, it may cause corrosion of both work and machine. The mixture may range from 1 part soluble oil to 5 parts water up to 1 part

Fig. 1. A Stream of Cooling Fluid Floods the Grinding Wheel Along the Line of Contact while Grinding a Long Cylindrical Surface on an Anti-aircraft Gun Tube

soluble oil and 50 or even 100 parts water. Soluble oils are easily mixed; but since the emulsion is of the oil-in-water type, it should always be prepared by pouring the *oil* into the water instead of pouring the water into the oil.

Mineral Oils.—This group includes all types of oils extracted from petroleum such as paraffin oil, mineral seal oil, and kerosene. Mineral oils are often blended with base stocks, but they are generally used in the original form for light machining operations on both free-machining steels and non-ferrous metals. The coolants in this class should be of a type that has a relatively high flash point. Care should be taken to see that they are non-toxic, so that they will not be injurious to the operator. The heavier mineral oils (paraffin oils) usually have a viscosity of about 100 seconds at 100 degrees F. Mineral seal oil and kerosene have a viscosity of 35 to 60 seconds at 100 degrees F.

Base Oils.—This name is applied to various types of highly sulphurized and chlorinated oils containing inorganic, animal, or fatty materials. This "base stock" usually is "cut back" or blended with a lighter oil, unless the chip-bearing pressures are high, as in cutting alloy steel, in which case the base stock may be used straight. Base oils usually have a viscosity range of from 300 to 900 seconds at 100 degrees F.

The sulphurized and chlorinated base oils when blended with mineral oils, produce metallic oxides or a *metallic*-film lubrication instead of fluid-film lubrication, as a result of the heat generated by the cutting tool. Chlorine, like sulphur, is added to mineral oils to obtain cutting fluids suitable for high chip-bearing pressures.

Base oils are usually dark in color. As a rule, they contain sulphur compounds resulting from a thermal or catalytic refinery process. When so processed, they are more suitable for industrial coolants than when they have had such compounds as flowers of sulphur added by hand. The adding of sulphur compounds by hand to the coolant reservoir is of temporary value only, and the non-uniformity of the solution may affect the machining operation.

Mineral Lard Oil.—Mixtures of mineral oil and lard oil may be used to obtain a cutting fluid having greater lubricating value than a straight mineral oil and much lower cost than a straight lard oil. They may be used when the chip pressures are moderate. The proportion of lard oil and mineral oil depends upon the character of the machining operation and the need for both cooling and lubricating effects. For light machining, straight mineral oil may be satisfactory; for heavier duty or where the metal is removed at comparatively high rate, the mineral oil may contain from 10 to 40 per cent of lard oil.

Aqueous Solutions.—When the function of a cutting fluid is merely to cool the work and possibly wash away chips, water containing some alkali has often been used, although these aqueous solutions have been replaced quite largely by modern cutting fluids. They do not, of course, provide the lubricating film that is important for many classes of work and they also cause corrosion of both work and the machine. These aqueous solutions may contain carbonate of soda (sal-soda), borax, caustic soda, etc. Lard oil and soft soap may be added to improve the properties.

What is the general practice in selecting cutting fluids?

The selection of a cutting fluid may depend upon the kind of material to be cut and also upon the type of machining operation. In general, if cooling effect is required chiefly, an oil-and-water emulsion is used, but if lubrication of chip bearing surfaces must be combined with cooling, then some mineral oil combination is employed. Between these extremes there are many border-line cases, and, consequently, differences of opinion. The general recommendations which follow represent common practice, although different cutting fluids and mixtures are often employed for a given class of work, and in some cases it may be difficult to determine which gives the best results.

Low-Carbon Steels.—(Free-cutting steels such as screw stock and machinery steels.) *For Turning:* Use either soluble oils (mixed with water), straight mineral oils of low viscosity, or, for roughing cuts, 75 per cent mineral oil and 25 per cent lard oil. If a soluble oil is suitable, use 1 part oil and 10 to 20 parts water. Mineral-oil or mineral-lard-oil combinations may be used in preference to soluble oils when the latter tend to corrode the work. *Drilling and Milling:* Use soluble oil. *Tapping:* Use mineral oil with 25 to 40 per cent lard oil; or 75 per cent mineral oil and 25 per cent sulphur base oil. *Grinding:* Soluble oil emulsions or emulsions made from paste compounds are used extensively in grinding all classes of steel, although mineral oils are preferred in some cases to improve the quality of the ground surface. For cylindrical grinding, use 1 part soluble oil and from 70 to 80 parts water; for centerless grinding, use 1 part oil to 50 parts water. Mineral oils are used with vitrified wheels but are not recommended for wheels with rubber or shellac bonds. *Broaching:* For steel, use a heavy mineral oil such as sulphurized oil of 300 to 500 Saybolt viscosity at 100 degrees F. to provide both adequate lubricating effect and a dampening of the shock loads. Soluble oil emulsions may be used for the lighter broaching operations. *Thread Cutting:* For steel, use either 1 part soluble oil and 15 parts water or a sulphurized cutting oil containing 2 to 4 per cent active sulphur with Saybolt viscosity varying from 125 to 300 at 100 degrees F.

Alloy Steels.—For turning; use 75 per cent mineral oil and 25 per cent sulphur base oil, on account of the high chip-bearing pressure on the tool. *Milling:* Use 90 per cent mineral oil and 10 per cent lard oil. *Drilling:* Use soluble oil. *Tapping:* Use 70 per cent mineral oil and 20 per cent lard oil.

Cast Iron.—While cast iron ordinarily is machined dry, a soluble oil emulsion may be used to avoid an excessive amount of dust around the machine.

Brass Rod.—*For Turning:* Use either straight mineral oil or 90 per cent mineral and 10 per cent lard oil. *Milling:* Use soluble oil with about 95 per cent water. *Drilling:* Use either soluble oil with 75 to 90 per cent water or 70 per cent mineral oil and 30 per cent lard oil. *Tapping:* Use 80 to 90 per cent mineral oil with 20 to 10 per cent lard oil.

Cast Brass.—Brass castings usually are machined dry.

Aluminum.—*For Turning:* Use 90 per cent mineral oil and 10 per cent lard oil; or 50 to 90 per cent kerosene and 50 to 10 per cent mineral oil; or use soluble oil. *Milling:* Use soluble oil with about 95 per cent water; or mineral seal oil; or mineral oil. *Drilling:* Use soluble oil with 75 to 90 per cent water or 90 per cent mineral oil with 10 per cent lard oil. *Tapping:* Use either lard oil, sperm oil or wool grease. Sulphurized oils ordinarily are not recommended for tapping aluminum; however, in some cases they have proved very satisfactory, but the work should be slushed in a solvent right after machining to prevent discoloration. Use 75 per cent mineral oil with 25 per cent sulphur base oil.

Magnesium.—Use either an ample supply of mineral oil (4 to 5 gallons per minute) or machine dry. *Soluble oils or emulsions should never be used for magnesium.* A cutting fluid serves primarily to cool the work and also eliminate a possible fire hazard, especially when dull tools are operated at high speeds with fine feeds. Even when using sharp tools, the cut should not be less than 0.001 inch because fine chips are more likely to become ignited at high speeds. While a variety of mineral oils may be used, the following properties are recommended: Specific gravity 0.79 to 0.86; viscosity (Saybolt) at 100 degrees F., up to 55 seconds; flash point, minimum value (closed cup), 160 degrees F.; saponification No. 16 (max.); free acid (max.) 0.2 per cent. Oil-water emulsions, while good coolants, are objectionable because water will greatly intensify any accidental chip fire.

Grinding Magnesium: As a general rule, magnesium is ground dry. The highly inflammable dust should be formed into a sludge by means of a spray of water or low-viscosity mineral oil. Accumulations of dust or sludge should be avoided. For surface grinding, when a fine finish is desirable, a low-viscosity mineral oil may be used.

In cutting steel is some fluid always used?

In many cases, cutting fluids are not used even when machining steel. This may be due to the nature of the work or to the inconvenience of supplying a lubricant when the machine is not equipped for it. For instance, small turning operations in the lathe are usually performed dry or without a lubricant, regardless of the material being turned, especially when the cuts are light and the application of a fluid to the tool would interfere with the work. When there is considerable superfluous metal to be removed and long roughing cuts must be taken, a good cutting fluid, while not necessary, is very desirable, as it permits higher cutting speeds and preserves the edge of the tool.

Cutting fluids are more generally used on turning and milling machines of various types than on planing and slotting machines. In fact, cutting fluids are not often used for rough planing operations, although, in many cases, they would be desirable. The same is true of many other operations which are ordinarily performed dry. Frequently a fluid, such as soda-water, is used on a planer or shaper when taking light finishing cuts. The object, however, is to secure a smooth surface rather than to increase the durability of the tool or permit higher cutting speeds.

In producing an emulsion for general machining operations what ingredients are used?

There are many formulas for cutting fluids. The following is used in a large automobile plant for all ordinary operations, such as drilling, turning, milling, light reaming, and grinding, unless conditions demand a different fluid. The soluble or "base oil" (which is mixed with water to form the emulsion) consists of paraffin oil, 27 gallons; oleic acid, 4 gallons; denatured alcohol, 2 gallons; caustic soda solution at 31 degrees Baumé, 1 gallon. Water in the proportion of 24 to 1 is added to the base oil to obtain the soluble oil, which has the consistency and appearance of milk. This emulsion is commonly called "soda water." To avoid infection from bacteria, which might develop if impure compound got into slight cuts or scratches, a phenol disinfectant is added to the soluble oil daily in the proportion of one gallon of disinfectant to 1000 gallons of compound. This disinfectant is fifteen times stronger than a 5 per cent solution of carbolic acid. Disinfectant is also used in the other cutting compounds.

When are cutting fluids used which also lubricate machine parts and prevent corrosion?

In the automobile plant referred to in the preceding paragraph, automatic screw machines, gear generators, and similar equipment are ordinarily supplied with common paraffin oil. This oil, in addition to facilitating the cut, lubricates the intricate moving parts of the machines. If a soluble oil were employed for this purpose, the machine parts might rust when the plant was shut down over week-ends. For certain jobs on automatic screw machines, heavy threading cuts may necessitate the use of a heavier cutting compound in order to avoid torn threads. For such operations, a spe-

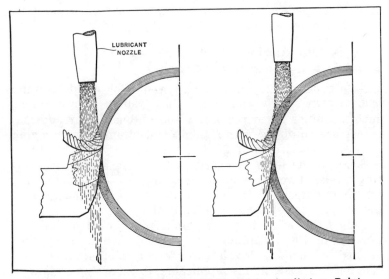

Fig. 2. In Turning, Cooling Fluid Should be Applied at Point
where Chip is Being Severed

cial oil is supplied which is made up by adding 5 gallons of
heavy gear oil and 10 gallons of animal fat to a 55-gallon
drum of paraffin oil. This compound is considered an ex-
cellent substitute for the comparatively expensive lard oil.

Where should the stream of cutting fluid be applied in turning?

The stream of lubricant for a turning tool should fall
directly upon the chip at the point where it is being removed
by the tool. The diagram at the left of Fig. 2 shows how
the stream should fall upon the tool and chip. Very often
the water is thrown upon the work at a point above the
chip to prevent splashing, as illustrated in the right-hand
view. This method, however, of applying lubricant is less
effective and results in a slower cutting speed. Cutting
fluids should be applied where the cutting action is taking
place and as rapidly as possible without causing splashing.
As a general rule, it is preferable to supply from 3 to 5 gallons per minute for each single-point tool on a machine such
as a turret lathe or automatic. The temperature of the cutting fluid should be kept below 110 degrees F. If the volume

of fluid used is not sufficient to maintain the proper temperature, means of cooling it should be provided.

How is the cutting fluid circulated for obtaining a continuous supply?

As a general rule, each machine requiring a cutting fluid has its own supply and circulating system. For example, such machines as turret lathes and automatic turning machines are equipped with a pump and piping for supplying a continuous stream of fluid to the turning or other tools.

Some plants have a general distributing system for cutting fluids. Two types of systems are in use for delivering oils and compounds from a central station to machines in the shop. One of these is arranged to pump the purified cutting fluid up to a storage tank from which it flows by gravity to the machines on different floors. The other pumps the coolant directly to different machines. General distributing systems are applicable when a single class of cutting fluid can be used throughout a plant or department.

How are cutting oils separated from chips and reclaimed?

Chips from screw machines and other classes of machine tools requiring oil for the cutting tools, may contain considerable oil even after the chips have been drained by gravity. The average amount of oil on screw machine chips is about 3 gallons per 100 pounds, and by gravity draining only about 30 per cent of this oil is reclaimed; hence, oil extractors are used, especially in the machine tool-using plants which have continually a lot of oil-soaked chips. These extractors operate on the centrifugal principle. The chips are placed in a perforated pan or basket which is rotated rapidly, thus causing the oil to fly out through the perforations. With these centrifugal oil extractors, from 1 to 5 gallons of oil per 100 pounds of chips may be reclaimed. About 2 gallons per 100 pounds is a fair average, but the amount varies considerably, depending upon the extent of previous draining by gravity and the viscosity of the lubricant. By this centrifugal method practically all of the oil is reclaimed and the process requires only 2 or 3 minutes. Centrifugal separator speeds vary from 500 or 600 R.P.M. up to about 1000 or 1200 R.P.M.

Screw Thread Standards and Their Application

Most of the screw threads used in machine construction conform to some established standard. These screw thread standards include the profile or cross-sectional shape of the thread, a range of screw thread diameters, and a standard number of threads per inch for each diameter. Tolerances and allowances for obtaining varying degrees of accuracy and different classes of fits are also included in modern screw thread standardization. While screw threads, as a general rule, conform to some standard, a screw thread may be standard as to thread *form* but not standard as to *pitch* or number of threads per inch. These special screw threads are used when there is some mechanical advantage. For example, a thread that is smaller in pitch than standard may be used when a fine adjustment is required. The present American (Unified) standard includes a fine series of pitches so that special pitches are seldom required.

Why are different forms of screw threads used?

Different screw-thread forms and standards have been originated and adopted at various times, either because they were considered superior to other forms or because of the special requirements of screws used on a certain class of work. Some of the more important and desirable features of a screw thread are as follows: 1. The thread should be of such a shape that the tool for producing it can easily be made. 2. The shape should be such that the cutting edges of the tool will not be so pointed or delicate as to be worn away easily by the cutting action. 3. The crest of the thread should not be sharp and easily battered. 4. It should be possible to test the diameter and form of the thread with a minimum of measuring and gaging. 5. The form should be such that a good bearing between a screw and nut may be obtained without unnecessary refinement.

Standard Screw-Thread Forms and General Dimensions – 1

AMERICAN STANDARD

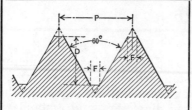

Formulas for revised American Standards are given on page 171.

BRITISH STANDARD WHITWORTH

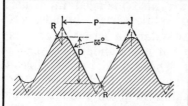

Depth D = 0.6403 × pitch
Radius R at crest and root =
            0.137329 × pitch
Angle = 55 degrees in plane of axis

BRITISH ASSOCIATION THREAD

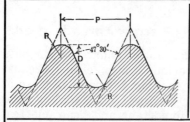

Depth D = 0.6 × pitch
Radius R at crest and root =
            2 × pitch ÷ 11
Angle = 47½ degrees in plane of axis

INTERNATIONAL STANDARD METRIC THREAD

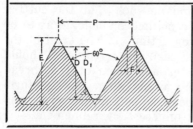

Max. depth D = 0.7035 × pitch
Min. depth D_1 = 0.6855 × pitch
Root radius
         Max. = 0.0633 × pitch
         Min. = 0.054 × pitch
Angle = 60 degrees in plane of axis.

Standard Screw-Thread Forms and General Dimensions — 2

AMERICAN STANDARD ACME THREADS

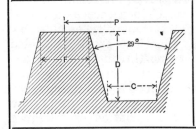

Information on the revised American Standard Acme threads is given on page 174.

29-DEGREE WORM THREAD

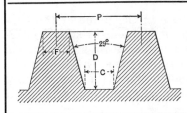

Depth D = 0.6866 × pitch
Width F = 0.335 × pitch
Width C = 0.310 × pitch
Angle = 29 degrees in plane of axis

SQUARE THREAD

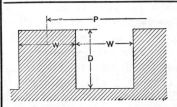

Depth D = 0.5 × pitch
Width W for screw = 0.5 × pitch
Width thread groove in nut = 0.5 × pitch + 0.001 to 0.002 inch clearance

SHARP V-THREAD

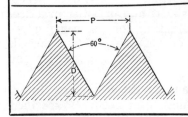

Depth D = 0.866 × pitch
Angle = 60 degrees in plane of axis
Note: Crest and root theoretically are sharp, but in actual practice slightly flat or rounded. This form is nearly obsolete.

What is the American Standard (Unified) screw thread system?

The American Standard for screw threads is the Unified system agreed upon by the United Kingdom, Canada, and the United States to obtain screw thread interchangeability among these three nations. These Unified threads are now the basic American Standard for fastening types of screw threads. In relation to previous American practice, Unified threads have substantially the same thread form and are mechanically interchangeable with the former American National threads of the same diameter and pitch. The principal differences between the two systems lie in: (1) the application of allowances; (2) the variation of tolerance with size; (3) difference with amount of pitch diameter tolerance on external and internal threads; and (4) differences in thread designations.

Thread Form.—The thread angle in the plane of the axis is 60 degrees. The general form of Unified threads is practically the same as the previous American standard for 60-degree threads. The external thread may have either a flat or a rounded root (as shown by the accompanying diagram). In practice, the amount of rounding varies with and is the result of tool wear.

Series of Pitches.—Unified threads consist of a Coarse-thread Series, Table 1, a Fine-thread Series, and an Extra Fine-thread Series, Table 2. There are also 4-, 6-, 8-, 12-, 16-, 20-, 27-, 28-, and 32-thread series, the pitch in each of these three cases being constant for all diameters. The Coarse Series is recommended for general use where conditions do not require a fine thread. The Fine- and Extra-fine Series are particularly useful in the automotive and aircraft industries. The series having 8 threads per inch for all sizes (1 to 6 inches) is for high-pressure pipe flanges, cylinder head studs, or wherever an initial pressure-resisting tension is required in a fastening. The 12-thread series is widely used for thin nuts on shafts and in boiler practice. The 16 thread series is for adjusting collars, bearing retaining nuts or other application requiring a fine thread. It provides a continuation of the Extra Fine series for diameters larger than 2 inches.

Classes of Limits and Tolerances.—In producing interchangeable screw threads, the degree of accuracy specified depends upon the class or quality of the work. When a given quality of fit is desired, whatever standard class of limits needed to obtain it is utilized (see page 383). Tables giving these limits will be found in engineering handbooks (see pages 1124 to 1146 of MACHINERY'S HANDBOOK, 16th Edition).

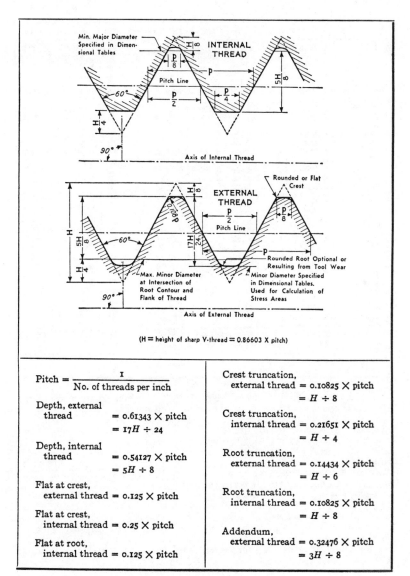

(H = height of sharp V-thread = 0.86603 X pitch)

Pitch = $\dfrac{1}{\text{No. of threads per inch}}$

Depth, external
thread = 0.61343 X pitch
= 17H ÷ 24

Depth, internal
thread = 0.54127 X pitch
= 5H ÷ 8

Flat at crest,
external thread = 0.125 X pitch

Flat at crest,
internal thread = 0.25 X pitch

Flat at root,
internal thread = 0.125 X pitch

Crest truncation,
external thread = 0.10825 X pitch
= H ÷ 8

Crest truncation,
internal thread = 0.21651 X pitch
= H ÷ 4

Root truncation,
external thread = 0.14434 X pitch
= H ÷ 6

Root truncation,
internal thread = 0.10825 X pitch
= H ÷ 8

Addendum,
external thread = 0.32476 X pitch
= 3H ÷ 8

Table 1. American Standard Unified Coarse-Thread Series — Basic Dimensions

Sizes	Basic Major Diam., D	Thds. per Inch, n	Basic Pitch Diam.,a E	Minor Diameter Ext. Thds., K_s	Minor Diameter Int. Thds., K_n	Lead Angle at Basic P.D. Deg.	Min.	Area of Minor Diam. at $D-2h_b$	Tensile Stress Area
	Inches		Inches	Inches	Inches	Deg.	Min.	Sq. In.	Sq. In.
1 (.073)*	0.0730	64	0.0629	0.0538	0.0561	4	31	0.00218	0.00263
2 (.086)	0.0860	56	0.0744	0.0641	0.0667	4	22	0.00310	0.00370
3 (.099)*	0.0990	48	0.0855	0.0734	0.0764	4	26	0.00406	0.00487
4 (.112)	0.1120	40	0.0958	0.0813	0.0849	4	45	0.00496	0.00604
5 (.125)	0.1250	40	0.1088	0.0943	0.0979	4	11	0.00672	0.00796
6 (.138)	0.1380	32	0.1177	0.0997	0.1042	4	50	0.00745	0.00909
8 (.164)	0.1640	32	0.1437	0.1257	0.1302	3	58	0.01196	0.0140
10 (.190)	0.1900	24	0.1629	0.1389	0.1449	4	39	0.01450	0.0175
12 (.216)*	0.2160	24	0.1889	0.1649	0.1709	4	1	0.0206	0.0242
1/4	0.2500	20	0.2175	0.1887	0.1959	4	11	0.0269	0.0318
5/16	0.3125	18	0.2764	0.2443	0.2524	3	40	0.0454	0.0524
3/8	0.3750	16	0.3344	0.2983	0.3073	3	24	0.0678	0.0775
7/16	0.4375	14	0.3911	0.3499	0.3602	3	20	0.0933	0.1063
1/2	0.5000	13	0.4500	0.4056	0.4167	3	7	0.1257	0.1419
9/16	0.5625	12	0.5084	0.4603	0.4723	2	59	0.162	0.182
5/8	0.6250	11	0.5660	0.5135	0.5266	2	56	0.202	0.226
3/4	0.7500	10	0.6850	0.6273	0.6417	2	40	0.302	0.334
7/8	0.8750	9	0.8028	0.7387	0.7547	2	31	0.419	0.462
1	1.0000	8	0.9188	0.8466	0.8647	2	29	0.551	0.606
1 1/8	1.1250	7	1.0322	0.9497	0.9704	2	31	0.693	0.763
1 1/4	1.2500	7	1.1572	1.0747	1.0954	2	15	0.890	0.969
1 3/8	1.3750	6	1.2667	1.1705	1.1946	2	24	1.054	1.155
1 1/2	1.5000	6	1.3917	1.2955	1.3196	2	11	1.294	1.405
1 3/4	1.7500	5	1.6201	1.5046	1.5335	2	15	1.74	1.90
2	2.0000	4 1/2	1.8557	1.7274	1.7594	2	11	2.30	2.50
2 1/4	2.2500	4 1/2	2.1057	1.9774	2.0094	1	55	3.02	3.25
2 1/2	2.5000	4	2.3376	2.1933	2.2294	1	57	3.72	4.00
2 3/4	2.7500	4	2.5876	2.4433	2.4794	1	46	4.62	4.93
3	3.0000	4	2.8376	2.6933	2.7294	1	36	5.62	5.97
3 1/4	3.2500	4	3.0876	2.9433	2.9794	1	29	6.72	7.10
3 1/2	3.5000	4	3.3376	3.1933	3.2294	1	22	7.92	8.33
3 3/4	3.7500	4	3.5876	3.4433	3.4794	1	16	9.21	9.66
4	4.0000	4	3.8376	3.6933	3.7294	1	11	10.61	11.08

* Secondary sizes.
a British: Effective Diameter.

The area designated as "Stress Area" is based upon a diameter that is the mean of the pitch and minor diameters.

American Standard Unified screw threads include the various series of pitches given on page 170. The Coarse thread series is the one most commonly used in the bulk production of bolts, screws, nuts and other general engineering applications. It is also used for threading into lower tensile strength materials such as cast iron, mild steel and softer materials (bronze, brass, aluminum, magnesium and plastics) to obtain the optimum resistance to stripping of the internal thread. The Fine-thread Series is suitable for the production of bolts, screws, nuts and for other applications where the Coarse series is not applicable. External threads of this series have greater tensile stress area than comparable sizes of the Coarse series. The Extra-fine Thread Series is applicable where even finer pitches of threads are desirable, as for short lengths of engagement and for thin-walled tubes, nuts, ferrules, or couplings.

Table 2. American Standard Unified Fine and Extra-fine Thread Series — Basic Dimensions

Sizes	Basic Major Diam., D	Thds. per Inch, n	Basic Pitch Diam.,[a] E	Minor Diameter Ext. Thds., K_s	Minor Diameter Int. Thds., K_n	Lead Angle at Basic P.D.		Area of Minor Diam. at $D-2h_b$	Tensile Stress Area
	Inches		Inches	Inches	Inches	Deg.	Min.	Sq. In.	Sq. In.
FINE THREAD SERIES									
0 (.060)	0.0600	80	0.0519	0.0447	0.0465	4	23	0.00151	0.00180
1 (.073)*	0.0730	72	0.0640	0.0560	0.0580	3	57	0.00237	0.00278
2 (.086)	0.0860	64	0.0759	0.0668	0.0691	3	45	0.00339	0.00394
3 (.099)*	0.0990	56	0.0874	0.0771	0.0797	3	43	0.00451	0.00523
4 (.112)	0.1120	48	0.0985	0.0864	0.0894	3	51	0.00566	0.00661
5 (.125)	0.1250	44	0.1102	0.0971	0.1004	3	45	0.00716	0.00830
6 (.138)	0.1380	40	0.1218	0.1073	0.1109	3	44	0.00874	0.01015
8 (.164)	0.1640	36	0.1460	0.1299	0.1339	3	28	0.01285	0.01474
10 (.190)	0.1900	32	0.1697	0.1517	0.1562	3	21	0.0175	0.0200
12 (.216)*	0.2160	28	0.1928	0.1722	0.1773	3	22	0.0226	0.0258
¼	0.2500	28	0.2268	0.2062	0.2113	2	52	0.0326	0.0364
⁵⁄₁₆	0.3125	24	0.2854	0.2614	0.2674	2	40	0.0524	0.0580
³⁄₈	0.3750	24	0.3479	0.3239	0.3299	2	11	0.0809	0.0878
⁷⁄₁₆	0.4375	20	0.4050	0.3762	0.3834	2	15	0.1090	0.1187
½	0.5000	20	0.4675	0.4387	0.4459	1	57	0.1486	0.1599
⁹⁄₁₆	0.5625	18	0.5264	0.4943	0.5024	1	55	0.189	0.203
⁵⁄₈	0.6250	18	0.5889	0.5568	0.5649	1	43	0.240	0.256
¾	0.7500	16	0.7094	0.6733	0.6823	1	36	0.351	0.373
⅞	0.8750	14	0.8286	0.7874	0.7977	1	34	0.480	0.509
1	1.0000	12	0.9459	0.8978	0.9098	1	36	0.625	0.663
1⅛	1.1250	12	1.0709	1.0228	1.0348	1	25	0.812	0.856
1¼	1.2500	12	1.1959	1.1478	1.1598	1	16	1.024	1.073
1⅜	1.3750	12	1.3209	1.2728	1.2848	1	9	1.260	1.315
1½	1.5000	12	1.4459	1.3978	1.4098	1	3	1.521	1.581
EXTRA-FINE THREAD SERIES									
12 (.216)*	0.2160	32	0.1957	0.1777	0.1822	2	55	0.0242	0.0270
¼	0.2500	32	0.2297	0.2117	0.2162	2	29	0.0344	0.0379
⁵⁄₁₆	0.3125	32	0.2922	0.2742	0.2787	1	57	0.0581	0.0625
³⁄₈	0.3750	32	0.3547	0.3367	0.3412	1	36	0.0878	0.0932
⁷⁄₁₆	0.4375	28	0.4143	0.3937	0.3988	1	34	0.1201	0.1274
½	0.5000	28	0.4768	0.4562	0.4613	1	22	0.162	0.170
⁹⁄₁₆	0.5625	24	0.5354	0.5114	0.5174	1	25	0.203	0.214
⁵⁄₈	0.6250	24	0.5979	0.5739	0.5799	1	16	0.256	0.268
¹¹⁄₁₆*	0.6875	24	0.6604	0.6364	0.6424	1	9	0.315	0.329
¾	0.7500	20	0.7175	0.6887	0.6959	1	16	0.369	0.386
¹³⁄₁₆*	0.8125	20	0.7800	0.7512	0.7584	1	10	0.439	0.458
⅞	0.8750	20	0.8425	0.8137	0.8209	1	5	0.515	0.536
¹⁵⁄₁₆*	0.9375	20	0.9050	0.8762	0.8834	1	0	0.598	0.620
1	1.0000	20	0.9675	0.9387	0.9459	0	57	0.687	0.711
1¹⁄₁₆*	1.0625	18	1.0264	0.9943	1.0024	0	59	0.770	0.799
1⅛	1.1250	18	1.0889	1.0568	1.0649	0	56	0.871	0.901
1³⁄₁₆*	1.1875	18	1.1514	1.1193	1.1274	0	53	0.977	1.009
1¼	1.2500	18	1.2139	1.1818	1.1899	0	50	1.090	1.123
1⁵⁄₁₆*	1.3125	18	1.2764	1.2443	1.2524	0	48	1.208	1.244
1⅜	1.3750	18	1.3389	1.3068	1.3149	0	45	1.333	1.370
1⁷⁄₁₆*	1.4375	18	1.4014	1.3693	1.3774	0	43	1.464	1.503
1½	1.5000	18	1.4639	1.4318	1.4399	0	42	1.60	1.64
1⁹⁄₁₆*	1.5625	18	1.5264	1.4943	1.5024	0	40	1.74	1.79
1⅝	1.6250	18	1.5889	1.5568	1.5649	0	38	1.89	1.94
1¹¹⁄₁₆*	1.6875	18	1.6514	1.6193	1.6274	0	37	2.05	2.10

* Secondary sizes.
a British: Effective Diameter.

What are the advantages of the revised American Standard?

Modern practice in producing both external and internal screw threads makes it possible to obtain very precise dimensions. One of the difficulties arising from these small tolerances has been that the mating threaded parts may approach or have the same basic dimensions; hence a nut thread made to the minimum allowed limit, and a bolt thread made to the maximum limit, may not assemble readily. The new American Unified standard corrects such faults by introducing limits of Classes 1A, 1B and 2B, 2B which provide a *minimum clearance* between mating parts. Thus, tight fits during wrenching and seizure at high temperatures are prevented, and room is allowed for plating.

Increase in Working Tolerance.—The revised standard is designed to correct certain production difficulties resulting from the former standard. Often, under the old system, the tolerances of the product were practically absorbed by the combined tool and gage tolerances, leaving little for a working tolerance in manufacture. Somewhat greater tolerances are now provided for nut threads. As contrasted with the old "classes of fit" 1, 2, and 3, for each of which the pitch diameter tolerance on the external and internal threads were equal, the Classes 1B, 2B, and 3B (internal) threads in the new standard have, respectively, a 30 per cent larger pitch diameter tolerance than the 1A, 2A, and 3A (external) threads. Relatively more tolerance is provided for fine threads than for coarse threads of the same pitch.

What is the standard form for Acme screw threads?

The American Standard for Acme screw threads provides for two types of Acme thread according to intended application, namely, General Purpose and Centralizing. General Purpose Acme threads have sufficient clearance on all diameters for free movement whereas Centralizing Acme threads have the clearance at the major diameters of the external and internal threads limited so that bearing at the major diameter maintains approximate alignment of the thread axes thus preventing wedging of the thread flanks.

The included thread angle of these Standard Acme threads is 29 degrees; the basic thread depth is 0.5 times the pitch;

and the basic thread thickness, at a diameter less than the basic major diameter by 0.5 times the pitch, is 0.5 times the pitch. The crest corners of Centralizing threads are chamfered while with General Purpose threads the corners may be either sharp or chamfered. Basic dimensions of General Purpose Acme threads are given in Table 3. Other thread details are given in MACHINERY'S HANDBOOK.

What is the standard form for Stub Acme screw threads?

The American Standard provides a Stub Acme screw thread for those unusual applications where, due to mechanical or metallurgical considerations, a coarse-pitch thread of shallow depth is required. The included thread angle of these Stub Acme threads is 29 degrees; the basic thread depth is 0.3 times the pitch; and the basic thread thickness, at a diameter less than the basic major diameter by 0.3 times the pitch, is 0.5 times the pitch. The major and minor diameter clearances are the same for Stub Acme threads as those provided for General Purpose Acme threads.

What is the relation between the pitch and the diameter of an Acme screw thread?

For American Standard Acme threads, recommended combinations of pitch diameter and threads per inch are: $\frac{1}{4}$—16; $\frac{5}{16}$—14; $\frac{3}{8}$—12; $\frac{7}{16}$—12; $\frac{1}{2}$—10; $\frac{5}{8}$—8; $\frac{3}{4}$—6; $\frac{7}{8}$—6; 1—5; $1\frac{1}{8}$—5; $1\frac{1}{4}$—5; $1\frac{3}{8}$—1; $1\frac{1}{2}$—4; $1\frac{3}{4}$—4; 2—4; $2\frac{1}{4}$—3; $2\frac{1}{2}$—3; $2\frac{3}{4}$—3; 3—2; $3\frac{1}{2}$—2; 4—2; $4\frac{1}{2}$—2; 5—2. However, other combinations are used for many special applications. Thus, the Acme thread form is often used on multiple-threaded lead screws, etc., and for such applications the pitch and lead, with a given diameter, vary more or less, according to the class of service or other requirements. In some cases, Acme threads are used on lead-screws which are required to move a slide or other part a greater distance per revolution than would be possible with a single thread; then a multiple thread is used. For example, if the required lead for a given diameter exceeds that corresponding to the maximum pitch recommended, it is advisable to use a multiple thread of finer pitch rather than a single thread of coarser pitch.

Table 3. American Standard General Purpose Acme Threads—Basic Dimensions*

Thds. per Inch	Pitch,	Height of Thread (Basic),	Total Height of Thread,	Thread Thickness (Basic),	Width of Flat	
					Crest of Internal Thread (Basic),	Root of Internal Thread,
n	$p = 1/n$	$p/2$	$p/2 + \frac{1}{2}$ allowance†	$p/2$	$0.3707p$	$0.3707p -$ $0.259 \times$ allowance†
16	0.06250	0.03125	0.0362	0.03125	0.0232	0.0206
14	0.07143	0.03571	0.0407	0.03571	0.0265	0.0239
12	0.08333	0.04167	0.0467	0.04167	0.0309	0.0283
10	0.10000	0.05000	0.0600	0.05000	0.0371	0.0319
8	0.12500	0.06250	0.0725	0.06250	0.0463	0.0411
6	0.16667	0.08333	0.0933	0.08333	0.0618	0.0566
5	0.20000	0.10000	0.1100	0.10000	0.0741	0.0689
4	0.25000	0.12500	0.1350	0.12500	0.0927	0.0875
3	0.33333	0.16667	0.1767	0.16667	0.1236	0.1184
2½	0.40000	0.20000	0.2100	0.20000	0.1483	0.1431
2	0.50000	0.25000	0.2600	0.25000	0.1853	0.1802
1½	0.66667	0.33333	0.3433	0.33333	0.2471	0.2419
1⅓	0.75000	0.37500	0.3850	0.37500	0.2780	0.2728
1	1.00000	0.50000	0.5100	0.50000	0.3707	0.3655

* All dimensions are in inches.
† Allowance is 0.020 inch for 10 threads per inch and coarser, and 0.010 inch for finer threads.

What is a square thread and is there a standard square-thread system?

The square thread is so named because the section is square, the depth, in the case of a screw, being equal to the width or one-half the pitch. The thread groove in a square-threaded nut is made a little greater than one-half the pitch in order to provide a slight clearance for the screw; hence, the tools used for threading square-threaded taps are a little less in width at the point than one-half the pitch. The pitch of a square thread is usually twice the pitch of an American standard thread of corresponding diameter, but square threads have not been standardized. The square thread has been superseded quite largely by the Acme form, in present-day practice.

Why is the Acme thread frequently used in preference to a square thread?

The Acme thread is extensively used in preference to the square thread, especially for lead-screws and similar parts, because it has several advantages. The Acme form is stronger than the square thread, and it may be cut with a die more readily than a square thread. When an Acme thread is engaged by a sectional nut like the half-nut of a lathe apron, engagement or disengagement is more readily effected than with a square thread; an adjustable split nut may also be used in connection with an Acme screw thread to compensate for wear and to eliminate backlash or lost motion because it has angular sides.

Why is the sharp V-thread seldom used in modern machine construction?

The sharp V-thread is used very little at the present time, because thread forms like the American Standard and British Standard Whitworth have certain practical advantages. The American Standard has a flat top or crest and the British Standard Whitworth a rounded crest; consequently, these thread forms are not so likely to be injured or battered as the sharp V-thread; furthermore, taps and dies wear less at the points of the teeth and retain their size longer. The American Standard screw is from one-eighth to one-sixth stronger to resist tension than a V-thread screw, because for a given outside diameter the American Standard screw thread has a larger root diameter or effective area. Owing to the difficulties connected with the V-thread, the tap manufacturers agreed in 1909 to discontinue the making of sharp V-thread taps, except when ordered. One advantage of the V-thread is that the same cutting tool may be used for all pitches, whereas, with the American standard form, the width of the point or the flat varies according to the pitch. This is one of the reasons why V-threads are still used to some extent. The V-thread is regarded as a good form where a steam-tight joint is necessary, and many of the taps used on locomotive work have this form of thread.

What screw thread standard is applied to machine screws?

Screw threads for machine screws are included in the American Standard system and the thread form is the same as the American (National) form. The American Standard screw thread system for general use in machine construction includes a coarse series of pitches and a fine series as previously explained. This is also true of the smaller sizes adapted for machine screws; however, most machine screws (probably about 80 per cent) have the coarse-thread series. The sizes of American Standard machine screws are designated by numbers up to, but not including, the ¼-inch diameter. Sizes of ¼ inch and larger are designated by giving the actual dimensions. (See Table 4.)

Has the A.S.M.E. Machine Screw Standard been replaced entirely by the American Standard?

The A.S.M.E. Machine Screw Standard, which was the first one to be generally recognized by machine screw manufacturers, has been officially replaced by the American Standard. However, there is still occasional demand for certain sizes or pitches conforming to the older A.S.M.E. Standard. This continued use of the older standard applies particularly to the No. 4 size with 36 threads per inch. The No. 4 American Standard machine screw has 40 threads per inch in the coarse-thread series and 48 in the fine-thread

Table 4. American Standard Machine Screws

	Coarse-thread Series				Fine-thread Series		
Size	Threads per Inch	Major Diam., Max.	Minor Diam., Max.	Size	Threads per Inch	Major Diam., Max.	Minor Diam., Max.
. . . .	. .	. . . . . .	. . . . . .	0	80	0.0600	0.0447
1	64	0.0730	0.0538	1	72	0.0730	0.0560
2	56	0.0860	0.0641	2	64	0.0860	0.0668
3	48	0.0990	0.0734	3	56	0.0990	0.0771
4	40	0.1120	0.0813	4	48	0.1120	0.0864
5	40	0.1250	0.0943	5	44	0.1250	0.0971
6	32	0.1380	0.0997	6	40	0.1380	0.1073
8	32	0.1640	0.1257	8	36	0.1640	0.1299
10	24	0.1900	0.1389	10	32	0.1900	0.1517
12	24	0.2160	0.1649	12	28	0.2160	0.1722
1/4	20	0.2500	0.1887	1/4	28	0.2500	0.2062
5/16	18	0.3125	0.2443	5/16	24	0.3125	0.2614
3/8	16	0.3750	0.2983	3/8	24	0.3750	0.3239
7/16	14	0.4375	0.3499	7/16	20	0.4375	0.3762
1/2	13	0.5000	0.4056	1/2	20	0.5000	0.4387

This machine screw series includes that part of the regular American Standard Screw Thread Series within the range of ordinary machine screw sizes.

series. The No. 4-36 machine screw of the former A.S.M.E. Standard is extensively used in some shops and may be found in some hardware stores at the present time. Furthermore, manufacturers of taps and dies continue to supply No. 4-36 tools chiefly in response to the demand of the trade. Eventually, this No. 4-36 screw may be largely or entirely superseded by the American Standard. The A.S.M.E. No. 14-20 and No. 14-24 also continue to be used more or less, but present indications are that this No. 14 size (the diameter of which is 0.242 inch) is gradually being replaced by the ¼-inch size of the American Standard which has 20 threads per inch in the coarse-thread series and 28 in the fine-thread series.

What are the most important British screw thread standards?

The British Standard for Whitworth screw threads was comparable to the former American Standard in the United States; in other words, it was the standard intended for general machine construction. The diameters range from ¼ inch up to 6 inches. The included angle of the thread is 55 degrees, and the crest and root are rounded to a radius of 0.137329 times pitch. This makes the depth of the thread equal 0.640327 times pitch. This standard is to be replaced by the Unified thread standard.

British Standard Fine Thread.—This thread form is the same as the Standard Whitworth, but the pitch is finer, there being a larger number of threads per inch for a given diameter. The British Standard Fine Thread System covers a range of diameters from 7/32 up to 3 inches, inclusive. For sizes below ¼ inch, the British Association Standard is used. The fine thread standard is intended to supplement the regular British Standard Whitworth whenever finer pitches are required. These threads are to be replaced eventually by Unified threads.

British Association Thread.—This standard is for small screws. The diameters are designated by numbers and range from 6 millimeters (0.2362 inch) up to 0.29 millimeters (0.011 inch). The smaller sizes, from No. 17 up, are not in general use. The thread has an included angle of 47.5 degrees. The root and crest are rounded to make the depth

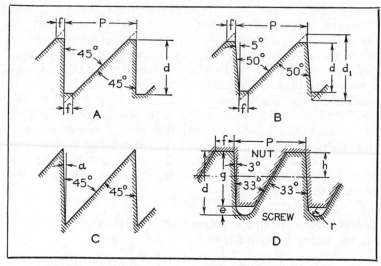

Fig. 1. Threads of Buttress Type

equal 0.6 times pitch approximately. The abbreviation B.A. is used to designate the British Association Thread.

There are other British Standards for screw threads, but the four mentioned are the most prominent ones.

What standard thread form is used for pipes?

The American Standard pipe thread is used in the United States. This thread has an angle of 60 degrees like the regular American Standard thread, and the pipe thread is also truncated or flattened at the top and crest. This flattening, however, is less than for the regular American Standard thread; consequently, the depth of a pipe thread is greater and equals 0.8 × pitch, except for 8 threads per inch which is 0.788 × pitch. The tapering pipe thread has a standard taper of ¾ inch per foot. The American Standard pipe thread was formerly known as the Briggs Standard.

Why are buttress threads used and is there a standard form?

Screw threads of the buttress type (see diagrams, Fig. 1) have one face which is either perpendicular to the axis or nearly so in order to resist heavy loads in one direction. The form shown at *A* has a vertical face or one that is square with the axis, and the included angle is 45 degrees. Sometimes the thread depth *d* is made equal to 0.75 times pitch, thus making the flat *f* equal 0.125 times pitch. This depth *d* may also be reduced to two-thirds of the pitch, thus making the flat equal one-sixth of the pitch. American Standard Buttress threads have the face inclined at a 7-degree angle, the trailing flank at a 45-degree angle, and the thread depth equal to 0.6 times the pitch.

The front side of buttress threads may be inclined slightly to avoid cutter interference when the threads are cut by milling. If the angle of the front face is 5 degrees as shown by diagram *B*, making the included angle 50 degrees, and width of the flat *f* of both crest and root equals 0.125 times pitch, then thread depth equals 0.69 times pitch, or three-fourths of the height of the triangle d_1.

Diagram *C* shows a buttress thread of the sharp vee form with a front face angle *a* of 1 degree; some flat or rounding, however, at the crest and root of any screw thread is preferable.

The "saw-tooth" form of thread illustrated by diagram *D* is known in Germany as the "Sägengewinde" and in Italy as the "Fillettatura a dente di Sega." Pitches are standardized from 2 millimeters up to 48 millimeters in the German and Italian specifications. The front face inclines 3 degrees from the perpendicular and the included angle is 33 degrees.

The thread depth *d* for the screw $= 0.86777 \times$ pitch *P*. The thread depth *g* for the nut $= 0.75 \times$ pitch. Dimension $h = 0.341 \times P$. The width *f* of flat at the crest of the thread on the screw $= 0.26384 \times$ pitch. Radius *r* at the root $= 0.12427 \times$ pitch. The clearance space *e* between the root of the screw thread and the crest of the nut $= 0.11777 \times$ pitch.

What are the principal features of the International Metric Thread System?

The International Metric Thread System (Systeme Internationale) has been adopted as standard by most European countries using the metric system, and also by Japan and Russia. The thread form is similar to the American Stand-

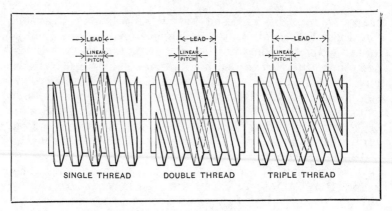

Fig. 2. Single and Multiple Screw Threads

ard, excepting the depth which is slightly greater. The included angle of the thread is 60 degrees, and the crest has a flat like the American Standard. The width of this flat is equal to one-eighth of the pitch. The root of the thread is rounded which provides a clearance between the root and the crest of the mating thread. The thread depth equals 0.7035 times pitch, maximum, and 0.6855 times pitch, minimum. This depth is greater than that of the American Standard. Incidentally, the German metric thread form is like the International Standard, and the thread depth equals 0.6945 times pitch.

What is the difference between "pitch" and "lead" of a screw thread?

Pitch is the distance from the center of one thread to the center of the next thread, measured parallel to the axis of the screw. This definition applies whether the screw has a single thread or is of the multiple-threaded form.

Lead is the distance that a thread advances in a single turn, or the distance that a nut would advance in an axial direction if turned one complete revolution. The lead may also be expressed as the distance from center to center of the *same* thread, after one turn. The lead and pitch of a single screw thread are equal; the lead of a double thread is twice the pitch; the lead of a triple thread is three times

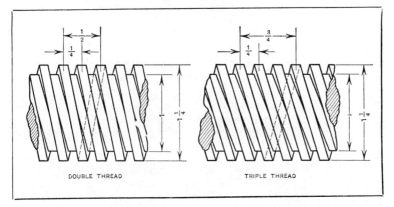

Fig. 3. Relation between Pitch and Lead of Multiple Threads

the pitch, and so on. For example, the double thread and the triple thread shown in Fig. 3 each has a pitch of ¼ inch. The lead of the double thread is ½ inch and the lead of the triple thread is ¾ inch.

What are multiple screw threads and why are they used?

Most screw threads are the single type. (See diagram at left in Fig. 2.) This means that the screw thread consists of a single ridge and groove. A double thread differs from a single thread in that it has two threads and grooves, starting diametrically opposite as shown by the central diagram. A triple thread has three grooves starting at three equally spaced points around the circumference. (See diagram at right.) Multiple threads may also have four or more threads.

The object in using multiple threads is to obtain an increase in lead without weakening the screw. For example, the lead of the triple-threaded screw (Fig. 2) is 1.5 times that of the one with a double thread; consequently, a nut would advance ¾ inch in one revolution instead of ½ inch. This method of increasing the movement per screw revolution often is very desirable. To obtain the same lead with a single thread, the pitch would have to be ¾ inch, thus making the thread much coarser. This would weaken the screw, unless its diameter were increased.

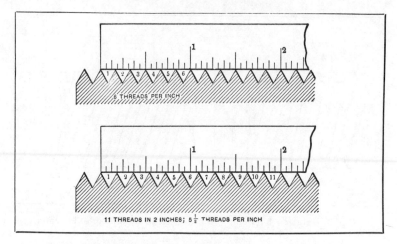

Fig. 4. Method of Counting the Number of Threads per Inch

How is the pitch of a screw thread designated on drawings?

Since pitch represents a dimension it should, to be strictly accurate, be expressed in inches (or in millimeters in the case of metric threads). To illustrate, if a screw thread has 8 threads per inch, the pitch is 0.125 inch and not 8. However, the word "pitch" is often used to denote the *number of threads per inch* because this number is related to the pitch. It is said that screws have an 8-pitch thread, or 16-pitch thread, when 8 threads per inch and 16 threads per inch is what is really meant.

The number of threads per inch is the number of threads counted in the length of one inch, when, for example, a scale is held against the side of the screw, and the threads are counted, as shown in Fig. 4. If there is not a whole number of threads in one inch, count the threads in two or more inches, until the center of one thread comes opposite an inch-mark, and then divide by the number of inches to find the number of threads in one inch, as shown by the lower diagram. The number of threads per inch equals 1 divided by the pitch, or, expressed as a formula:

$$\text{Number of threads per inch} = \frac{1}{\text{pitch}}.$$

The pitch of a screw equals 1 divided by the number of threads per inch, or

$$\text{Pitch} = \frac{1}{\text{number of threads per inch}}.$$

Thus if the number of threads per inch equals 16, the pitch equals 1/16. If the pitch equals 0.05, the number of threads per inch equals $1 \div 0.05 = 20$. If the pitch equals 2/5 inch, the number of threads per inch equals $1 \div 2/5 = 2\frac{1}{2}$ threads per inch.

On drawings, the number of threads per inch usually is given, especially if the screw thread is standard. This number follows the diameter. For example, $\frac{3}{4} - 10$ means a $\frac{3}{4}$-inch screw thread having 10 threads per inch, which is the American Standard number for this diameter. A machine screw of No. 6 size might be specified as No. 6—32.

What designation is preferable for multiple screw threads?

Confusion is often caused by indefinite designation of multiple-thread (double, triple, quadruple, etc.) screws. One way of expressing that a double-thread screw is required is to say, for instance: "3 threads per inch double," which means that the screw is cut with 3 *double* threads, or 6 threads per inch, counting the threads by a scale placed alongside of the screw. The pitch of this screw is 1/6 inch, and the lead twice this, or 1/3 inch. To cut this screw, the lathe would be geared to cut 3 threads per inch, but the thread depth is that required for 6 threads per inch. "Four threads per inch triple" means that there are 4 times 3, or 12 threads along one inch of the screw, when counted by a scale; the pitch of the screw is 1/12 inch, but, being a triple screw, the lead of the thread is 3 times the pitch, or $\frac{1}{4}$ inch. The best way of expressing that a multiple-thread screw is to be cut is to give the lead and pitch; for example, a triple Acme thread, $4\frac{1}{2}$ inches lead, $1\frac{1}{2}$ inch pitch. In the case of single-threaded screws, the number of threads per inch and the form of the thread only are given. The word "single" is not required.

Cutting Screw Threads
in the Lathe

The lathe is indispensable for many screw-cutting operations, partly because it is adapted to a wide range of pitches and diameters. The swing of the lathe equals, approximately, the maximum diameter of external screw thread that can be cut, and the number of pitches varies according to the change-gear mechanism, but usually is large enough for all ordinary requirements. There is also an advantage in most instances in being able to cut threads on the same machine that is used for the turning operation, to insure cutting the thread concentric with other finished surfaces. A well-constructed lathe is also capable of very accurate thread cutting. When exceptional accuracy is required, the cut thread is finished by grinding, especially if the screw thread is hardened after cutting.

In order to cut a thread, it is necessary to know about the thread form or its cross-sectional shape; the diameter of the screw thread; the number of threads per inch or the pitch, if the thread is the usual single form. If the thread is a double, triple or some other multiple type, the *lead* of the thread and the number of single threads or "starts" must be known, as explained later in connection with multiple thread cutting. All of this information should be given on the drawing.

Is a lathe adapted for cutting all classes of screw threads?

All of the various forms or classes of screw threads used in machine construction may be cut on a lathe, but it does not follow that a lathe should always be used. For example, threads in holes for receiving studs, cap-screws, etc., are cut rapidly and accurately by tapping, and threads on bolts, cap-screws, machine screws, etc., may either be cut by dies or be formed by a rolling process. Large coarse threads on worms, lead-screws, etc., frequently are cut by milling in special thread-milling machines. The conditions under which the lathe is commonly used for cutting screw threads are as follows:

1. When a part has been turned and one or more screw threads must be cut to complete it.

2. When the screw thread is not standard or is so large in diameter that the use of a tap or die is not practicable.

3. When there is not enough thread cutting to warrant the use of machines or equipment designed primarily for screw cutting.

4. When the lathe is the only means available, in which case it is sometimes applied to screw-cutting operations which could be done more efficiently in some other way.

5. When the lathe is the only machine available that will cut threads of the required standard of accuracy.

When is a lathe generally used for thread cutting?

The engine lathe equipped with a single-point tool is almost invariably used for cutting screw threads on parts that are turned in it, but it is seldom used for threading operations on parts that have been previously turned in another type of machine; in fact, when threading operations are preceded by turning operations, the former are, as a rule, performed in the machine that did the turning, whether it is an engine lathe or some other form of lathe or turning machine. For instance, in the turret lathe and automatic screw machine practice, dies are used for most external thread-cutting operations and taps for internal work. The object of cutting the screw threads in the same machine is to avoid a second operation on another machine, and, at the same time, to secure accuracy by cutting the threads before the position of the work has been disturbed. If, for example, a piston-rod has been turned in the engine lathe and a screw thread is required at the piston end for receiving a nut, the lathe would be used for cutting that thread. On the other hand, if cutting a screw thread is the principal operation, the engine lathe may not be the type of machine to use, especially if a lot of duplicate parts must be threaded.

In such cases, a special threading machine of the die class or a thread milling machine might be used in preference to the lathe.

How is a screw thread of given pitch cut in a lathe?

The main spindle of a lathe and the lead-screw which moves the carriage along the bed for thread cutting, are connected by gearing through which motion is transmitted from the spindle to the lead-screw. The ratio of this gearing can be changed to make the carriage and thread cutting tool move whatever distance per spindle and work revolution is required to cut a thread of given pitch. For example, suppose the lathe is to be arranged to cut a 1½-inch American Standard screw thread. A table giving American Standard diameters and corresponding pitches or numbers of threads per inch shows that the 1 1/2-inch diameter has 6 threads per inch; consequently, in cutting this thread, the gearing ratio must be such as to move the carriage and tool 1/6 inch for each spindle or work revolution, or, expressed differently, the work must make six revolutions while the tool and carriage are moving one inch.

There are two general methods of changing the gear combination or ratio to suit the pitch of the thread, and the method depends upon the type of lathe being used. Most modern lathes, excepting some of the very large sizes or comparatively inexpensive ones, are equipped with what is known as a "quick change-gear" mechanism. This mechanism consists of gearing so arranged that the ratio can easily be changed to obtain any one of a large range of pitches. An instruction plate or table on the housing of the mechanism shows the various numbers of threads per inch which can be obtained. If, for example, 6 threads per inch are to be cut, the gearing is arranged to cut this number merely by shifting certain controlling handles or levers. Simple instructions given in connection with the table or chart show clearly the position of each controlling handle or lever required to obtain any given number of threads per inch. The exact arrangement varies more or less on lathes of different make; but in a few minutes anyone can see just how the changes are made on any particular lathe, as shown by the following descriptions of these quick-change mechanisms as applied to thread cutting.

How is a change-gear mechanism adjusted for cutting a given number of threads per inch?

Quick change-gear mechanisms provide the changes required both for turning and thread cutting, and in adjusting the quick-change mechanisms for cutting a thread of given pitch or lead, the procedure is the same as previously explained in connection with adjustments for obtaining a given rate of feed. The chart or instruction plate, which shows the range of feeds obtainable, also shows the range of threads per inch obtainable, and the control levers are positioned with reference to the number of threads per inch. For example, suppose the quick-change mechanism (Fig. 3, page 24) is to be set for cutting 10 threads per inch. Then lever C is placed in the notch indicated on plate A; lever B is placed directly below the vertical column containing "10" (threads per inch); lever D is placed in the "A" position because the letter A is at the end of the horizontal row containing the figure 10; and lever E is placed in the position marked "thread" so that motion will be transmitted to the carriage through the lead-screw. The lead-screw should be used only when cutting threads. For all other operations, motion is transmitted through the feed-rod. This practice is to preserve the accuracy of the lead-screw.

In setting the quick-change mechanism shown on page 32 (Fig. 8) the procedure would be as follows: For 10 threads per inch, engage lever B with that hole directly under the column containing the figure 10. Place top lever C in the right-hand position and the sliding gear knob (at the end of the lathe but not shown) in the "in" position.

If the quick-change mechanism shown on page 33 (Fig. 10) is to be set for 10 threads per inch, note that the letters BE are opposite the horizontal row containing the figure 10; consequently, set lever 1 (which has A, B and C positions) in its B position, and lever 3 (which has D and E positions) in its E position. Lever 2 is, of course, placed directly below the vertical row containing the figure 10. Some plates or charts (as in this case) give, in addition to the numbers of threads per inch, the equivalent leads to permit setting the mechanism for a given lead if this should be required.

It is impracticable to illustrate and describe every design of quick change-gear mechanism. While some differ considerably from the designs here illustrated, they all are similar in principle, and the lathe operator can soon determine the changes required for obtaining any given feed or number of threads per inch.

If a lathe is not equipped with quick change-gears, how is it arranged for thread cutting?

If a lathe is not equipped with a quick change-gear mechanism, it is necessary to place the required gears in position by hand. These so-called "change-gears" serve exactly the same purpose as quick change-gears. They are located at the end of the headstock and are so arranged that whatever combination is required may be placed in position by hand and adjusted so that the spindle and lead-screw will have the correct relative speeds. A set of these change-gears accompanies the lathe, and the ones required are placed in position each time a thread of different pitch must be cut. The change-gears to use for obtaining a certain number of threads per inch are shown by a table or index-plate attached to the headstock of the lathe. (The calculation of change-gears is explained in a separate section which follows.)

Before cutting a thread, to what diameter is the part turned?

Suppose a 1½-inch American Standard screw thread is to be cut upon the end of a shaft. In that case, the 1½-inch diameter represents ordinarily the maximum allowable major or outside diameter of the screw thread. In cutting screw threads according to the American standard dimensions for obtaining different classes of fits, there is a *minimum* as well as a *maximum* major diameter. The difference between the maximum and minimum major diameters varies with different sizes, and for any given size is smaller for the Fine-thread Series than for the Coarse-thread Series. Engineering handbooks contain tables showing these maximum and minimum dimensions for the various sizes and classes of fits. For example, the 1½-inch American Standard in the Coarse-thread Series and Class 2 fit, has a minimum major diameter of 1.4798 inches which is about 0.020 inch less than the maximum size of 1.500. This difference decreases as the diameter decreases. To illustrate, a ⅜-inch screw thread in the Coarse-thread Series and Class 2 fit has a minimum major diameter of 0.366 or 0.009 inch under the maximum of 0.375.

It is common practice, in cutting ordinary screw threads, to merely turn the major diameter to the approximate nominal size, using ordinary calipers and a machinist's scale, or a micrometer, to check the diameter, and without considering minimum or maximum sizes. The more precise method, however, should be understood.

Why are maximum and minimum major diameters allowed?

The reason why screw threads and many other machine parts may conform to any dimension within certain maximum and minimum limits, is because absolute perfection is impossible; hence, if *some* error is to be allowed, the amount should be definitely specified and controlled. But you may think that the 0.020 inch, referred to previously, is a large error for a 1½-inch screw thread. It is not, however, excessive for the outside or major diameter. The bearing between the screw and nut should be on the sloping sides of the thread and not at the top and bottom; therefore, a little clearance at the crest or root is desirable, but it is important not to exceed the maximum major diameter as this would result in a bearing on the narrow crest or top of the thread. To avoid this, it is better to be a little under size than a little over, and that is what occurs when the diameter is somewhere below the maximum. This difference between maximum and minimum limits or sizes is called a *tolerance*. Tolerances are dealt with in another section.

How is the shape of the thread-cutting tool determined?

The shape of the cutting end of the tool conforms to the standard cross-sectional shape of the thread to be cut; con-

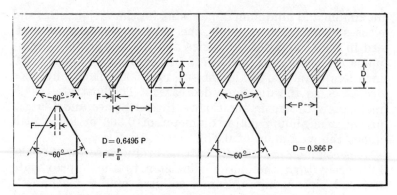

Fig. 1. American Standard Thread   **Fig. 2.** Sharp V-thread

$D = 0.6495 P$

$F = \frac{P}{8}$

$D = 0.866 P$

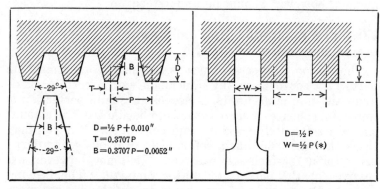

Fig. 3. Acme Standard Thread   **Fig. 4.** Square Thread

$D = \frac{1}{2} P + 0.010''$

$T = 0.3707 P$

$B = 0.3707 P - 0.0052''$

$D = \frac{1}{2} P$

$W = \frac{1}{2} P (*)$

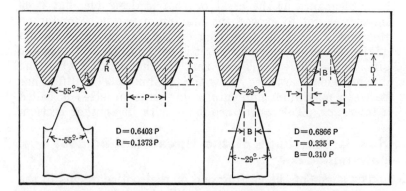

Fig. 5. Whitworth Standard Thread   **Fig. 6.** 29-degree Worm Thread

$D = 0.6403 P$

$R = 0.1373 P$

$D = 0.6866 P$

$T = 0.335 P$

$B = 0.310 P$

sequently, it is essential to know about the various important screw thread standards (see Screw Thread Standards and Their Application). Fig. 1 shows the cross-sectional shape of an American Standard thread and the point of a thread-cutting tool. The angle and other dimensions always represent the thread form in the plane of the axis. The included angle of an American Standard thread is 60 degrees; hence, if a tool point is ground to this angle, a screw thread cut with it will be correct as to angle, provided the tool is properly set, as explained later. The point of the tool is flattened, so that the width equals one-eighth the pitch cf the thread. When this tool has been fed in to the correct or standard depth, the width of the flat at the crest or top of the thread will also equal one-eighth of the pitch. In actual practice, the angle of the thread and width of flat may be checked by means of special gages.

Fig. 2 shows a cross-section of a sharp V-thread and also the tool for cutting it. This tool theoretically has a sharp point; hence it can be used for any pitch, because the point is not flattened to suit the pitch as in the case of an American Standard thread. The sharp V-form, however, is not very practical and is seldom used at the present time. Figs. 3 to 6 show four other screw thread forms and the tools used for cutting them. If a thread, such, for example, as the Acme, is coarse in pitch so that considerable metal must be removed in forming the thread groove, the bulk of this metal may be removed by using roughing tools which shape the thread approximately and are ground to make them cut much easier than the final finishing tool which has a flat top or no rake and, consequently, is not as effective in removing metal as a tool with rake. The reason why rake aids in metal cutting is explained in the section on Single-point Tool Forms and Tool Grinding.

What is the correct position of a thread-cutting tool?

The tool should be so located with reference to the part to be threaded that the angle of the thread cut by the tool will be the same as the tool angle, which should equal the standard thread angle; the tool should also be located so that the sides of the thread will incline equally with reference to the axis of the screw. To secure the correct thread angle (assuming that the tool is properly ground), the upper face must lie in a plane coinciding with the axis of the screw; in other words, if the upper face were flat and horizontal, it should be at the same height as the lathe centers. A common method of setting a tool so that each side will have the same inclination is by using the gage intended for testing the tool when grinding it. This gage (one form of which is shown at A, Fig. 19) is simply placed against the turned surface to be threaded, in case the thread is straight or cylindrical, and the tool is adjusted until the cutting point fits accurately into the V-shaped notch in the gage.

Special gages are sometimes used for setting threading tools, especially when making thread gages of the plug form or cutting other precision screw threads. The tool setting gage may be in the form of a cylindrical plug which is accurately centered and has a 60-degree groove cut into it, assuming that the gage is for American Standard thread tools. When a tool is to be set, the gage is simply placed between the centers of the lathe and the tool is adjusted until the cutting end accurately coincides with the groove of the gage. The latter may also be provided with means for setting the tool at the correct height or so that the top surface lies in a plane intersecting the axis of the work. A simple arrangement for testing the vertical position of the tool consists of a small plug which is inserted in a hole extending crosswise through the body of the gage. This hole is so located that one side is exactly in line with the axis or centerline of the gage. The plug projects far enough so that its lower side can be used for setting the tool, which is done by simply adjusting the tool until the upper face bears evenly on the lower side of the plug.

Some gages of this general type consist of a centered arbor upon which is mounted two close-fitting sleeves. The inner end of each sleeve is beveled to an angle of 30 degrees, so that, as the sleeves are placed in contact, they form a 60-degree groove. The opposite end of each bushing may also be ground to form a 55-degree groove for Whitworth thread tools. In setting a tool, these bushings are pushed up against the cutting end, and a piece of white paper is held beneath the line of contact to reflect the light so that any error in adjustment may easily be observed.

How are successive cuts taken in order to form a complete thread?

In order to form a complete thread with a single-point tool, a number of cuts are required, the number depending upon the pitch of the thread and the corresponding depth of the thread groove. The tool is fed in a little farther for each successive cut until the thread is finished. When these cuts are being taken, the carriage is moved along the bed by the lead-screw a distance, per work revolution, equal to the *pitch* of a single threaded screw or equal to the *lead* in case of a multiple thread. The carriage is engaged with the lead-screw by a lever on the carriage, which causes the halves of a split nut to close around the screw. (This lever is at *G*—see Figs. 9, 11 and 12, pages 32, 36 and 37.)

The way a lathe is handled when cutting a thread is as follows: After the lathe is started, the carriage is moved until the tool-point is slightly beyond the right end of the work, and the tool is fed in far enough to take the first cut. The carriage is then engaged with the lead-screw, and the tool moves to the left and cuts a winding groove as at *A*, Fig. 7 When the tool has traveled as far as the thread is required, it is withdrawn by a quick turn of cross-slide handle and the carriage is returned to the starting point for another cut. The tool is then fed in a little farther and a second cut is taken as at *B*, and this operation is repeated as at *C* and *D* until a "full" or complete thread is cut.

In taking successive cuts, will the thread-cutting tool always follow the first cut?

If the number of threads per inch on the screw being cut is a multiple of a number per inch on the lead-screw, the carriage may be disengaged and reengaged with the lead-screw at random and the tool will always follow the original or first thread groove that was cut; when the number, however, is not a multiple of the number on the lead-screw, the tool may not engage the thread properly.

There are two ways of returning the lathe carriage and tool to the starting point for taking another cut after one

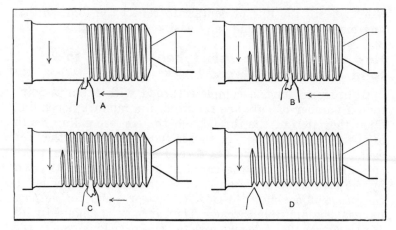

Fig. 7. Thread is Formed by Taking a Number of Successive Cuts

or more cuts have been completed. One method is by disengaging the carriage from the lead-screw and returning it by hand; the other is by allowing the carriage to remain in engagement with the lead-screw and reversing the lathe and lead-screw, or the lead-screw only, at the completion of each cut. If it is necessary to adopt some method of keeping the tool in the right relation to the thread groove and if the screw is quite short, the carriage may remain in engagement with the lead-screw until the thread is finished; but, for cutting comparatively long screw threads, this method of returning the carriage would require too much time and it can be returned more quickly by hand after disengagement with the lead-screw. Most modern lathes are equipped with an indicator or thread chasing dial for "catching the threads" or engaging with the revolving lead-screw at the right time to make the tool follow the thread groove that was first cut.

What is a chasing dial or thread indicator and how is it used in thread cutting?

The thread chasing dial or indicator of an engine lathe is attached to the carriage and has a worm-wheel that meshes with the lead-screw. (This indicator is illustrated by the diagrams, Fig. 8). The vertical spindle or shaft of this worm-wheel carries a graduated dial which shows when to reengage the carriage with the lead-screw in cutting screw threads which are not a multiple of the number per inch on the lead-screw.

The number of teeth on the worm-wheel of the indicator should be a multiple of the number of threads per inch on the lead-screw, and the number of main divisions on the dial should equal the number of teeth on the worm-wheel divided by the number of threads per inch on the lead-screw. Each main division will then represent an inch of carriage travel. For instance, if the lead-screw has six threads per inch and the worm-wheel twenty-four teeth, then there should be 24/6 = 4 main divisions or graduations on the dial (see diagrams, Fig. 8.)

Assume that 11 threads per inch are being cut and that the carriage was engaged with the lead-screw when graduation line No. 1 was opposite the zero line on a stationary part of the indicator as illustrated at A. If the tool were withdrawn from the thread groove and moved back a distance equal to one-sixth inch, or one lead-screw thread, it would not be opposite a thread groove on the work; the same would be true for a backward movement equal to two,

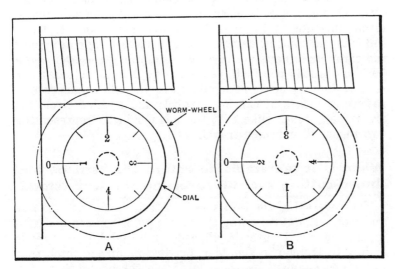

Fig. 8. Diagrams Illustrating Arrangement of Thread
Chasing Dial or Indicator

three, four, or five threads on the lead-screw, but a movement of six lead-screw threads, or one inch (as indicated by B), would bring the tool in line with a thread groove eleven threads away from the point of disengagement; therefore, by always reengaging the carriage with the lead-screw when one of the graduations representing an inch of travel is in line with the zero mark, the tool will follow the original cut.

If in the preceding example the number of threads per inch being cut were ten instead of eleven, or any other even number, a half-inch of backward movement would have located the tool directly opposite a thread groove; hence, if the four main divisions on the indicator dial previously referred to were subdivided, making eight divisions in all, any of these half divisions could also be used for "catching the thread" when cutting an even number of threads per inch. If 11½ threads per inch were being cut, those graduations on the dial representing a movement equivalent to two inches or twenty-three threads on the work would be used in reengaging the carriage and lead-screw. For instance, suppose there are four main divisions on the dial, each representing one inch of carriage travel and numbered 1, 2, 3, and 4, as shown; then if engagement were made for the first cut when, say, line No. 1 was opposite the zero mark, either this line or line No. 3, two divisions from it, would indicate the point of engagement for succeeding cuts. Some indicator dials have a circle of graduations for even numbers of threads per inch, representing a half-inch carriage travel; another circle of graduations for odd numbers representing inches of carriage travel; and a third circle for fractional pitches (like 11½ threads per inch) representing two inches of carriage travel.

When is it preferable to return the carriage and thread-cutting tool by reversing the lead-screw?

The reversal of the lead-screw for returning the carriage and tool, without releasing the half-nuts, is especially useful in cutting short threads, threads in blind holes, threads ending in front of a shoulder, or threads of odd pitch that cannot be engaged by the use of the thread-chasing dial. This lead-screw reverse method may be employed when the

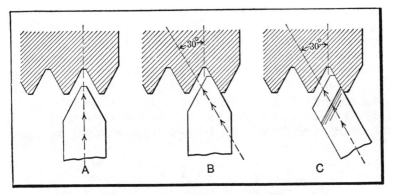

Fig. 9. Straight and Angular Methods of Feeding Tool when
Cutting Thread in Lathe

lathe is equipped with a reverse control lever at the carriage or operating position. This lever (*R*, Fig. 11, page
36) connects with a rod extending along the bed of the
lathe. This rod operates a reversing clutch which changes
the rotation of the lead-screw and feed-rod without changing the direction of the spindle rotation. In using the lead-
screw reverse, the general practice is to stop the travel of
the carriage automatically both at the end of the cutting
movement and the end of the reverse movement. This automatic control is by means of stop-collars on the reverse rod
which are adjusted to disengage the carriage traverse at
the right points. At the end of the cutting movement, the
tool is backed out to clear the work, and the lead-screw and
carriage movements are reversed by the hand control lever,
so that it is not necessary to disengage the half-nuts from
the lead-screw during the thread-cutting operation. The
clutch controlled by reverse lever *R* is a single-tooth type
in order to insure correct timing between the headstock
spindle and lead-screw after they have been disengaged for
reversing the movement of the carriage.

In what direction is the thread tool moved inward for taking successive cuts?

The inward feeding movement of a tool for each successive cut may be either at right angles to the axis of the

screw thread, as indicated at *A*, Fig. 9, or at an angle of 30 degrees as shown at *B*. With the latter method the compound rest is set at an angle of 30 degrees and is used to feed the tool in before each cut. The objection to method *A* is that the cutting action is not as good as when one edge of the tool does practically all the cutting, as at *B*, and the other edge moves parallel to the opposite side of the thread. The angular method of feeding the tool does not tend to tear the thread as when the tool is fed straight in, and a smoother thread is cut. After most of the metal has been removed by the angular feeding method, the tool may be moved straight in to take a light finishing cut.

The thread tool illustrated at *C* is intended especially for feeding in at an angle. This tool is given top rake as shown at *A*, Fig. 10, and all the cutting is done on one side. The compound rest *E* is set at an angle of 30 degrees for cutting 60-degree threads such as the American Standard. The point of the tool forms one side of the thread as it feeds in at this angle and the cutting edge forms the opposite side.

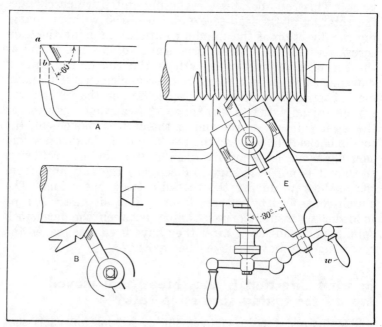

Fig. 10. Tool-holding Slide Set for Cutting Thread by Angular Method

The cutting edge may be located to suit the thread angle by using the point of a thread gage as shown at *B*. This form of tool cuts easily, because of the top rake or slope, and it is particularly adapted for coarse threading operations. Sometimes an ordinary thread tool is used for taking a light finishing cut after roughing out the thread with a tool of the type referred to. The cutting edge *a–b* is ground to an angle of 60 degrees (or slightly less, if anything) with the side.

How is the thread depth used as a preliminary guide in cutting screw threads to standard size?

Many lathes have graduated collars on the cross-feed screws which permit moving the slide and tool any given amount. These graduations may be used in feeding the tool in to the thread depth required for a given pitch. Suppose the thread is a ⅞-inch American Standard with 9 threads per inch (Coarse-thread Series). In this case, the basic thread depth is about 0.068 inch (one-half difference between major and minor diameters. See Table 1, page 172.) Assume that the major diameter of the unthreaded blank is ⅞ inch and the tool is adjusted to graze the outer surface. Then, if successive cuts are taken until the tool has been moved inward 0.068 inch, the screw should be very close to the finished size. A dial on the cross-feed screw graduated to show cross-slide movements of 0.001 inch is convenient for work of this kind. This use of the thread depth as a guide is merely to avoid unnecessary testing for size. It is necessary, however, finally to check the size either by using some form of standard gage or by utilizing the mating threaded part as a gage.

The root or minor diameter is often used as a sizing guide. First turn the blank to the outside diameter *D* (Fig. 11) and then turn a small part of the end to diameter *r* of the thread at the root. The finishing cut for the thread is then taken with the tool point set to just graze diameter *r*.

The dimensions of screw threads for use in interchangeable work should be obtained from tables giving the standard limits. Such tables will be found in MACHINERY'S HANDBOOK.

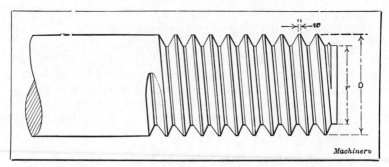

Fig. 11. Diagram Illustrating How Root Diameter is Used as a
Preliminary Guide in Cutting Thread to Standard Depth

In replacing a sharpened thread tool, how is it set in alignment with the unfinished thread?

If it is necessary to sharpen the thread-cutting tool before the thread is finished, the tool should be reset square with the work by testing with the thread gage; also set top face at same height as lathe centers. The carriage is then engaged with the lead-screw and the lathe is turned forward to bring the tool opposite the partly finished thread and also to take up any backlash or lost motion in the gears or half-nut. If the tool-point is not in line with the thread groove previously cut, either re-adjust the tool, or, if the driving dog is clamped to a cylindrical end, release the dog and turn the work slightly in order to align the groove with the tool.

In cutting an internal thread, is the procedure the same as for external thread cutting?

Internal threading, or cutting threads in holes, is an operation performed on work held in the chuck or on a faceplate, as for boring. The tool used is similar to a boring tool except that the cutting end is shaped to conform to the thread to be cut. The method of procedure, in cutting an internal thread, is similar to that for outside work, as far as handling the lathe is concerned. The hole to be threaded is first bored to the root diameter D, Fig. 12, of the screw that is to fit into the threaded hole. The tool-point (of a tool for an American Standard thread) is then

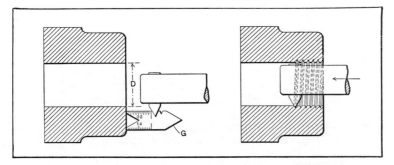

Fig. 12. Method of Setting and Using Inside Thread Tool

set square by holding a gage G against the true side of the work and adjusting the point to fit the notch in the gage as shown. The view to the right shows the tool taking the first cut.

Very often the size of a threaded hole can be tested by using as a gage the threaded part that is to fit into it. It is rather difficult to cut an accurate thread in a small hole, especially if the hole is quite deep, owing to the flexibility of the tool; for this reason threads are sometimes cut slightly under size with the tool, after which a tap with its shank end held straight by the tailstock center is run through the hole. In such a case the thread should be cut small enough with the thread tool to leave a light cut for the tap. Small Acme and square-threaded holes are often finished in this way, and if a number of pieces are to be threaded, the use of a tap makes the holes uniform in size.

How is the depth of each successive cut regulated by an adjustable stop?

In cutting a thread, it is rather difficult to feed in the tool just the right amount for each successive cut, because the tool is moved in before it feeds up to the work. A stop is sometimes used for threading which overcomes this difficulty. This stop when arranged as shown in Fig. 13 consists of a screw S which enters the tool slide and passes through a block B clamped in front of the slide. The hole in the block through which the stop-screw passes is not threaded, but is large enough to permit the screw to move

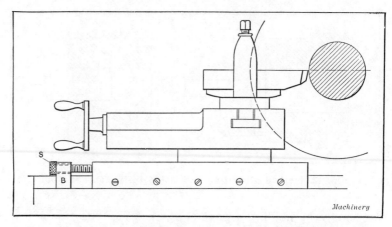

Fig. 13. Cross-slide Equipped with Stop for Regulating Depth
of Successive Cuts when Threading

freely. In cutting a thread, the tool is set for the first cut
and the screw is adjusted until the head is against the fixed
block. After taking the first cut, the stop-screw is backed
cut, say one-half revolution, which allows the tool to be
fed in far enough for a second cut. If this cut is about
right for depth, the screw is again turned about one-half
revolution for the next cut and this is continued for each
successive cut until the thread is finished. By using a stop
of this kind, there is no danger of feeding the tool in too
far as is often done when the setting of the tool depends
upon judgment only. If this form of stop is used for internal threading, the screw, instead of passing through the
fixed block, is placed in the slide so that the end or head
will come against the stop B. This change is made because
the tool is fed outward for cutting an internal thread.

In cutting a taper screw thread, what is the correct position of the tool?

When a taper thread is to be cut, the tool should be set
square with axis $a–a$ as at A, Fig. 14, and not by the tapering surface as at B. If there is a cylindrical part, the
tool can be set as indicated by the dotted lines. When the tool
is set as shown at A, the sides of the thread will incline

equally with reference to the axis of the screw. One reason why taper threads should be cut with the tool in this position is that taper taps are made in this way or with the threads normal (square) to the axis. If the tool were set in the position shown at *B* or so that the sides of the thread incline equally with reference to the tapering surface, obviously such a thread would be a poor fit in a hole tapped with an ordinary taper tap having threads normal to the axis as at *A*. If the hole and the tapering part which screws into it were both threaded normal to the surface as at *B*, the thread would be satisfactory unless there were an unusual amount of taper. In extreme cases, one side of the thread might exert an excessive radial or bursting pressure on the nut owing to the wedging action.

The top cutting face of the tool should lie in a horizontal plane coinciding with the axis of the work for all taper thread cutting. It is especially important to have the tool at the same height as the lathe centers in cutting taper threads because a section parallel to the axis of a cone, but offset relative to the axis, is not straight but curved; consequently, a tool improperly adjusted for height not only changes the angle of the thread but also produces a curved tapering thread.

Why is a taper attachment preferable for taper thread cutting?

An engine lathe equipped with a taper attachment should be used for taper thread cutting, if possible. When the re-

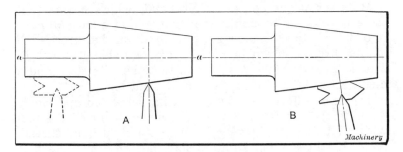

Fig. 14. Correct and Incorrect Positions of Tool for
Taper Thread Cutting

quired taper is obtained by setting the tailstock off center, the thread will not advance at a uniform rate or form a true helix, especially if an ordinary bent-tail driving dog is used. This "drunken thread" or error is caused by the angularity between the driving dog and the face-plate, which causes the rotating speed of the work to vary during each revolution. The bearing surface between the lathe centers and the work-centers when the tailstock is offset is another cause of inaccuracy, because as the work-centers wear rapidly on account of the poor bearing surface, the angle of the taper is changed as the tailstock spindle is tightened. The amount of these errors depends upon the angle of the taper and the distance that the centers must be offset.

If a plain (not threaded) gage of the required taper is available this may be used for adjusting the taper attachment accurately prior to the thread-cutting operation. The taper gage is placed between the centers (which should be in line) and a dial indicator is fastened in the tool-holder. The carriage is then traversed while the indicator is in contact with the taper gage, and the taper attachment is adjusted until the hand of the indicator remains practically stationary as it is traversed from one end of the gage to the other. This method has been employed in making thread gages of the plug form.

What is the procedure in cutting a left-hand thread?

Most screw threads are right-hand, which means that the grooves wind around to the right so that a nut will have to be turned toward the right to enter it on the thread. All of the threads shown in Fig. 15 are right hand except D. This left-hand thread D winds in the other direction and a nut is screwed onto it by turning the nut to the left.

The only difference between cutting left-hand and right-hand threads in the lathe is in the movement of the tool with relation to the work. In cutting a right-hand thread, the tool moves from right to left, but this movement is reversed for left-hand threads because the thread winds around in the opposite direction. To make the carriage

travel from left to right, the lead-screw is rotated backwards by means of reversing gears. Lathes differ somewhat
in regard to the location of the lead-screw reversing lever.
In cutting a left-hand thread, the tool starts at a (Fig. 15)
instead of at the right-hand end. Sometimes a small hole
is drilled at the starting point to provide a space for beginning a cut.

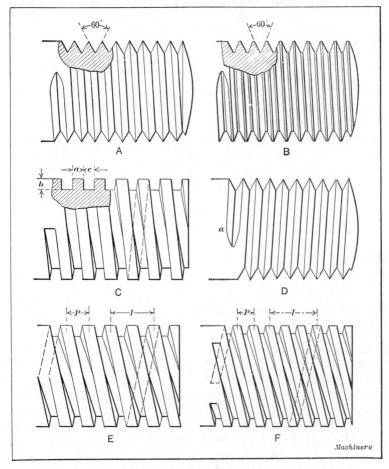

Fig. 15. (A) V-thread. (B) American Standard Thread. (C) Square
Thread. (D) Left-hand Thread. (E) Double Square
Thread. (F) Triple Square Thread

In cutting square threads should the tool point width equal one-half the pitch?

Acme threads are used instead of square threads in most cases, because of superior features. If a square thread is to be cut, it is necessary to provide clearance between the threads of a square-threaded screw and nut. To obtain clearance, the width of the thread groove in the nut is made somewhat greater than one-half the pitch of the thread. The width of the point of the tool for cutting external screws with square threads should be exactly equal to one-half the thread pitch, but the width of a tool used for cutting the threads on taps which are afterward to be used for tapping nuts should be slightly less than one-half the pitch so that the cutting teeth are a little wider than the theoretical standard width. The thread groove cut in the nut will then be slightly wider than the thread on the screw, thus providing the necessary clearance. An inside threading tool for threading nuts evidently should be of the same width as the teeth on the tap, or slightly wider than one-half the pitch. Usually the tool width is increased from 0.001 to 0.002 inch, depending upon the pitch of the thread.

Square threads may bind against the sides of the tool unless the cutting end is inclined to suit the lead angle. This is particularly true of multiple threads. Side interference is more likely to occur with square threads than with angular forms.

What is the procedure in cutting multiple threads?

Multiple threads are shown at E and F, Fig. 15. Thread E is double and thread F is triple. Dimension p is the pitch and l is the lead in each case.

In cutting multiple screw threads, the general method of procedure is about the same as for single screw threads, except that the lathe must be geared according to the number of *single* threads per inch, or with reference to the *lead* of the thread, not the pitch; provision must also be made for obtaining the correct spacing of the different thread grooves. The lead of the double thread, shown at B, Fig. 16, is one-half inch, or twice the pitch, and the number of sin-

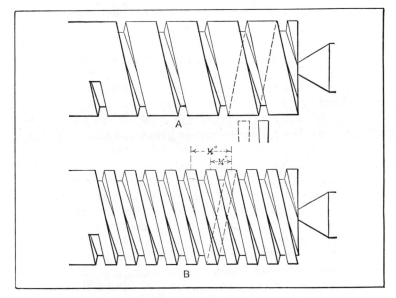

Fig. 16. Views Illustrating How a Double Square Thread is Cut

gle threads to the inch equals $1 \div \frac{1}{2} = 2$; therefore, the lathe is geared for cutting two threads per inch or for a lead of $\frac{1}{2}$ inch. The first cut is taken just as though a single thread were being cut, leaving the work as shown at A. When this cut is finished, assume that the work is turned one-half a revolution (for a double thread) without disturbing the position of the lead-screw or carriage; then the tool will be midway between the grooves of the single thread as indicated by dotted lines. The second groove is then cut, producing a double thread as shown at B.

What are the different methods of cutting equally spaced multiple thread grooves?

The dividing or spacing of multiple threads may be done (1) by indexing or turning the piece being threaded a fractional part of a revolution as explained in connection with Fig. 16; (2) by setting the compound slide parallel with the screw thread being cut so that the slide can be used for adjusting the tool; (3) by disengaging the lock-nut from the lead-screw while the lathe spindle is stationary, moving the carriage the required distance; (4) by engaging the lead-screw at the proper time (with the lathe in motion), as shown by graduations on the thread chasing dial or indicator. The different thread grooves of a multiple screw thread may also be cut at the same time by using a tool for each groove, the tools being spaced according to the pitch of the thread.

When the screw is indexed for locating the tool in connection with thread cutting, it is given one-half turn for a double thread, one-third turn for a triple thread, one-fourth turn for a quadruple thread, and so on. An easy method of indexing for a double thread when the work is held between centers is simply to remove the part from the lathe and turn it one-half revolution by placing the driving end of the dog in the opposite slot of the faceplate. The objection to this method is that any error in the location of the faceplate slot would be reproduced in the screw thread. A convenient method of indexing multiple-threaded screws is by means of a special indexing type of faceplate.

How is the indexing type of faceplate used for multiple thread cutting?

The indexing faceplate has an adjustable section which makes it possible to index or rotate the work whatever fractional part of a turn is required. The design shown in Fig. 17 has a notched work-driving section which may be turned whatever fractional part of a revolution is required, by disengaging the indexing latch. This plate usually has 60 notches. These notches are numbered, and the indexing movement is determined merely by dividing 60 by the number of threads on a multiple screw. For example, a triple thread would be indexed $60 \div 3 = 20$ notches for cutting each thread groove.

Some indexing faceplates are graduated with numbers 2, 3, 4, etc., indicating double, triple, quadruple or other multiple screw threads. If a triple thread, for example, is being cut, the three graduations marked "3" are used to index cr turn the movable part of the faceplate one-third revolution after cutting each thread groove. This general type of faceplate is very useful, especially where multiple thread cutting is done frequently.

How is the compound rest used for indexing the tool in cutting a multiple thread?

The compound rest may be used for adjusting the tool to obtain correct spacing in cutting the different thread grooves of a multiple screw thread. It is set parallel to the axis of the screw and after one thread groove is cut, the tool is moved a distance equal to the *pitch* of the thread or one-half the lead for a double thread, one-third the lead for a triple thread, etc. When the feed-screw has a graduated dial, this adjustment of the tool can easily be made. The compound-rest method is very convenient and it may be applied in threading parts which are held in the chuck for internal threading operations. The accuracy of the tool adjustment and of the screw that is cut depends upon the accuracy of the feed-screw of the compound-rest slide; ordinarily, the errors from this source would be so small as to be negligible. Errors due to play or lost motion should be avoided by always moving the slide in one direction for indexing the tool.

Fig. 17. Indexing Faceplate
for Multiple Thread Cutting

Fig. 18. Speed Reducer for Cutting
Screw Threads of Large Lead

Is it practicable to shift the carriage for dividing a multiple thread?

If a tool is located for cutting different thread grooves of a multiple screw thread by shifting the carriage and tool, the adjustment must be such that the lock-nut may be re-engaged with the lead-screw when the tool is in the correct position. If a double thread is being cut having a lead of, say, one inch, the tool could be located for cutting the second thread groove by disengaging the lock-nut (with the lathe spindle stationary) and moving the carriage back a distance equal to the pitch of the thread, or one-half inch. If the adjustment were equal to the pitch plus the lead or the pitch plus any multiple of the lead, the tool would still be in position for cutting the second thread groove. In actually cutting a screw thread, it would, of course, be necessary to move the carriage far enough for the tool to clear the end of the work before starting another cut; for instance, if the tool were 10 inches from the starting end and a double thread having a one-inch lead were being cut, the carriage should be moved at least 10½ inches. This adjustment could also be obtained in this particular case, if the lead-screw had an even number of threads per inch, by moving the carriage and tool ½ inch (pitch of thread) and then, after reengaging the lock-nut, turning the lathe backward to secure the necessary additional movement.

Whether or not the lock-nut can be reengaged with the lead-screw after shifting the carriage a given distance may be determined as follows: If the carriage is moved a whole or even number of inches (not fractional), the lock-nut can be reengaged with any lead-screw having a whole number of threads per inch. If the number representing the carriage adjustment is fractional, the number of threads per inch on the lead-screw must be divisible by the denominator of the fraction.

Is the thread indicator ever used for dividing a multiple thread?

The thread chasing dial or indicator may sometimes be used for engaging the tool with the different multiple thread grooves when cutting a screw thread of this kind. By means of the indicator, the engagement of the lock-nut with the lead-screw is so timed that the tool, after taking a cut through one thread groove, will be in position to cut the other groove or grooves, as the case may be, before feeding the tool inward, instead of finishing one groove at a time. To illustrate, suppose a double-threaded screw is to be cut having a lead of ½ inch (¼-inch pitch) or two single threads per inch. Assume that the lead-screw of the lathe has 4 threads per inch, the indicator worm-wheel 24 teeth, and the dial 6 main divisions, representing inches of carriage travel, and 6 subdivisions representing half-inches of carriage travel. Since the number of threads per inch is even in this case, the lock-nut may be engaged with the lead-screw when any division line on the dial is opposite the zero mark, and the tool will follow the original cut. After taking a cut in one thread groove and moving the carriage back to the starting point, the lock-nuts are next engaged when the zero line is midway between any two lines on the dial; the tool will then cut another groove midway between the first one, or a distance from it equal to the pitch of the thread. If there were an odd number of single threads per inch, say, three, engagement would be made on any main division line for cutting one groove of a double thread, and on any subdivision for the other groove.

In cutting multiple threads of large lead, why are special drives or speed reducers used?

When a lathe is used for cutting a screw thread of exceptionally large lead, or steep pitch, the change-gear mechanism may be subjected to excessive stresses if the power for traversing the carriage along the bed is transmitted from the lathe spindle to the lead-screw in the usual manner. This is due to the unusual distance that the carriage must move along the bed per revolution of the work in order to obtain a large lead. For instance, if the lead is such that the lead-screw must be revolved quite rapidly to move the carriage and tool a distance equal to the lead of the thread, each time the spindle makes one revolution, the teeth, especially on the first gear of the train, may be broken as a result of the excessive stress. One method of avoiding trouble of this kind is to apply power directly to the lead-screw, instead of to the spindle; motion is then transmitted from the high-speed member of the gear train to the low-speed member, as the lead-screw drives the spindle and the load on the gear teeth is reduced.

Special Drive from Cone Pulley.—Another method of overcoming this difficulty on a lathe having a cone pulley, is by driving the lead-screw from the gear on the cone pulley, special gearing being used to transmit the motion. On one design of lathe arranged in this way, the cone pulley has a velocity ten times that of the spindle when the back-gears are engaged; consequently, by using the rapidly revolving cone gear as the driver in the train of gearing connecting with the lead-screw, the stress on the teeth is reduced proportionately. If it is assumed that the lead of a screw to be cut is 3½ inches and that there are 4 threads per inch on the lathe lead-screw, the speed of the lead-screw relative to the spindle speed is 14 to 1. By driving directly from the cone gear, however, the ratio will be changed to 14 to 10, because the cone pulley revolves ten times as fast as the spindle; therefore, the power necessary for traversing the carriage is easily transmitted through the gearing, and without overstressing the teeth. The gearing on a coarse-threading attachment of this kind may be arranged as follows: A double sliding gear on the reversing shaft inside of the headstock can be engaged either with the regular driving gear on the spindle or with a small gear at the end of the cone pulley. For cutting threads of large lead, the sliding gear is engaged with the cone gear and the back-gears are thrown into mesh. The sliding gear will then make ten revolutions to one of the spindle; consequently, if the lathe were geared to cut one thread per inch, it would cut a thread groove having a lead of ten inches when driving through the sliding gear and cone pinion. An attachment of this kind may be used for cutting oil-grooves in cylindrical parts and for similar operations, as well as for cutting screws of large lead.

Special Lead-screw for Coarse Pitches.—A special lead-screw for cutting threads of large lead is applied to some lathes. With one arrangement, this auxiliary lead-screw extends along the rear side of the bed, and when in use the back-gearing of the headstock is engaged; the drive is then from the large back-gear, through change-gearing, to the special lead-screw. A long half-nut at the back of the carriage engages the threads of the lead-screw and is so arranged that it may be raised or lowered by a cam operated by a handwheel at the front of the apron. The lathe is equipped with the regular quick-change gear mechanism and a lead-screw at the front for ordinary thread-cutting operations. The coarse-pitch threading attachment is used for leads varying from 2 to 15 inches.

Speed-Reducing Faceplate.—The speed-reducing faceplate simply reduces the speed of the work so that the lead of the thread is increased proportionately. One of these speed reducers is shown in Fig. 18. Motion is transmitted from the headstock spindle to the work-driving plate, through a planetary gear train which reduces the work speed in the ratio of 6 to 1, relative to the headstock spindle and the lead-screw; consequently, it is possible to cut threads six times coarser in lead than are indicated on the instruction plate attached to the headstock. This speed reducer is mounted on the cam-lock spindle nose in the same manner as the faceplate. By locking the parts together, the speed reducer may be used the same as an ordinary work-driver. It is also equipped with a 60-notch index-plate for indexing the work in connection with multiple thread cutting. A small lever is used to lock the index-plate in the successive positions required.

Under what conditions is the work held stationary and the tool revolved for thread cutting?

When it is necessary to thread a part that will not swing in the lathe on account of a projecting member that will not clear the lathe bed, it is sometimes possible to mount the work on the carriage and revolve the tool. The work is bolted or otherwise attached to the carriage so that whatever surface is to be threaded is concentric with the lathe spindle. If the thread is short, the tool may be fastened to one of the chuck jaws for radial adjustment; the thread is then cut in the usual manner. This method may be applied either to external or internal thread cutting.

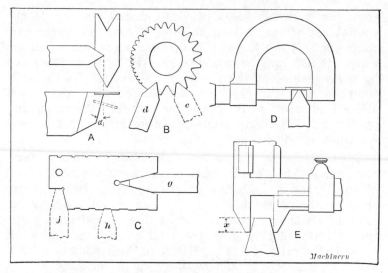

Fig. 19. Methods of Gaging Thread-cutting Tools

What types of gages are used for testing the shapes of thread cutting tools?

The simple type of notched gage A (Fig. 19) is often used for checking the angle of 60-degree thread cutting tools. However, for American Standard thread tools, a gage of type B is preferable because it checks both the angle between the cutting edges and the width of the flat point. Opposite each notch around the circumference of the gage is stamped the number of threads per inch which the different notches or tool point sizes are used for. The tool is first ground to a 60-degree angle, the V-shaped notch in the gage being used as shown at d. The point is then ground off to the right width or until the tool fits into a notch corresponding to the required pitch, as illustrated at e.

In using a gage of the type shown at A and B, the gage should be held in the same plane as the cutting edge, as at A, and not at right angles to the front side, as shown by the dotted lines, assuming that the notch in the gage conforms to the standard thread angle. If the clearance angle a of a tool is 15 degrees, the angle in a plane at right angles to the front face is about 61 degrees 45 minutes, when the angle in the plane of the cutting edge is 60 degrees; hence, if the tool were ground to fit a gage held as shown by the dotted lines at A, the angle of the cutting edge would be too small.

If the thread tool angle is to be measured as indicated by the dotted lines at A, Fig. 19, or with the gage held perpendicular to the end clearance surface, this angle may be determined as follows:

Rule.—Divide the tangent of ½ the standard thread angle by the cosine of the clearance angle of the tool; the quotient thus obtained equals the tangent of ½ the required angle as measured perpendicular to the front end of the tool.

Example.—A thread tool gage is to be made for checking the angle of the tool as indicated by the dotted lines at A, Fig. 19. Determine the angle of the V-shaped notch in the gage.

Tan 30 degrees = 0.57735; cosine 15 degrees = 0.96592

0.57735 ÷ 0.96592 = 0.5977, which is the tangent of 30 degrees 52 minutes; hence, this angle is doubled to obtain the total or included angle of the notch in the thread tool gage which is 61 degrees 44 minutes.

What type of gage is used for Acme thread tools?

An Acme thread gage is shown at C, Fig. 19. This gage also has notches for different pitches. The 29-degree notch at the end of the gage is used first for testing the angular sides of the tool when grinding, as at g. The shallow notches are used simply for testing the width of the cutting edge at the end as at h. Numbers opposite the notches represent the number of threads per inch. The angle between the side and the end may be tested as illustrated at j. The tool may also be set square with the work by placing one edge of the gage against the turned surface and adjusting the tool unit it coincides with the gage, as indicated by the dotted lines at j.

Width of Tool Point.—If the depth of an Acme thread equals 0.5 times pitch, there being no allowance for clearance, then the width at the root of the thread or the width of the tool point equals 0.3707 times pitch. There is some variation in practice regarding the thread depth and the amount of clearance.

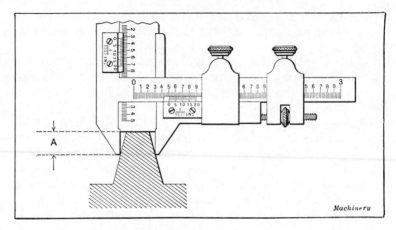

Fig. 20. Measuring Width of Acme Thread Tool with
Vernier Gear-tooth Caliper

If the depth equals 0.5 times pitch plus 0.010 inch (thus making the thread deeper to provide clearance between crest and root), the tool point width equals 0.3707 times pitch minus 0.0052 inch.

If depth equals 0.5 times pitch plus 0.005, tool point width equals 0.3707 times pitch minus 0.0026 inch.

As these widths apply to the axial plane of the screw thread, the top face of the tool should coincide with this plane.

How is the end width of an Acme thread tool measured with a vernier caliper?

In case it should be necessary to measure the end width of an Acme thread tool, for a pitch not on the regular gage, this can be done by using a vernier gear-tooth caliper, as indicated at E, Fig. 19, and also in Fig. 20. If we assume that the caliper jaws bear on the sides of the tool at a distance A (Fig. 20) from the top, equal to ¼ inch, then the width of the tool point equals the caliper reading (as shown by the horizontal scale) minus 0.1293 inch. For example, if the caliper reading was 0.315 inch, the width at the point would equal 0.315 — 0.1293 = 0.1857 inch, assuming that the sides were ground to the standard angle of 29 degrees. (This end width is for a tool set in the plane of the axis.) The constant to be subtracted from the caliper reading equals tan 14° 30′ multiplied by twice the dimension A, or, in this case, $2 \times 0.25 \times 0.2586 = 0.1293$.

The end width, when the top of the tool is perpendicular to the sides of the thread, equals the end width in the plane of the axis multiplied by the cosine of the lead angle at the root of the thread. (Cotangent of lead angle equals circumference at root or minor diameter divided by lead of thread.)

Fig. 21 shows how a commercial thread tool gage of the vernier type is used to test the angle of the tool and the width of the point. The sliding jaw is set for whatever point width is required for the pitch to be cut. The tool point is then ground so that the flat point "bottoms" or rests on a hardened steel strip when the sides bear evenly against the angular edges of the gage. The vernier scale makes it possible to set the gage to a given point width with considerable accuracy. These thread tool verniers are made to the American Standard of 60 degrees, to the British Standard Whitworth angle of 55 degrees, and also to 29 degrees which is the standard for Acme threads and is also

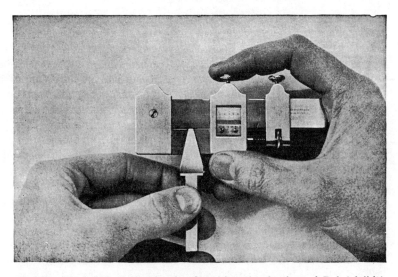

Fig. 21. Thread Tool Vernier for Checking the Angle and Point Width of a Thread-cutting Tool

the angle used for many worm threads, especially of single-threaded form.

How is an ordinary micrometer used for testing the width of the flat end of a thread tool?

The width of the flat or end of either an American Standard or an Acme thread tool may be measured by using an ordinary micrometer as illustrated at D, Fig. 19. In measuring the tool, a scale is held against the spindle and anvil of the micrometer and the end of the tool is placed against this scale. The micrometer is then adjusted to the position shown.

Rule.— For an American Standard thread tool, subtract 0.2887 inch from the reading; the result equals the width cf the tool point which should equal one-eighth the pitch.

Rule.—For an Acme thread tool, subtract 0.1293 inch from the micrometer reading to obtain the width of the tool point. The constants (0.2887 and 0.1293) which are subtracted from the micrometer reading are only correct when the micrometer spindle has the usual diameter of 0.25 inch. The value or constant for any other spindle diameter could be obtained by multiplying twice the spindle diameter by the tangent of one-half the thread tool angle.

In cutting threads, is it practicable to increase or decrease the pitch slightly?

Some tool steels are liable to shrink more or less when they are hardened; consequently, if a very accurate hardened screw is required, it is possible to cut it so that the pitch is slightly greater than standard, to compensate for the shrinkage due to the hardening operation, although finishing the hardened thread by grinding is preferable. As the amount of contraction incident to hardening is very small, it is not practicable to use change-gears that will give the exact pitch required. A method of obtaining this increase of pitch is by the use of a taper attachment.

Example.—Suppose a tap having 8 threads per inch is to be threaded, and, owing to the contraction of the steel, the pitch must be 0.12502 inch instead of 0.125 inch.

The lathe is geared to cut 8 threads per inch, or 0.125-inch pitch, and then the taper attachment is set to an angle a,

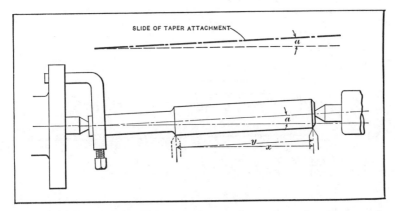

SLIDE OF TAPER ATTACHMENT

Fig. 22. Diagram Illustrating Method of Cutting a Thread to Compensate
for the Error in Pitch Due to Shrinkage in Hardening

Fig. 22, the cosine of which equals $\dfrac{0.125}{0.12502}$; that is, the
cosine of angle a equals *the pitch required after hardening*
divided by *the pitch necessary to compensate for shrinkage.*
The angle is then found by referring to a table of cosines.
The tap blank is also set to the same angle a by adjusting
the tailstock center, thus locating the axis of the work
parallel with the slide of the taper attachment. When the
carriage moves a distance x, the tool point will have moved
a greater distance y along the work, the difference between x and y depending upon angle a; hence, the tool will
cut a thread of slightly greater pitch than the lathe is
geared to cut.

To illustrate, by using the preceding example, cosine of
angle $a = \dfrac{0.125}{0.12502} = 0.99984$. By referring to a table of
cosines, it is found that 0.99984 is the cosine of 1 degree,
approximately; hence, the taper-attachment slide and the
work should be set to this angle. (The angle a, has been exaggerated in order to more clearly illustrate the principle.)

As is well known, it is objectionable to cut a thread with
the tailstock center offset, because the work is not rotated
at a uniform velocity, owing to the fact that the driving
dog is at an angle with the faceplate. For a small angle,
such as 1 degree, however, the error resulting from this

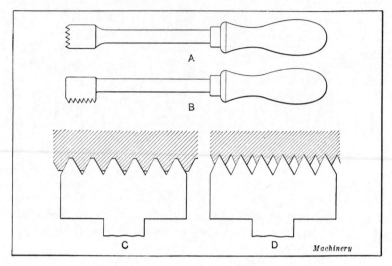

Fig. 23. Hand Chasers—Threading Tool Chasers

cause would be very small. It is advisable, however, to use a driving dog of the compensating type.

Pitch Less Than Standard.—If a thread having a pitch slightly less than standard is needed to fit a threaded part which has contracted in hardening, the taper attachment can also be used, provided the lathe is equipped with special gears to cut a little less than the required pitch.

Example.—Suppose a screw having a pitch of 0.198 inch is required to fit the thread of a nut the pitch of which has been reduced from 0.200 to 0.198 inch.

If gears having 83 and 84 teeth are available, these can be inserted in a compound train, so as to reduce the 0.200-inch pitch that would be obtained with the regular gearing to $\frac{83}{84}$ of 0.200, or 0.19762 inch. This pitch, which is less than the 0.198-inch pitch required, is then increased by using the taper attachment as previously described.

What is a thread chaser and how is it used?

A thread chaser is a form of threading tool having a number of teeth instead of a single point like the threading tools commonly used for screw cutting in the engine lathe,

although the term "thread chasing" is often used to indicate the cutting of a thread with a single-point tool. The
two general classes of chasers (exclusive of those used in
dies) are hand chasers and threading tool chasers. The
former are hand-controlled, and the latter are rigidly held
in a tool-holder and used like an ordinary lathe threading
tool. Two types of hand chasers are shown at A and B in
Fig. 23. Form A is used for chasing external threads and
form B for internal threads. When the tool is in use, the
cutting end is supported by some form of rest held in the
toolpost. These hand chasers are convenient for truing up
battered threads or for reducing the size of a part which
has been threaded either by a die or a single-point tool.
Tools of this kind are especially adapted for brass work.
The chaser has teeth spaced to correspond to the pitch of
the thread. This form of tool can be applied to the work
quickly and without gearing the lathe for a thread-cutting
operation.

Threading tool chasers which are held rigidly in the tool-
holder are used practically the same as a single-point tool,
the lathe being geared for traversing the tool along the
work in order to control the lead of the thread. Tools of
this kind cut threads rapidly, especially in brass or any
soft alloy. A threading tool chaser for an American Standard thread is shown at C. The spaces between the teeth
extend to a sharp vee instead of having flats the same as the
cutting ends, in order to provide clearance for the top of
the thread. The pitch of the chaser teeth does not always
equal the pitch of the thread to be cut. For instance, the
chaser illustrated at D has a pitch double that of the screw
thread. Every alternate groove is engaged, but as the lathe
is geared for the pitch of thread to be cut, each tooth of
the chaser follows the thread groove the same as though
it were a single tool. Chasers are sometimes made as shown
at D for cutting very fine threads, because larger and
stronger chaser teeth are obtained.

How to Calculate Change-Gears for Cutting Screw Threads

Ordinarily, the lathe operator does not need to determine by calculation the ratio or combination of gears required for cutting a screw thread of given pitch. Occasionally, however, such a calculation may be necessary, particularly for some special thread-cutting operation. Furthermore, it is advisable to know how to figure the gearing ratio in order to understand clearly the fundamental principle upon which the design of a change-gear mechanism is based. These change-gear calculations apply particularly to the simple change-gear type of lathe, but the ratios obtained with a quick change-gear mechanism are based upon the same fundamental principle.

What principle governs the cutting of a given number of threads per inch?

Before referring to any rules, it should be understood why a lathe cuts a certain number of threads to the inch and how this number is changed by the use of different gears. As the carriage and the tool are moved by the lead-screw which is connected by gearing with the lathe spindle, the number of threads to the inch that are cut depends, in every case, upon the number of turns the work makes while the lead-screw is moving the carriage one inch. If the lead-screw has six threads per inch, it will make six revolutions while the carriage and the thread tool travel one inch along the piece to be threaded. Now, if the change-gears a and c (see diagram A of accompanying illustration) are so proportioned that the spindle makes the same number of revolutions as the lead-screw, in a given time, it is evident that the tool will cut six threads per inch. If the spindle revolved twice as fast as the lead-screw, it would make twelve turns while the tool moved one inch, and, consequently, twelve threads per inch would be cut; but to obtain this difference in speeds, it is necessary to use a combination of gearing that will cause the lead-screw to revolve once while the lathe spindle and work make two revolutions.

Example.—Suppose that 9 threads to the inch are to be cut and the lead-screw has 6 threads per inch. What gearing ratio or combination of gears is required?

In this case, the work must make nine revolutions while the lead-screw makes six and causes the carriage and thread tool to move one inch, or, in other words, one revolution of the lead-screw corresponds to one and one-half revolutions of the spindle; therefore, if the lead-screw gear *c* has 36 teeth, the gear *a* on the spindle stud should have only 24 teeth. The spindle will then revolve one and one-half times faster than the lead-screw, provided the stud rotates at the same rate of speed as the main lathe spindle.

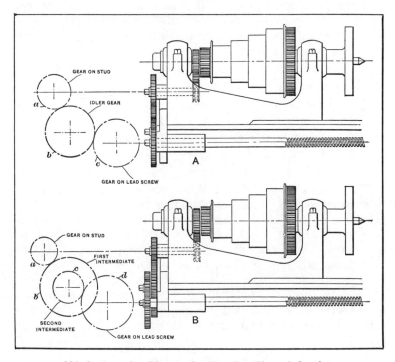

(A) Lathe with Simple Gearing for Thread Cutting.
(B) Compound Geared Lathe

How is the required ratio for change-gears determined?

Rule.—First find the number of threads per inch that is cut when gears of the same size are placed on the lead-screw and spindle stud, either by trial or by referring to the index plate. Then place this number (called the "lathe screw constant") as the numerator of a fraction, and the number of threads per inch to be cut, as the denominator; multiply both the numerator and denominator by some trial number, until numbers are obtained which correspond to numbers of teeth in gears that are available. The product of the trial number and the numerator (or "lathe screw constant") represents the gear a for the spindle stud, and the product of the trial number and the denominator, the gear c for the lead-screw. The size of the idler gear b does not affect the ratio.

If the gearing connecting the main spindle and stud are equal in size or have a ratio of 1 to 1, then the lathe screw constant equals the number of threads per inch on the lead-screw. Then we have

$$\frac{\text{Threads per inch of lead screw}}{\text{Threads per inch to be cut}} = \frac{\text{teeth in gear on spindle stud}}{\text{teeth in gear on lead-screw}}$$

Example.—Again assume that 9 threads per inch are to be cut and lathe lead-screw has 6 threads per inch (which number also equals the lathe screw constant). Then,

$$\frac{6}{9} = \frac{6 \times 4}{9 \times 4} = \frac{24}{36}.$$

The values of 36 and 24 obtained by multiplying 6 and 9, respectively, by 4, do not change the proportion. Any other number could be used as a multiplier, and if gears having 24 and 36 teeth were not available, this might be necessary. For example, if there were no gears of this size, some other multiplier, such as 5 or 6, might be used.

Suppose the number of teeth in the change-gears supplied with the lathe are 24, 28, 32, 36, etc., increasing by four teeth up to 100, and assume that the lead-screw has 6 threads per inch and that 10 threads per inch are to be cut. Then,

$$\frac{6}{10} = \frac{6 \times 4}{10 \times 4} = \frac{24}{40}.$$

By multiplying both the numerator and the denominator by 4, two available gears having 24 and 40 teeth, respectively, are obtained. The 24-tooth gear goes on the spindle stud and the 40-tooth gear on the lead-screw. The number of teeth in the intermediate or "idler" gear b, which connects the stud and lead-screw gears, is not considered as it does not affect the ratios between gears a and c, but is used simply to transmit motion from one gear to the other. If this lathe had a quick change gear mechanism and a lead-screw with 6 threads per inch, the ratio of the gearing between spindle and lead-screw, when set for cutting 9 threads per inch, would be represented by the fraction 6/10, the same as in the preceding example.

When compound gearing must be used, how are the gear sizes determined?

When gearing is arranged as shown at A, in the diagram, it is referred to as *simple* gearing, but sometimes it is necessary to use four gears, as at B, or *compound* gearing. The method of calculating compound gearing is practically the same as that for simple gearing.

Rule.—To find the change-gears used in compound gearing, place the "screw constant" obtained by the foregoing rule, as the numerator, and the number of threads per inch to be cut as the denominator of a fraction; resolve both numerator and denominator into two factors each, and multiply each "pair" of factors by the same number, until values are obtained representing numbers of teeth in available change-gears. (One factor in the numerator and one in the denominator make a "pair" of factors.)

Example.—Assume that the lathe cuts 6 threads per inch when gears of equal size are used, and that the number of teeth in the gears available are 30, 35, 40, and so on, increasing by 5 up to 100. What gears are required to cut 24 threads per inch?

The screw constant 6 is placed in the numerator and 24 in the denominator. The numerator and denominator are then divided into factors and each pair of factors is multiplied by the same number to find the gears, thus:

$$\frac{6}{24} = \frac{2 \times 3}{4 \times 6} = \frac{(2 \times 20) \times (3 \times 10)}{(4 \times 20) \times (6 \times 10)} = \frac{40 \times 30}{80 \times 60}.$$

The last four numbers indicate the gears which should be used. The upper two having 40 and 30 teeth are the *driving* gears and the lower two having 80 and 60 teeth are the *driven* gears. The driving gears are gear *a* on the spindle stud and gear *c* on the intermediate stud, meshing with the lead-screw gear, and the driven gears are gears *b* and *d*. It makes no difference which of the driving gears is placed on the spindle stud, or which of the driven is placed on the lead-screw.

If a special screw thread has 2⅔ threads per inch, how are the change gears calculated?

In this case the number of threads per inch is given, but sometimes the *lead* of a thread is given instead of the number of threads per inch. For example, a thread may be required having a ⅜-inch lead. The expression "⅜-inch lead" should first be transformed to "number of threads per inch." The number of threads per inch (the thread being single) equals:

$$\frac{1}{\frac{3}{8}} = \frac{1}{1} \times \frac{8}{3} = 2\,2/3.$$

Example 1.—Find the change-gears to cut 2 2/3 threads per inch in a lathe having a screw constant of 8 and change-gears varying from 24 to 100 teeth, increasing by 4.

$$\frac{8}{2\,2/3} = \frac{2 \times 4}{1 \times 2\,2/3} = \frac{(2 \times 36) \times (4 \times 24)}{(1 \times 36) \times (2\,2/3 \times 24)} = \frac{72 \times 96}{36 \times 64}.$$

Example 2.—As another illustration, suppose it is desired to cut 1¾ threads per inch on a lathe having a screw constant of 8. Assume that the gears have 24, 28, 32, 36, 40 teeth, etc., increasing by 4 up to 100. Following the rule:

$$\frac{8}{1\frac{3}{4}} = \frac{2 \times 4}{1 \times 1\frac{3}{4}} = \frac{(2 \times 36) \times (4 \times 16)}{(1 \times 36) \times (1\frac{3}{4} \times 16)} = \frac{72 \times 64}{36 \times 28}.$$

The gears having 72 and 64 teeth are the *driving* gears, and those with 36 and 28 teeth are the *driven* gears.

What number of threads per inch will be cut with a given combination of change-gears?

A general rule for determining the number of threads per inch that will be obtained with a given combination of change-gears on an engine lathe is as follows:

Rule.—Multiply the lathe screw constant by the number of teeth in the driven gear (or by the product of the numbers of teeth in both driven gears in case of compound gearing), and divide the product thus obtained by the number of teeth in the driving gear (or by the product of the numbers of teeth in the two driving gears of a compound train). The quotient equals the number of threads per inch obtained with that combination of gearing.

Example.—The driving gears in a compound train of change-gears have 72 and 64 teeth; the driven gears have 36 and 28 teeth. The screw constant is 8. Find the number of threads per inch that would be cut, using these gears.

$$\text{Threads per inch} = \frac{8 \times 36 \times 28}{72 \times 64} = 1\tfrac{3}{4}$$

Note: When a lathe is equipped with a quick change-gear mechanism, the operator obtains the gear combination for cutting any pitch or thread within the range of the mechanism, merely by shifting the control levers to indicated positions, as explained previously in this treatise. In some cases, however, the change-gear mechanism is so arranged that auxiliary change-gears may be used in conjunction with it for cutting special pitches which are outside the range of the regular gear box combinations. The method of calculating these auxiliary change-gears is explained in the last chapter containing Miscellaneous Rules and Formulas (see pages 550 to 553).

If the pitch of a screw thread is in millimeters, what change-gears are required?

Screw threads based on the metric system of measurement have the pitch (or lead if the thread is multiple) of the thread expressed in millimeters. If the lathe to be used has a lead-screw cut according to the English system of measurement, the change-gears may be calculated as follows:

Rule.—Multiply the lathe screw constant by the pitch of the thread in millimeters and the product by 5, to find the number of teeth in the spindle stud gear. The gear on the lead-screw should have 127 teeth.

Just how this rule is derived will be apparent by considering a simple example. Suppose the screw is to have a pitch of 3 millimeters and the lathe screw constant is 4. The number of threads per inch equals 25.4 ÷ 3, because there are 25.4 millimeters per inch. The ratio of the change-gears may be expressed by a fraction having the screw constant as the numerator and the number of threads per inch as the denominator. Thus:

$$\frac{4}{\frac{25.4}{3}} = \frac{4 \times 3}{25.4}.$$

The first whole number by which 25.4 can be multiplied and obtain a whole number as the product is 5; hence, the numerator and denominator of the fractional expression are multiplied by 5. Thus:

$$\frac{4 \times 3 \times 5}{25.4 \times 5} = \frac{60}{127}.$$

Therefore, a thread of 3 millimeters pitch would require a 60-tooth gear on the spindle stud and a 127-tooth gear on the lead-screw.

When Lathe has a Metric Lead-Screw.—If a screw having a given number of threads per inch is to be cut on a lathe having a metric lead-screw, first determine the "metric screw constant" or the lead of the thread in millimeters that would be cut with change-gears of equal size on the spindle stud and the lead-screw. The product of the number of threads per inch multiplied by the metric screw constant multiplied by 5 equals the number of teeth for the lead-screw gear. The gear on the spindle stud should have 127 teeth.

How are translating gears used for metric pitches?

Lathes used for cutting threads based on either the English or the metric systems of measurement may be provided with translating gears. There are two gears having 50 and 127 teeth, respectively. The numbers of teeth in these gears represent the relation between the English and the metric systems of measurement; thus,

1 inch is equivalent to 2.54 centimeters, and $\frac{1 \times 50}{2.54 \times 50} = \frac{50}{127}$

When these gears are in the train of gearing connecting

the lathe spindle and lead-screw, the lathe may be geared for cutting a given number of threads per centimeter by using, in addition to the translating gears, the same gears that would be employed for cutting a similar number of threads per inch. For example, if a metric thread is to be cut having a pitch of 2 millimeters, or 5 threads to the centimeter, and translating gears are used, change-gears for cutting 5 threads per inch could be employed. In this case, 5 threads to the centimeter will actually be cut and not 5 threads to the inch, because the translating gears are used in conjunction with the regular gears, thus forming a compound train of gearing. If the gears for cutting 5 threads per inch should have 36 and 30 teeth, respectively, on the stud and lead-screw, the compound train of gearing for cutting 5 threads per centimeter would consist of driving gears having 50 and 36 teeth and driven gears having 127 and 30 teeth. The positions of either the driving or the driven gears could be transposed, if necessary, in order to make the gears mesh together properly.

In cutting worm threads to a given diametral pitch, what change gears are required?

Ordinary engine lathes are used quite extensively for cutting worm threads. Whether or not lathes can be used to advantage depends on such factors as output required and size and nature of the work. When worms are to be cut to mesh with a worm-wheel of given diametral pitch, the ratio of change-gearing for obtaining the required worm-thread lead may be calculated by a simple method. First, the "lathe screw constant" is determined or the number of threads per inch cut by the lathe when the gears on the spindle stud and lead-screw are of equal size. This number is equal to the number of threads per inch on the lead-screw, assuming that the headstock spindle and stud are geared together in the ratio of 1 to 1.

Rule.—To determine the ratio of the change-gears, first multiply the lathe screw constant by 22, thus obtaining the numerator of a fraction representing the ratio. Next, multiply the diametral pitch of the worm-gear by 7, thus obtaining the denominator of the fraction. Change-gears having this ratio are then selected.

Example.—Assume that the diametral pitch of the worm-gear is 5, and the lathe screw constant is 4. Then, $\dfrac{4 \times 22}{5 \times 7} = \dfrac{88}{35}$ If this simple combination of gearing were used, the gear on the stud would have 88 teeth, and the gear on the lead-screw, 35 teeth. Of course, any other combination of gearing having this same ratio could be used, as for example, the following compound train of gearing:

$$\frac{24 \times 66}{30 \times 21}$$

The reason why the constants 22 and 7 are used in determining the ratio of change-gears for cutting worm threads, is because $\dfrac{22}{7}$ equals, very nearly, 3.1416, which is the circular pitch equivalent to 1 diametral pitch.

If the lathe screw constant is 4, as previously assumed, then the number of threads per inch obtained with gearing having a ratio of $\dfrac{88}{35} = \dfrac{4 \times 35}{88} = 1.5909$; hence, the pitch of the worm thread equals $1 \div 1.5909 = 0.628 +$, which is the circular pitch equivalent to 5 diametral pitch, correct to the third decimal place.

Measuring Pitch Diameters of Screw Threads

In ordinary thread cutting practice, the method of checking the size of a screw thread may depend upon the equipment available and the accuracy required. The mating nut or threaded hole sometimes is used as a gage, especially in repair work; but in manufacturing plants, a gaging or measuring device commonly is employed. Threaded bolts, shafts, pins, or other external screw threads usually are checked by means of a ring gage which is threaded to represent the hole or nut. Gages of the threaded plug type are commonly used for internal threads or threaded holes. These ring and plug gages may have "Go" and "Not Go" sizes to insure cutting screw threads within whatever limits of accuracy are desired. Approved forms of these ring and plug gages have been standardized, and they may be obtained from firms specializing in gage work. Many other forms of gaging or checking devices are in use.

What is the pitch diameter of a screw thread?

The pitch diameter of a screw thread is equal to the diameter of an imaginary cylinder, the surface of which would pass through the threads on all sides at such points as to make the width of the groove equal one-half of the pitch (see Fig. 1.). If the thread were perfect, this would occur where the widths of the thread and groove are equal. In actual practice, the pitch diameter specified would depend upon the degree of accuracy required. Suppose as an example we take a ¾-inch American Standard screw thread (external) with 10 threads per inch. Then according to this standard as revised in 1949, the pitch diameter for Class 1A limits would be 0.6832 maximum and 0.6744 minimum, but if Class 2A limits were required then the pitch diameter would be 0.6832 maximum and 0.6773 minimum, thus indicating that greater accuracy is required. If Class 3A limits were specified, the degree of accuracy would be even higher.

Why is the pitch diameter a very important dimension?

Why bother with the pitch diameter? Why not rely upon the major and minor diameters for obtaining any class of fit required? The pitch diameter is more important because contact between any threaded plug, bolt, etc., and a threaded hole, should be on the sloping sides of the thread and not at the crest or root. This is the reason why some method of checking the diameter that is related to these angular sides is desirable. The pitch diameter serves this purpose because it is across the angular sides of the thread. This will be more apparent when the method of measuring the pitch diameter is understood. Pitch diameter is also known

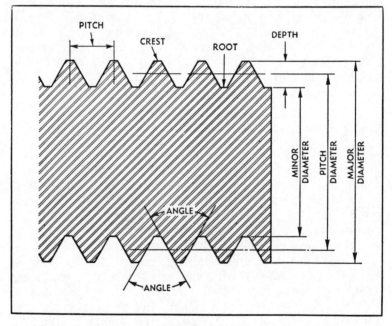

Fig. 1.   Diagram Illustrating Meaning of Terms Applied
to Screw Threads

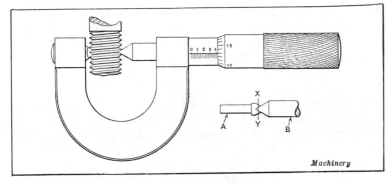

Fig. 2. Screw Thread Micrometer

as the "effective diameter" and sometimes as the "angle diameter."

What type of micrometer is used for measuring the pitch diameter of a screw thread?

A thread micrometer may be used for measuring or checking pitch diameters. This micrometer has a fixed anvil which is V-shaped so as to fit over the thread while the movable point or spindle is cone-shaped at the end so that it will enter the space between two threads. (See Fig. 2.) The anvil and the spindle make contact with the sides of the thread, thus enabling the pitch diameter to be determined. The cone-shaped point of the measuring screw is slightly rounded so that it will not bear at the bottom of the thread. There is also sufficient clearance at the bottom of the groove in the V-shaped anvil to prevent it from bearing at the top of the thread. When the micrometer is closed and the 60-degree point B and the anvil A are together (as shown by the diagram), the zero on the micrometer barrel represents a line drawn through the plane $X-Y$, and, if the micrometer is opened, say, 0.5 inch, this reading represents the distance that two such planes are apart; hence, the micrometer reading equals the pitch diameter or angle diameter, as it is sometimes called. The thread micrometer does not give an absolutely accurate pitch diameter measurement, there being a slight error which depends upon the lead angle of the screw thread. Usually this error is not large enough to be of practical importance. There is no error when the thread micrometer is set to a standard thread gage of the plug type and is then used for measuring screw threads having the same pitch and diameter as the gage.

In using a thread micrometer for measuring screw threads like the American and Whitworth Standards, it is evident that the actual outside diameter of a screw or tap does not affect the micrometer reading, and as screws are not intended to bear upon the top of the thread but on the angular sides, obviously the pitch diameter test should always be employed when accuracy is necessary.

All thread micrometers are not arranged in the same way as the one illustrated in Fig. 2. For instance, there is a type which has a pointed anvil that enters the thread groove instead of spanning the thread; that is, both the anvil and spindle have conical points which are ground to fit the thread angle. The anvil is provided with a lateral adjustment so that it can be moved lengthwise of the screw a distance equal to one-half the pitch of the thread. This adjustment is provided so that the measuring points will enter the thread grooves at right angles to the screw axis.

What is the three-wire method of checking the pitch diameter of a screw thread?

The pitch diameter may be checked very accurately by what is known as the "three-wire method." This wire method is especially useful in checking very accurate work, such, for example, as thread gages, and ordinarily it would not be employed in checking parts in connection with ordinary manufacturing practice because thread gages require much less time and are preferable for shop measurements. The three-wire method, however, is so generally used for precision work that it should be understood. Three wires or pins of the same diameter (within very close limits) are placed in contact with the screw thread, as illustrated by the diagram, Fig. 3. Two wires are placed in contact with the thread on one side and a third wire on the opposite side. When the micrometer is in contact with all three wires, this insures measuring perpendicular to the axis of the screw thread. The following simple rule and formula are for determining what measurement M over the wires should be when the pitch diameter of the screw thread is correct.

Rule.—Multiply 1.5155 by pitch of thread (1 ÷ no. threads per inch) and subtract product from standard major or outside diameter; then add to difference 3 times the wire diameter. Expressed as a formula

$$M = D - (1.5155 \times P) + (3 \times W)$$

This rule or formula applies to the American Standard thread form.

Example.—A screw 1½ inches in diameter and having 12 threads per inch of the American Standard form, is to be measured by the three-wire method; the wires are 0.050 inch in diameter. What is the correct micrometer reading?

$$1\frac{1}{2} - (1.5155 \times \frac{1}{12}) + (3 \times 0.050) = 1.5237 \text{ inches.}$$

If the micrometer reading is, say, 1.5360 inches, this indicates that the pitch diameter of the screw is too large. The amount of the error is the difference between the actual micrometer reading when the screw thread is measured,

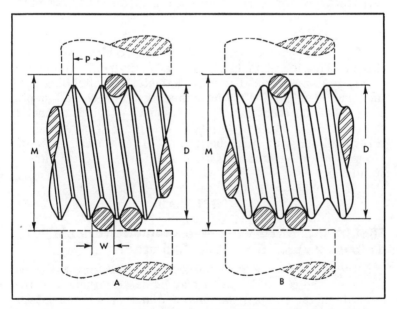

Fig. 3. Method of Checking Pitch Diameter by Three-wire Method

and the theoretical reading as found from the formula. In this case, then, 1.5360 — 1.5237 = 0.0123 inch, which is the amount that the pitch diameter is too large.

Measurement M over the wires may be made by using an ordinary micrometer. Special measuring fixtures of the micrometer type have also been developed for use with the three-wire method. These fixtures provide convenient means of holding the wires in position and the micrometer is mounted so that it can move freely either parallel or perpendicular to the axis of the screw thread which is held in a horizontal position between adjustable centers.

What rule or formula is used for checking British Standard screw threads by the 3-wire method?

The British Standard Whitworth screw thread is the standard that is used principally in Great Britain. The rule or formula used in checking this screw thread by the three-wire method is as follows:

Rule.—Multiply 1.6008 by pitch and subtract product from standard major or outside diameter; then add to difference 3.1657 times wire diameter. Expressed as a formula,

$$M = D — (1.6008 \times P) + (3.1657 \times W)$$

Example.—Determine measurement M (Fig. 3), for checking a ¾-inch British Standard Whitworth screw thread. This diameter has 10 threads per inch, making the pitch equal 0.10 inch. The wire diameter for pitch-line contact equals 0.056 inch approximately. The thread depth equals 0.06405 inch; hence, the effective or pitch diameter equals 0.75 — 0.06405 = 0.68595 inch. (These standard thread dimensions will be found in engineering handbooks containing data relating to important screw thread standards.)

$$M = 0.75 — (1.6008 \times 0.1) + (3 1657 \times 0.056)$$
$$= 0.7672 \text{ inch.}$$

Should the three-wire measurement formula be based upon the pitch diameter?

Although the three-wire method is for checking the pitch diameter, the rule or formula may be based either upon the pitch diameter or upon the outside diameter without affecting the final result. The rules or formulas generally found in engineering handbooks are based upon the standard or *basic* major or outside diameter. This kind of formula will now be applied to an example, and will be followed by the application, to the same example, of a formula based upon the pitch diameter.

Example.—An American Standard screw thread having a major diameter of 2½ inches and 4 threads per inch is to be checked by the three-wire method. Determine measurement M over the wires equivalent to the correct pitch diameter. The wire diameter is 0.1443 inch. (A paragraph to follow will explain how the wire sizes are determined.) The pitch of this thread is 0.25 inch. Applying the formula based upon the outside diameter

$$M = 2.5 — (1.5155 \times 0.25) + (3 \times 0.1443)$$
$$= 2.554 \text{ inches.}$$

This shows that measurement M is 2.554 inches when the pitch diameter is absolutely correct.

Now a rule or formula based upon pitch diameter will be applied to this same example. This formula is the same as the one based upon the outside diameter, excepting the constant 1.5155 is replaced by the constant 0.86603 and the basic major or outside diameter D is replaced by the effective or pitch diameter E, making the formula

$$M = E — (0.86603 \times P) + (3 \times W)$$

The pitch diameter of a 2½-inch American Standard screw thread having 4 threads per inch equals 2.5 — 0.1624 (thread depth) = 2.3376 inches; consequently,

$$M = 2.3376 — (0.86603 \times 0.25) + (3 \times 0.1443)$$
$$= 2.554 \text{ inches.}$$

As will be seen, the dimension M is the same as obtained by the formula based upon the major diameter. The pitch diameter formula, however, is preferable in checking screw threads having pitch diameter tolerances; for example, in measuring gages, taps, etc., such a formula shows the correct measurement M when the pitch diameter E is within the maximum and minimum limits specified for any given class of work. The pitch diameter is the most important dimension and in determining dimension M, the maximum and minimum pitch diameters for a standard tap or screw thread may be taken directly from tables giving these standard dimensions.

What rule or formula shows the pitch diameter equivalent to a given measurement over the wires?

When a screw thread is being checked by the three-wire method, the problem may be to determine the *pitch diameter* equivalent to a given measurement M over the wires instead of measurement M equivalent to the correct pitch diameter. This can be done merely by rearranging the formula for dimension M as follows:

Pitch diameter $E = M + (0.86603 \times P) - (3 \times W)$

Example.—Assume that a 2½-inch American Standard screw thread (Coarse-thread Series) has a measurement M over the wires of 2.556 inches, using wires of 0.1443 inch diameter. What pitch diameter does this measurement M represent? Applying the formula, we have

$E = 2.556 + (0.86603 \times 0.25) - (3 \times 0.1443) = 2.3396$

If this screw thread is a Class 3 fit, the maximum pitch diameter is 2.3376 and the minimum 2.3279 inches; hence, in this case, the formula shows that when measurement M is 2.556 inches, the pitch diameter is 0.002 inch larger than the maximum allowable pitch diameter of 2.3376 inches.

In checking screw threads by the three-wire method, how is the wire diameter found?

Any wire diameter W, Fig. 3, may be used provided the wires are small enough to enter the thread and contact with the sloping sides and are large enough to project above the top or crest of the thread, thus permitting proper contact with the micrometer or other measuring instrument. It is preferable, however, to use wires of the size required to make contact at the pitch line or mid-slope of the thread, because then measurement of the pitch diameter is least affected by any error in the thread angle. The term "best size" is commonly applied to wires making pitch-line contact.

Best Size Wire.—To determine the best size wire, divide one-half the pitch by the cosine of one-half the included thread angle in the axial plane or by the cosine of 30 degrees for an American Standard thread form. The best size may also be obtained by multiplying one-half of the pitch by the secant of one-half included thread angle. For the

American Standard or other 60-degree threads, this rule may be simplified as follows:

Best size wire for American Standard = 0.57735 × pitch.

Best size wire for Whitworth Standard = 0.56368 × pitch.

Best size wire for Acme thread = 0.51645 × pitch.

Largest and Smallest Wires.—The largest wire diameter for an American Standard thread equals 0.90 × pitch; the sn.allest wire diameter equals 0.56 × pitch.

For a British Standard Whitworth thread, the largest wire diameter equals 0.76 × pitch; the smallest wire diameter equals 0.54 × pitch.

Is the Whitworth three-wire formula applicable to the British Association Standard thread?

In checking the British Association Standard thread which is applied to small screws, a different rule or formula is required because of a change in the thread angle.

Rule.—Multiply 1.7363 by pitch and subtract product from standard major or outside diameter; then add to difference 3.4829 times diameter of wire.

$$M = D - (1.7363 \times P) + (3.4829 \times W)$$

Example.—Determine the micrometer reading M over the wires for checking a No. 10 British Association Standard screw thread. A table applying to this standard shows that the outside diameter is 1.7 millimeters, and the pitch is 0.35 millimeters. Assume that the wire diameter is 0.19 millimeters.

$$M = 1.7 - (1.7363 \times 0.35) + (3.4829 \times 0.19)$$
$$= 1.754 \text{ millimeters.}$$

In the foregoing example, assume that the dimensions were given in inches. In that case, the diameter equals 0.0669 inch, and the pitch, 0.0138 inch. A wire 0.19 millimeters in diameter is equivalent to a diameter of 0.0075 inch very nearly; hence,

$$M = 0.0669 - (1.7363 \times 0.0138) + (3.4829 \times 0.0075)$$
$$= 0.06906 \text{ inch.}$$

This measurement M, in inches, is equivalent to the measurement M in millimeters previously determined.

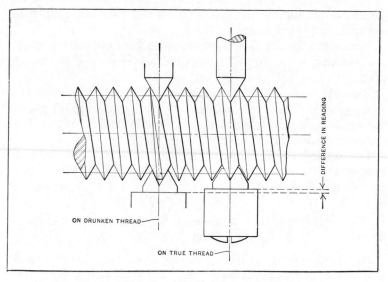

Fig. 4.   The Anvil Type of Thread Micrometer Gives Varying
Measurements on True and Drunken Threads

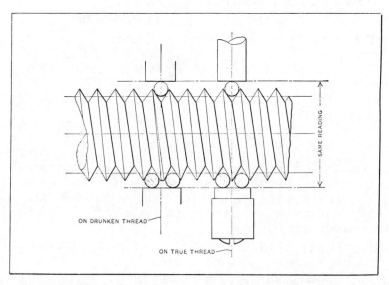

Fig. 5.   The Three-wire Method of Thread Measurement Makes no
Distinction between True and Drunken Threads

Can a sharp V-thread be checked by using the American Standard thread rule or formula?

If the rule or formula for the American Standard is based upon *pitch* diameter, it may be applied to any 60-degree thread form (see rule previously given). The sharp V-thread (which is seldom used) has the same standard angle (60 degrees) as the American Standard thread form. The following rule or formula for sharp V-threads is based upon the outside diameter.

Rule.—Multiply 1.732 by pitch and subtract product from basic major or outside diameter; then add to the difference 3 times wire diameter.

$$M = D - (1.732 \times P) + (3 \times W)$$

Example 1.—Determine measurement M for a ¾-inch sharp V-thread having 10 threads per inch, using the pitch diameter formula for 60-degree threads. The wire size is 0.070 inch. The thread depth = 0.0866; hence, pitch diameter = 0.75 — 0.0866 = 0.6634 inch.

$$M = 0.6634 - (0.86603 \times 0.1) + (3 \times 0.070)$$
$$= 0.7868 \text{ inch.}$$

Example 2.—Calculate measurement M for the screw thread in Example 1, using the formula based upon the basic outside diameter.

$$M = 0.75 - (1.732 \times 0.1) + (3 \times 0.070)$$
$$= 0.7868 \text{ inch.}$$

Will a diameter measurement by the three-wire method indicate a "drunken" thread?

When the thread is correct in form, either the thread micrometer or the three-wire method will give equally good results; but if the thread is not of the correct shape, but is "drunken," as indicated to the left in the illustrations Figs. 4 and 5, then the anvil type of thread micrometer only shows this variation, while the three-wire method would not indicate any error, provided the thread angle is correct. This is because the three-wire system measures the grooves cut by the thread tool, which is always at the same depth and is unvarying in shape; hence, the error, if any, would not be detected. The same condition is met with in the ball-

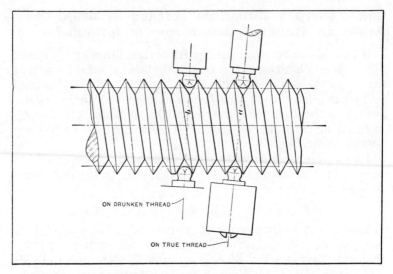

ON DRUNKEN THREAD

ON TRUE THREAD

Fig. 6. The Only Difference in Measurement on True and Drunken Threads Made by the Ball-point Micrometer is Due to the Very Slight Difference in Inclination — too Slight to be Appreciable

point micrometer. (See Fig. 6.) The lower anvil point of a regular thread micrometer, however, since it spans the abnormal thread, as shown in Fig. 4, instead of making contact with the sides of the adjacent threads, indicates the irregularity by giving an increased reading for the pitch diameter.

This does not mean that the three-wire method of measuring pitch diameters is unreliable for ordinary use. With the methods used for accurate thread cutting in general, a drunken thread is seldom produced. If the thread is drunken, the thread micrometer will indicate this defect, but the three-wire system nevertheless measures the pitch diameter correctly under all circumstances, as the principle of its use depends on the bearing of the wire on the sides of the thread groove.

The ball-point type of micrometer (Fig. 6) is especially useful for comparing the pitch diameter of a tap or screw thread with that of a standard thread plug gage. Since the purpose is to compare pitch diameters instead of measuring them, an exact relation between the pitch and the diameter of the ball points is not necessary. An approximate relationship, however, is necessary, since the ball point must be small enough to enter the thread groove and bear on the angular sides. If the thread is an American Standard, the ball diameter for pitch-line contact is 0.577 × the pitch, but this diameter might vary anywhere from 0.6 to 0.8 × the pitch.

In checking Acme and worm threads, how is the measurement over the wires calculated?

In measuring single-thread screws, the effect of the lead angle usually is very small. The first rule and formula which follow do not include the effect of the lead angle, and they may be applied to worm threads, Acme threads, or other forms, provided the lead angle can be ignored as in the case of most single-threaded screws. (A rule and formula which include the effect of the lead angle will be given later.)

Rule.—Find, in a table of trigonometrical functions, the tangent of one-half the thread angle (the tangent of 30 degrees for an American Standard thread, 14½ degrees for an Acme Standard thread, etc.) ; divide one-half the pitch by this tangent and subtract the quotient from the pitch diameter; then add to this difference the product of the wire diameter multiplied by one plus the cosecant of one-half the thread angle.

This rule is rather cumbersome and the equivalent formula is more convenient to use. In this formula,

M = measurement over the wires when pitch diameter is correct;

E = pitch diameter of screw thread;

W = wire diameter;

t = one-half the thread angle in the plane of the axis
= 30 degrees for American Standard thread, 27½ degrees for British Standard Whitworth, 14½ degrees for Acme Standard.

$$M = E - \frac{0.5\,P}{\tan t} + W\,(1 + \cosec t)$$

Example.—An Acme screw thread has an outside diameter of 2 inches and 4 threads per inch, making the pitch equal 0.25 inch. The basic thread depth is 0.125 inch;

hence, the pitch diameter equals 2.000 — 0.125 = 1.875 inches. The best wire size equals 0.51645 × pitch = 0.1291 inch. Acme threads have an included angle of 29 degrees; therefore, the tangent of one-half the included angle or 14½ degrees is 0.25862 and the cosecant 3.9939. These values are inserted in the formula to obtain measurement M equivalent to the correct pitch diameter.

$$M = 1.875 - \frac{0.5 \times 0.25}{0.25862} + 0.1291 \times (1 + 3.9939)$$
$$= 2.036 \text{ inches.}$$

This dimension M of 2.036 inches is slightly less than the true dimension owing to the effect of the lead angle on the position of the wires. This increase is very little for a single-thread screw; but if the Acme thread referred to in the preceding example had a quadruple thread, this would increase the lead angle to 9.635 degrees, the lead angle of the single-thread screw being 2.43 degrees; consequently, measurement M over the wires would be approximately 2.043 inches or an increase of about 0.007 inch due to the increased lead angle and resulting change in the position of the wires.   (See page 248 for effect of lead angle.)

Should Acme threads be checked by measuring the thread thickness?

While the wire method may be applied to Acme threads in order to check either the diameter direct, or the thickness by taking a diameter measurement, the chances of wire measurement errors increase as the angle of any thread decreases. To illustrate by taking an extreme example, it is evident that the wire method could not be applied to a square thread because the sides are parallel. Although the inclination of 14½ degrees on each side of an Acme thread groove provides a bearing for wires, this relatively small angle increases the chance of measurement error which might result either from slight errors in the wire sizes or from differences in the amounts of pressure applied in taking the measurement; consequently, in the case of an Acme thread, it may be preferable to check the quality of the fit by measuring the thread thickness rather than the pitch diameter.

In a report of the National Screw Thread Commission, a formula is given for checking Acme thread thickness. This formula is intended for application to any thread having an included angle of less than 45 degrees; however, it includes a measurement M over wires; hence the chances of error involved in applying the wire method to screw threads of relatively small angles are not eliminated.

Is there a simple direct method of checking the thread thickness?

A simple direct method that is especially applicable to the larger pitches is to use a vernier gear-tooth caliper for measuring the thickness normal or square to the sides of the thread. This measurement is usually made at the pitch-line depth or at a distance from the top of the thread equal to one-fourth of the pitch. The thickness normal or square to the sides of the thread will be less than in the plane of the axis, the difference depending upon the lead angle.

Rule.—To find width or thickness of thread normal or square to the sides, multiply the thread width in the plane of the axis by the cosine of the lead angle.

To find the lead angle, divide the pitch *circumference* by the pitch, or by the lead if a multiple thread, thus obtaining the cotangent of the angle.

Example.—An Acme screw thread has an outside diameter of 3 inches and a quadruple thread of 0.5 inch pitch, making the lead equal 2 inches. Find the normal thread thickness at the pitch line or at one-half depth.

The pitch diameter equals 3 — 0.25 inch (depth of one thread) = 2.75 inches; hence, the pitch circumference equals 8.6394 inches. Therefore,

$$\text{Cotangent lead angle} = \frac{8.6394}{2} = 4.3197$$

A table of trigonometric functions shows that the angle equivalent to this cotangent is 13 degrees 2 minutes and the cosine of this angle is 0.97424.

$$\text{Normal thread thickness} = 0.97424 \times 0.25$$
$$= 0.244 \text{ inch nearly.}$$

The maximum thickness in the plane of the axis equals one-half the pitch, or, in this case, 0.25 inch; hence, the normal thickness is 0.006 inch less. This difference would, of course, be greater for a larger lead angle. In actual practice, an Acme thread of this size might have a thickness tolerance of 0.010 inch. Such a tolerance would be minus so that the actual normal thickness might vary between 0.244 and 0.234 inch.

How is the pitch diameter checked when effect of lead angle must be included?

If the lead angle is large as in the case of many multiple screw threads such as are found on worms, quick-traversing lead-screws, etc., the ordinary rule or formula for checking the pitch diameter by the three-wire method is inaccurate and the effect of the lead angle on the position of the wires should be taken into account. This effect depends not only upon the size of the lead angle, but to some extent upon the degree of accuracy required in checking the pitch diameter. To calculate dimension M over the wires, and allow for the effect of the lead angle, proceed as follows:

Rule.—First determine one-half the angle of the thread in a plane normal or perpendicular to the sides of the thread. Call this angle A to identify it. If the thread is milled, this angle A equals one-half the included or total angle of the cutter. If the thread is cut in a lathe with the top surface of the tool set square to the sides of the thread when in the cutting position, then angle A equals one-half the included angle of the tool. If the thread is cut in a lathe with the top of the tool in the plane of the axis, thus forming a straight-sided thread in the plane of the axis, then angle A in the normal plane or square to the sides of the thread, must be calculated as shown in connection with the example to follow.

After determining angle A, add 1 to its sine and multiply this sum by the wire diameter which we will identify as diameter W. Then add to this product the standard or basic pitch diameter of the screw thread to obtain measurement M over wires equivalent to this basic diameter. Expressed as a formula

$$\text{Measurement } M = D + W (1 + \sin A) \qquad (1)$$

Wire Size.—This simple solution is made possible by using a special wire size W which must be calculated in each case. Wire diameter W is determined as follows:

Multiply the cosine of the lead angle L of the screw thread by one-half of its pitch T; then divide the product by the cosine of angle A to obtain wire diameter W. Expressed as a formula

$$\text{Wire diameter} = \frac{T \times \cos L}{\cos A} \qquad (2)$$

Example.—Calculate dimension M over the wires and the wire diameter W for a triple-threaded worm which is to be milled. It has a pitch of $1\frac{1}{2}$ inches or a lead of $4\frac{1}{2}$ inches, a pitch diameter of 2.481 inches, and a lead angle of 30 degrees. (The helix angle of a screw thread is commonly referred to as the *lead angle* and it is measured from a plane perpendicular to the axis.) The included angle of the worm thread is 60 degrees, this being the angle in the plane of the axis. The angle in a plane normal or perpendicular to the sides of the thread is less than 60 degrees; consequently, the angle of the milling cutter will be reduced to conform to the normal angle, as shown in the solution to follow.

Thread Angle in Normal Plane.—In this example, the standard thread angle in the plane of the axis is 60 degrees.

Tangent of angle A in normal plane = tan one-half included thread angle in axial plane × cosine lead angle = tan 30 degrees × cosine 30 degrees = 0.57735 × 0.866025 = 0.5; hence, angle A = 26.565 degrees (making the included angle of the cutter = 53.13 degrees).

In determining the wire diameter W (by using formula 2), the cosine of angle A is required, and the sine of this angle is used later in the formula 1 for calculating the measurement M over the wires.

Cosine A = 0.89443; sine A = 0.44721

$$W = \frac{0.75 \times 0.866025}{0.89443} = 0.72618 \text{ inch}$$

$$M = 2.481 + [0.72618 \times (1 + 0.44721)]$$
$$= 3.5319 \text{ inches.}$$

The preceding rule or formula, while not theoretically correct, does combine simplicity with a degree of accuracy that meets all but the most exacting requirements. If the screw thread to be measured has a large lead-angle combined with a small thread angle (such as a 29-degree Acme or worm thread with a large lead-angle), then calculating the measurement over the wires for checking the pitch diameter accurately is a cumbersome operation. The simplest known method is explained in MACHINERY'S HANDBOOK (see section on Measuring Screw Threads and the paragraph headed "Buckingham Exact Involute Helicoid Formula Applied to Screw Threads"). These formulas for obtaining a precise measurement, while cumbersome to apply, have the merit of providing a direct solution; consequently, they are preferable to the indeterminate equations and lengthy successive trial solutions heretofore employed in obtaining very accurate results when lead-angles are large, and especially when such angles are combined with small thread angles.

Is it practicable to measure a taper screw thread by the three-wire method?

External taper threads on pipes, etc., usually are checked by means of a threaded ring.gage. Such a gage may screw onto the threaded part until the gage face, in the case of pipes, is within one turn plus or minus of the threaded end. While the ring gage is a convenient form for general shop use, the three-wire method may be applied in checking taper thread gages of the plug form or other precision work. In taking a measurement over three wires, the line of measurement is at an angle relative to the axis of the tapering screw thread. The formula which follows compensates for this inclination. This formula applies to the American Standard pipe thread, the taper of which is ¾ inch per foot. The formula is not theoretically correct, but is believed to be accurate enough for this taper. In the formula M equals measurement over wires, E equals effective or pitch diameter at given point, and W equals wire diameter.

$$M = \frac{E - (0.86603 \times \text{pitch}) + (3 \times W)}{1.00049}$$

Example.—Find dimension M for a 3-inch American Standard pipe thread gage. This size has a pitch of 0.125 inch and a pitch diameter at the gaging notch of 3.3885 inches. Assume that the wire diameter is 0.07217 inch; then when the pitch diameter is correct

$$M = \frac{3.3885 - (0.86603 \times 0.125) + (3 \times 0.07217)}{1.00049}$$
$$= 3.495 \text{ inches.}$$

The taper thread is measured over the wires in the usual manner, but the single wire must be located accurately in the thread at a point where the effective diameter is to be checked. The other wires are then placed on each side of that thread which is diametrically opposite the single wire.

How accurate is the three-wire method of measuring screw threads?

It is possible to check screw thread sizes very accurately by this method; however, the degree of accuracy depends very much upon the accuracy of the wires used as well as the accuracy of the measuring instrument. The measurement may also be affected appreciably by the amount of contact pressure against the wires in measuring. If the accuracy of the pitch diameter of a screw thread gage is to be checked within 0.0001 inch by the wire method, it is necessary to know the wire diameters to within 0.00002 inch. Each wire should be round within 0.00002 inch and should be straight within the same amount over any quarter-inch section. A set of three wires should have the same diameter within 0.00003 inch; moreover, this common diameter should be within 0.0001 inch of the "best size" for any given pitch. As previously explained, the "best size," as it is commonly called, is one which makes contact at the pitch line oi at one-half thread depth where any errors in the thread angle will have the least effect upon the measurement over the wires. Tests made to show the effect of contact pressure were made by measuring a 24-pitch thread gage of the plug type. The measurement, with a contact pressure of 5 pounds, was 0.00013 inch less than with a pressure of 2 pounds. If proper precautions are taken regarding wire accuracy and contact pressure, it should be possible to check plug gages within an accuracy of 0.0001 inch. If the wire diameters are accurate to only 0.0001 inch, then the pitch diameter measurement is not likely to be more accurate than 0.0003 inch. This, however, may be accurate enough for many classes of work.

Turret Lathes and Machines of Automatic Type

Turret lathes are designed primarily for the production of duplicate parts and are used in practically all machine-building plants, especially where one or more products are built on a manufacturing basis. Lathes of this type were used first for machining parts made from bar stock and later for castings, forgings, and separate pieces of stock held in a chuck. The principle of operation, however, is the same in each case, there being a turret mounted upon a carriage and arranged to hold a succession of tools which can be brought into action as required, by turning the turret. While it is impracticable to give a general rule covering the classes of work for which turret lathes are adapted, the ordinary practice is to use turret lathes in preference to engine lathes when the number of duplicate parts required is large enough to warrant making the necessary adjustments and equipping the turret lathe with whatever standard or special tools may be needed. If the number of parts is quite large and other conditions are favorable, some type of "automatic" may be used in preference to a hand-operated turret lathe; it is impossible to draw a definite dividing line between the classes and quantities of work adapted to these different types of machine tools. The best and, in fact, only practicable way to obtain information on the kinds of work suitable for turret lathes and other machine tools, is by studying good examples of modern practice.

Why is a turret lathe efficient for many classes of work?

A turret lathe derives its name from the turret which is so arranged that tools may be brought into the working position successively by indexing or rotating the turret. In many instances, all of the tools required cannot be held in the turret and it is necessary to use other tools held on a cross-slide, for cutting off the finished part, facing a radial surface, knurling, or for some other operation. Fig. 1 shows a "close-up" of a turret lathe drilling a hole. This drill is followed by the reamer shown, after the turret is indexed one-sixth of a turn to bring the reamer in line with the drilled hole.

After a turret lathe is equipped with the tools needed for machining a certain part, it produces the finished work m··ch more rapidly than would be possible by using an ordinary engine lathe, principally because each tool is carefully set for turning or boring to whatever size is required, and the turret makes it possible to place any tool quickly in the working position. Many turret lathes also have systems of stops or gages for controlling the travel of the turret carriage and cross-slide, in order to regulate the depth of a bored hole, the length of a cylindrical part or its diameter; hence, turning machines of this type are much

Fig. 1. Close-up View of Turret Lathe Showing Drilling Operation

more efficient than ordinary lathes for turning duplicate parts, unless the quantity is small, in which case the advantage of the turret lathe might be much more than offset by the cost of "setting up" the machine. This cost varies greatly for different jobs and depends largely upon the special tool equipment, if any, which may be required.

A typical turret lathe job is shown in Fig. 2. This lathe is machining pinion blanks and two series of operations are required. The first series on the front of the blank is to center, rough-face, turn, drill, rough-bore, finish-bore, and counter-bore; the second series on the rear side includes drilling, boring, turning, and facing. The illustration shows the machine taking two cuts at one time—turn-

Fig. 2. General View of a Turret Lathe Showing the Tool-holding Turret which is Indexed or Rotated Intermittently to Locate the Different Tools in the Working Position.

ing the outside diameter with the cross-slide and rough-boring with a tool held by the hexagon turret.

Are turret lathes made in both horizontal and vertical types?

The names given to turret lathes may either be based upon some prominent constructional feature, or they may be derived from the general nature of the work for which the lathe was designed primarily. All machines which belong to the turret-lathe class are not ordinarily known as turret lathes, and there is also considerable variation in the names used by the manufacturers to designate the different types. Considering first the broad classification of turret lathes, there are the *horizontal* and *vertical* designs. A large percentage of the turret lathes in use are of the horizontal design. Machines which are called *vertical turret lathes* by one manufacturer are classed as *side-head boring mills* by another manufacturer, owing to the fact that they are designed along the lines of a vertical boring mill with the addition of a side-head; therefore, the name vertical turret lathe is not one that is applied generally to this type of machine, although such a design may properly be classified as a vertical turret lathe, as it possesses the same general features as a horizontal machine designed for chuck work. When a machine is simply referred to as a "turret lathe," this is generally understood to be a horizontal machine (like the one shown in Fig. 2) and it may be designed either for handling bar stock, chuck work, or for both bar and chuck work, and the turret may or may not have a power feeding movement.

What types or forms of turrets are used on turret lathes?

The form of the turret is either hexagonal, round or flat. The *flat turret lathe* has a turret which is practically a low circular table upon which the tools are clamped. This flat plate-shaped tool-holder is mounted on a low carriage, the support for both turret and carriage being designed to obtain direct and rigid support from the machine bed. The tool-holders used on flat turret lathes differ considerably in shape from those used on machines having turrets of hexagonal or similar form, because the tool-holders are mounted *upon* a flat turret, whereas with the hexagonal form they are either held by shanks inserted in the turret holes or are bolted to the vertical sides.

The *tilted turret lathe* is so named because the turret is in an angular position. The *hollow-hexagon turret lathe* is still another machine which derives its name from the form of the turret, although some manufacturers of such lathes do not refer to them as the hollow-hexagon type.

The classification of a turret lathe, in some instances, indicates the arrangement of the turret slide. In many cases, the turret has only a longitudinal feeding movement in the direction of the bed; when there is a cross-slide between the turret and the main slide, the name *set-over turret lathe* is used by some manufacturers, but not very generally. The *full-swing side-carriage turret lathe* is a design having a toolpost carriage mounted on the side of the bed, so that it will pass the chuck and enable the turret carriage to be moved up close to the chuck, thus reducing the overhang of the tools to a minimum.

Is the term "screw machine" applied to some lathes of the turret type?

A turret lathe that is designed more particularly for turning comparatively small screws, pins, etc., from steel rods or bar stock, is commonly (although not invariably) known as a *screw machine*, a *wire-feed screw machine*, or as a *turret screw machine*. According to the practice of some manufacturers, the name screw machine is applied to small turret lathes which have a collet chuck in the spindle and a "wire feed" or a mechanism for feeding a wire rod or bar stock through the spindle. When the machine is intended for either bar or chuck work, or for chuck work exclusively, the name turret lathe is commonly used, and such a machine may or may not have a stock-feeding mechanism which operates in conjunction with the spindle chuck. The foregoing method of distinguishing between the two types, however, is not universal, and there is no general agreement in the use of these names.

Turret lathes of the screw-machine class are sometimes

given names which indicate rather definitely the type of machine; for instance, the name *hand screw machine* is often applied to turret screw machines in general, in order to distinguish between the hand-operated type and the automatic type, or the term "hand screw machine" may indicate a design not equipped with an automatic feeding mechanism for the turret slide. The name *wire-feed screw machine* has been used to indicate a design having a mechanism for automatically feeding the stock through the spindle and operating the chuck, whereas a machine not having this stock-feeding mechanism is designated as a *plain screw*

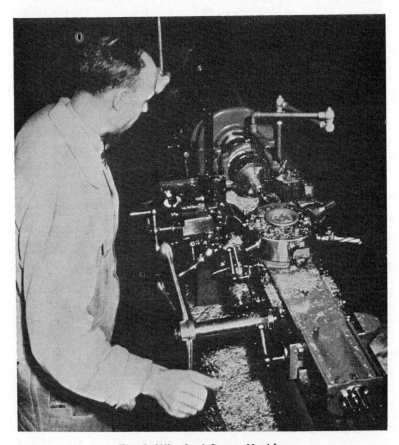

Fig. 3. Wire-feed Screw Machine

machine. A wire-feed screw machine is shown in Fig. 3. Machines of this general type can be set up quickly for turning various small parts and they are adapted especially to quantities of work that are not large enough to warrant the use of a fully automatic machine.

When are lathes of the turret type called "monitor lathes"?

Turret lathes which are intended principally for brass work are often referred to as *monitor lathes*, the name "monitor" in this connection indicating a revolving turret. This name is not applied to the same design of turret lathe by different manufacturers, although, in general, it indicates a comparatively small turret lathe which, in many cases, is provided with a thread-chasing attachment of the Fox lathe type and is designed principally for turning, boring, and threading parts made of brass. Some lathes which are listed as the monitor type have a stock-feeding mechanism, whereas others do not have this feature. The turret may or may not have power feed, and some monitor lathes have a cross-feed for the turret, whereas others have only the longitudinal feeding movement.

What is a "chucking lathe"?

Some turret lathes are used exclusively for operating on bar stock which is fed through the hollow spindle and is held by some form of collet chuck located in the end of the spindle, whereas other machines are equipped either for handling bar stock or larger work which must be held in a regular chuck that is attached to the spindle. There are also turret lathes which are not arranged for turning parts from bar stock, but are designed exclusively for machining castings or forgings which must be held in a chuck or upon a special form of arbor. Lathes of this latter class are frequently called *chucking machines* or *chucking lathes*, because the work is always held in a chuck. A *forming and chucking lathe* is intended particularly for chuck work, but the hollow spindle may be equipped with a collet chuck for bar work, if desired. Chucking machines are sometimes referred to as "boring, forming, and turning lathes," there being considerable variation in the names used by different manufacturers.

What types of tools are used in turret lathes?

There are two general classes of turret lathe work, namely, bar work and chuck work. The term "bar work" means that successive parts are turned from a bar of stock which is inserted through the hollow spindle; "chuck work" relates to the machining of parts which are in the form of separate castings or forgings that are held either in a regular jawed chuck, on a faceplate, or in some special fixture attached to the faceplate. Typical tools for bar work include the well-known box-tools and hollow mills (for reducing the diameter of the bar of stock to the required size); special designs of turning tools or "turners," such as are used extensively on flat turret lathes; forming tools, when there is an irregular surface to be machined; drills and reamers; dies, when the part must be threaded; cutting-off tools for severing finished parts; and many tools of special designs. In general, cutting-off and forming tools are mounted on a cross-slide between the turret and headstock, whereas box-tools, hollow mills, dies, etc., are carried in the turret. For some operations, a tool is mounted on every side or tool-holding position of the turret, whereas, for comparatively simple operations, the turret may not require tools in every position.

For chuck work, the turret tool equipment often includes tools such as drills, boring-bars, reamers, facing cutters, taps, dies, etc., and if there is a separate cross-slide on the machine, it is commonly used for operating forming tools and turning tools for turning and facing the rims of flywheels, and similar parts.

The operation of a turret lathe after the tools have been properly arranged is not particularly difficult, but designing and making the tools, determining what order of operations will give the most efficient and accurate results, and setting the tools on the machine require both skill and experience. For some classes of work, especially if of a rather complicated nature, many of the tools must be specially designed, although there are certain standard types

used on turret lathes which are adapted to general machining operations.

What is a box-tool?

In producing parts from bar stock, in turret lathes and
screw machines, the end of the bar projects from the chuck
and usually one of the first operations is to turn down all
or part of this projecting end to whatever diameter or
diameters may be required. A box-tool held on the turret
is commonly used for such turning operations. As a box-
tool operates on the unsupported end of the bar, it is
equipped with some form of back-rest opposite the turning
tool for supporting the work; it usually encloses or sur-
rounds the turned part to some extent, and, for that reason,
is known as a *box-tool*. Tools of this type are extensively
used on turret lathes and automatic screw machines. Box-
tools are made in a great variety of designs and types which
differ chiefly in regard to the number and arrangement of
the cutters and the method of supporting the part being
turned.

In what positions are box-tool cutters held?

Box-tool cutters are applied to the work either radially
as shown at A, Fig. 4, or tangentially as illustrated at B
and C. The radial position for the cutter is more commonly
used for brass work, whereas the tangential cutter is used
for all classes of steel work, and also for brass work in some
cases. The cutting edge of a radial cutter is set above the
horizontal center-line of the work an amount that is usually
about 0.02 times the diameter which is being turned. This
is the preferable method of applying the turning tool for
taking roughing cuts on brass rods. If the stock is rough
or of irregular shape, the cutter should precede the support
an amount varying from 0.010 to 0.020 inch, but, if the
bar is cylindrical and has a finished surface, the support
when taking roughing cuts, should precede the turning tool
as shown by the dotted lines at A. The tangential cutter
shown at B is set to take a roughing cut from a bar having
a comparatively rough surface. The tangential cutter shown
at C is set for taking a finishing cut in steel. The cutting

edge is located back of the center of the work an amount
equal to 0.10 of the diameter d, being turned. For cutting
brass, the tangential cutter is set in line with the center,
or, in some cases, slightly in advance of the center.

A method of applying two turning tools for roughing
steel work is shown at D, and at E three turning tools are
shown. For taking roughing cuts on brass, where considerable material is to be removed, a hollow mill is generally
used, but the method shown at D can sometimes be employed to advantage. At E no supports are used, as the
three equally spaced tools support the stock. These tools can
either be set radially as shown, and a slight amount in advance of each other, or tangentially and at varying heights,
so as to distribute the cuts equally among the tools. For
taking roughing cuts on steel, it is preferable to set the
cutters tangentially to the work.

At F is shown a method of applying two tangential turn-

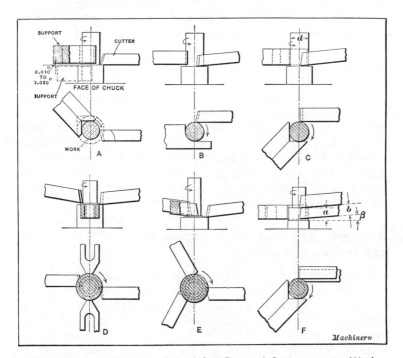

Fig. 4. Various Methods of Applying Box-tool Cutters to the Work

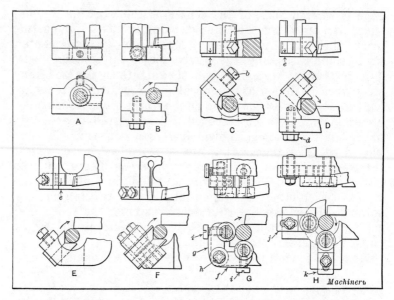

Fig. 5. Methods of Holding and Adjusting Box-tool Supports

ing tools for turning two diameters. This method is used when the distance a is not much greater than from $\frac{1}{2}$ to $\frac{5}{8}$ inch. For a larger dimension a, it is generally advisable to use two separate box-tools, provided there is sufficient room in the turret. When turning tools are used in this manner, the thickness b of the first tool should be such that the second tool, when set tightly against the first one, will turn the shoulder to the desired length. To illustrate, assume that $a = 0.375$ inch, angle $\beta = 10$ degrees; then $b = a \times \cos \beta = 0.375 \times 0.9848 = 0.369$ inch.

How are box-tool work supports applied and adjusted?

Various methods of holding and adjusting box-tool supports are shown in Fig. 5. At A is shown a common method of holding a bushing support. The support shown at B is tongued to the holder and is adjustable in an axial direction. At C is shown one method of holding a V-support. A rectangular hole is cut in the body of the holder in which the supports fit. When in position, the supports are held by the set-screw b. This method of holding a V-support is commonly used for both roughing and finishing box-tools, when one cutting tool is applied to the work, and sometimes when two cutting tools are used so close together that it is only necessary to support the work at one place. At D is shown a method of holding a V-support when it is necessary to apply more than one support to the work, as when turning more than one diameter at a time. This support is held in a movable block c, which is adjusted along the body of the holder. These last two methods are principally for box-tools used for turning brass or a similar class of materials, in which the cutter is set radially to the work. At E is shown a common method of applying the V-support to a box-tool used for cutting steel. This method is used when the cutting tool is set tangentially. The methods shown at C, D, and E are limited in their scope, to a certain extent, owing to the fact that they cannot be used in conjunction with a circular form tool when it is necessary to have the box-tool work closer to the forming tool than the thickness of the web e. For this class of work, the design shown at F is commonly used. This support is beveled and set in a beveled slot cut in the front end of the box-tool body. The body of the holder is split and screws bind the two parts together.

At G is shown a method of applying roller supports. These roller supports are held in two movable members, f and g, which, in turn, are fastened to the body of the holder by the clamping screw h. These roller-support holders are held in the correct position by large-headed screws i, which are screwed into the body of the holder. At H is shown another method of applying roller supports. In this case, the supports are held on two sliding holders, j and k, which slide in grooves cut in the box-tool body. They are adjusted in and out to the required diameter, and are held by the clamping screws. There are numerous other methods of holding roller supports, but they are all of a somewhat similar character to those already shown.

When are forming tools used?

When curved surfaces or those of irregular shape are required in connection with turret-lathe work, forming tools

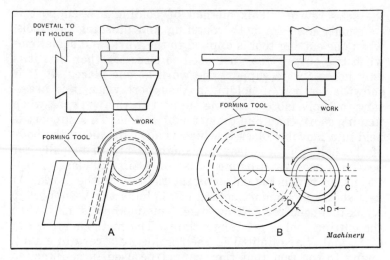

**Fig. 6. (A) Straight Forming Tool of Vertical Type.
(B) Circular Forming Tool**

are used. These tools are so made that the contour of the cutting edge corresponds to the shape required (see Fig. 6), and usually they may be ground repeatedly without changing the shape of the cutting edge. There are two general classes of forming tools—the straight type *A* and the circular type *B*. The circular forming tool is generally used on small narrow forms, whereas the straight type is more suitable for wide forming operations. Some straight forming tools are clamped in a horizontal position upon the cut-off slide, whereas others are held in a vertical position in a special holder. A common form of holder for these vertical tools is one having a dovetail slot in which the forming tool is clamped. In many cases, two forming tools are used, especially when a very smooth surface is required, one being employed for roughing and the other for finishing.

To provide sufficient periphery clearance on circular forming tools, the cutting face is off-set with relation to the center of the tool a distance *C*. Whenever a circular tool has two or more diameters, the difference in the radii of the steps on the tool will, therefore, not correspond exactly to the difference in the steps on the work. The form produced with the tool also changes, although the change is very slight, unless the amount of off-set C is considerable. As-sume that a circular tool is required to produce a part hav-ing two diameters as shown. If the difference D_1 between the large and small radii of the tool were made equal to dimension D required on the work, D would be a certain amount over-size, depending upon the off-set C of the cut-ting edge; hence, in determining the radii of circular form-ing tools for turning parts to different diameters the off-set must be allowed for.

How are screw threads cut on a turret lathe?

Most threading operations in the turret lathe are done by using taps and dies, but, for some classes of work, thread-chasing attachments are used. Such attachments cover a wide range of diameters and may be used, either because the screw thread is too large for a tap or die, because of the location of the screw thread, or because the number of parts required is not large enough to warrant the pur-chase of special taps and dies. Another advantage of the thread-chasing attachment is that it enables a screw thread to be produced which is known to be true with other cuts that have been taken at the same setting of the work.

One form of chasing attachment consists of a leader or short lead-screw which is mounted upon the feed-rod of the machine, and a brass follower that is engaged or disengaged by a lever pivoted in a bracket bolted to the carriage. A bar carrying a single-point chasing cutter is held in a holder clamped onto the turret. When the attachment is in use, the entire turret carriage is traversed along the bed which in-sures that threaded parts are true with the turned surfaces.

Is there an automatic type of turret lathe?

Some machines which are similar in principle to a turret lathe are automatic in operation excepting for the insertion and removal of the work. The machines which might be classed as automatic turret lathes are often called "auto-matic chucking and turning machines," or simply "auto-matic chucking machines." Machines of this class are designed for turning, boring, drilling, reaming, and other operations on castings, forgings, or separate pieces of stock

Fig. 7. Automatic Chucking and Turning Machine

which have previously been cut off from the bar. The machine shown in Fig. 7 is a representative design. After the work is placed in the chuck, the feeding of the tools, indexing of the turret, the movement of the turret-slide and cross-slide, and the necessary speed and feed changes are all controlled automatically by cams. The cross-slide may be provided with front and rear tools that are adjusted to work at the same time as the turret tools, or separately, the order of operation depending upon the nature of the work. The turret has different stations or faces to which various types of tools may be attached. The turret is advanced, revolved, and returned automatically; these movements are performed at a comparatively rapid rate of speed until the cutting point of a tool is about to engage the work, when it is automatically given a slower movement for feeding. The turret-slide, as well as the cross-slide, is operated by cams. There are automatic changes of spindle speed, and the range of speeds may be varied by means of change-gears. The time at which these speed changes occur is governed to suit the work. These machines are either equipped with ordinary

Fig. 8. Tooling Employed on an Automatic Chucking and Turning
Machine for the Taking of Roughing and Semi-finishing
Cuts on Three Arms of a Propeller Spider

chucks, air-operated chucks or collets, or special work-holding fixtures.

Figs. 7 and 8 show an automatic chucking and turning machine equipped for certain operations on the spider forging of an airplane propeller. The tool equipment shown in Fig. 7 is used for such operations as drilling, boring, and turning. The "pilots" or long extensions seen on some of these tools pass through the center of the work-holding chuck and into the spindle of the machine in order to steady the tool and hold it in alignment while at work. The tools shown in Fig. 8 are used for drilling, turning, and facing. The spider, which has been partly finished in previous operations, is securely and accurately held by certain finished surfaces in a special work-holding chuck mounted on the machine spindle. This spider has three arms or extensions and could not be held properly in an ordinary or standard chuck. Machines of this general type are adapted to an endless variety of work and are intended for producing duplicate parts when the number is large enough to justify the use of such a machine.

What are the principal features of automatic screw machines?

The automatic screw machine originally was classed as an "automatic turret lathe" by its inventor, Christopher N. Spencer, who was then connected with the Billings & Spencer Co. Characteristic features of screw machines in general are means for automatically locating successive tools in the correct working position, the automatic changing of feeds and speeds to secure economical operation, and the presenting of new stock to the tools for a similar series of operations. These various movements, which are entirely automatic, are obtained principally from cams which are rotated at pre-determined speeds, and are so formed and set relative to one another that the parts of the machine which they control all operate at the proper time, and at suitable speeds.

There are two general classes of screw machines, one class having a single work-spindle and the other, several work-spindles—usually four, five or six spindles. The single-spindle machines operate on one part at a time, as there is only one work-holding spindle. For instance, when operating on a bar of stock, the tools perform whatever turning, drilling, reaming, counterboring, threading, or other operations may be necessary, and then the finished piece is cut off. Each spindle of the multiple-spindle type holds a bar of stock, and tool-holders feed tools forward to operate on these bars of stock held in the opposing work-spindles. After a tool-holder has concluded its working stroke and returned to the starting position, the work-spindle carrier or head is revolved, bringing each bar of stock to the next tool in rotation. The final tool position provides for a cut-off blade, and a complete piece is finished and cut off at each indexing. One or more forming slides also operate at the different spindle positions if necessary. With this type of machine, all the cutting tools are working on each feeding stroke, as each has a bar of stock presented to it, whereas, with a single-spindle machine, the various tools of the turret operate successively on a single bar.

The time required to complete a part on a single-spindle machine is equal to the total time necessary for all of the individual operations, which includes the time for withdrawing the tools at the completion of the cut, indexing the turret and presenting the succeeding tools to the work. Single-spindle machines, however, are capable of very rapid production. With a multiple-spindle machine, the total time required to complete a piece is equal to the time necessary for the longest single operation plus the time for the idle movements; in some cases, the time is reduced by dividing the longest operation into two operations. Each type has its own field of application.

Is the automatic screw machine applicable to a large variety of work?

The original field of the automatic screw machine was, as its name implies, the making of screws. This field was quickly enlarged to include the making of all kinds of small nuts, washers, pins, collars, etc., and, at the present time, machines of this class are capable of a great variety of operations, not only on parts which are turned from bar stock, but on separate castings or forgings that are automatically fed to the machine by a special feeding mechanism. Since automatic screw machines are used in producing an endless variety of work, some typical examples will be shown to illustrate the general principles involved.

How are machine parts produced on a single-spindle type of automatic screw machine?

The method of using a single-spindle machine will be illustrated by showing the successive operations for producing a steel sleeve (see the diagrams, Fig. 9). This special sleeve requires drilling, forming, recessing, and tapping. The operations are in the following order:

1. Gage the stock to length by a gage stop A in the first hole in the turret. (The bar is moved through the chuck automatically until the end encounters this stop.)

2. Index the turret and rough-turn the large diameter with cutter a, using an overhanging turning attachment B, and at the same time drill a large hole full depth, using the

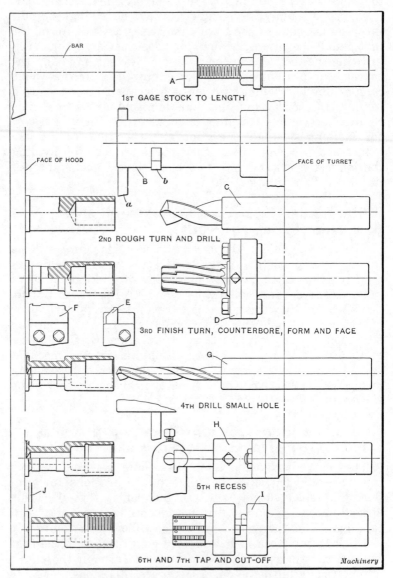

Fig. 9. Tool Equipment and Operations for Making a Steel
Sleeve on a Single-spindle Automatic

drill in holder C which is held in the second hole in the turret.

3. Index the turret and finish-turn the large diameter with the second cutter b held in a turning attachment, and at the same time counterbore a large hole, using a counterbore and holder D held in the third hole in the turret. As no tools are in the way on the front side, forming tools E and F can be brought into operation to face the end and to form the rear diameters, using flat forming tools on the front of the cross-slide.

4. Index the turret and drill a small hole, using a drill and holder G in the fourth hole in the turret.

5. Index the turret, recess, using a recessing tool and holder H in the fifth hole in the turret.

6. Index the turret and tap the hole with a tap held in the sixth hole.

7. Cut off, using the cut-off blade J held in a cut-off toolpost on the rear of the cross-slide.

When the tools have been set in their proper relation to each other, and the feed-regulating cams have been so adjusted as to give the proper feeds for the various tools, the position of the various cams is noted and recorded on a chart. All the tools used are also recorded on this chart, so that the machine can easily and quickly be equipped and adjusted for reproducing this same part, if necessary, at any future time.

How are parts produced on a multiple-spindle type of machine?

In using a multiple-spindle machine, the different tools operate simultaneously. Fig. 10 shows how a small brass binder post is machined on a five-spindle automatic. A bar of stock ⅜ inch in diameter is held in each of the five work-holding spindles and directly opposite there are five tool-spindles for holding whatever tools are presented in an endwise direction. Automatic screw machines also have front and rear tool-slides and supplementary tool-arms for use in holding whatever tools may be fed in laterally. In position A, two surfaces are turned on the work, as illustrated diagrammatically, by means of tools held in a special head mounted in the tool-head spindle corresponding to

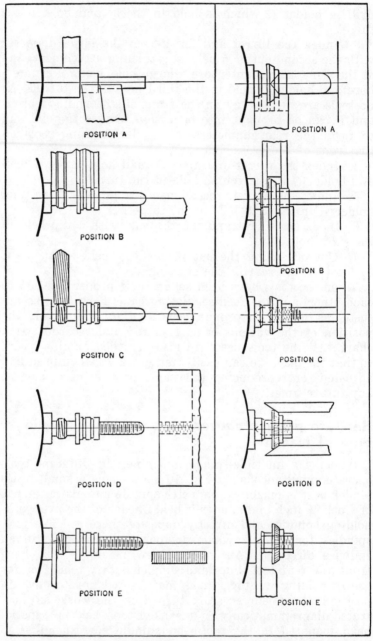

POSITION A

POSITION A

POSITION B

POSITION B

POSITION C

POSITION C

POSITION D

POSITION D

POSITION E

POSITION E

Fig. 10. Successive Operations   Fig. 11. Successive Operations
in Producing Part Shown at E   in Producing Part Shown at E

position *A*. When the work has been indexed into position *B*, a circular forming cutter on the rear arm is swung forward to turn and form the surfaces as shown, while the projecting end of the work is pointed and held rigidly by a combination tool and support, mounted in the tool-head spindle of position *B*. A thread-rolling tool on the rear slide is advanced to produce the thread on the left-hand end, after the work reaches position *C*, and at the same time a cutter in the tool-head spindle advances to counterbore the right-hand shoulder. In position *D* the long thread on the right-hand end of the piece is cut by means of a self-opening die-head mounted on the tool-head spindle for this position. Finally, when the piece reaches position *E*, the face of the right-hand shoulder is knurled by a knurling roll mounted on the tool-head spindle, and then the part is cut off by a tool mounted on the front tool-arm. A finished part is cut from the end of the bar every 3 seconds.

In what order should operations be performed on an automatic screw machine?

The successive order of operations must be varied to suit the shape and character of the work. In general, the main turning or other operations are performed first, and these are followed by whatever additional operations may be required. Determining the exact order and the types of tools to use requires expert knowledge of screw machine practice. The shape of the work is the chief factor in establishing the successive applications of different tools but the degree of accuracy necessary may have a bearing upon the types of tools used.

The production of the brass piece shown in Fig. 11 will be used as another example. First, the projecting end of the work is centered by a drill held in a combination stock-stop and drill-holder, which is mounted on the corresponding tool-head spindle. Simultaneously, a forming cutter on the front cross-slide forms seven different surfaces. In position *B*, the piece is drilled the entire length by means of a drill held in the tool-head spindle, and at the same time a sizing form cutter swings forward and sizes all turned and faced surfaces. This tool is provided with a roller which backs up the work on the rear side.

When the piece reaches position C, the end is tapped, and in position D, a beveled surface is knurled by means of rolls attached to the opposing tool-head spindle. Finally, in position E, the part is cut off by a tool mounted on the front tool-arm, and while this cutting-off tool is operating, the projecting end of the part is gripped in the collet of a transferring spider. This spider carries it to the front of the machine where a slot (not shown) is formed by the milling cutter of a slotting attachment. This brass piece is made in 3 seconds.

When screw machine parts are made from bars or rods, are round shapes always used?

Rods or bars of round cross-section are generally used, but hexagonal or other forms may be preferable in certain cases, as, for example, when some of the original bar forms part of the finished piece so that a hexagonal or other section is obtained without machining. The chuck which holds the bar must conform to its shape. Fig. 12 shows how a brass bar of rectangular shape is utilized. This bar, which is 7/16 inch wide and 0.234 inch thick, has a small shank that is off center; hence, the bar is held in a special form of chuck and off center. When the stock reaches position A, part of the material that is to be cut down to form the shank has already been removed by tools that operated while the preceding piece was being produced. In position A, a hollow mill attached to the corresponding tool-head spindle advances and rough-turns the shank to a diameter of $\frac{1}{8}$ inch. Another hollow mill attached to the tool-head spindle of position B finish-turns the shank to the outside diameter of a section that is to be threaded later, while a circular forming cutter on the rear cross-slide cuts down the stock on the opposite side of the head to start making the shank of the next piece. The second hollow mill is held in a floating holder.

In position C, the corresponding tool-head spindle is provided with a bushing that slips over the work shank as the tool-spindle advances, so as to support the part during the operation. A pointing tool, also mounted on this tool-head spindle, reduces the diameter in front of the portion to the right of the supporting bushing. At the same time, a circu-

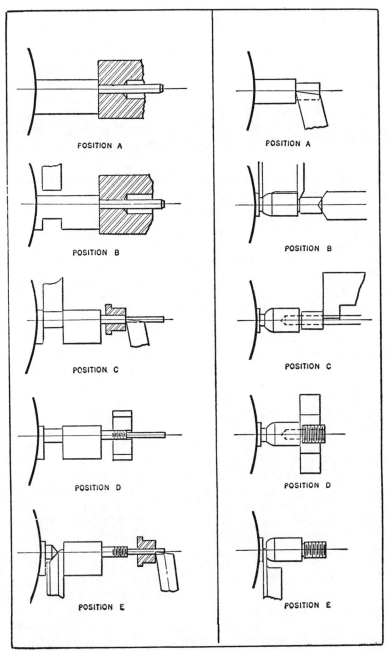

FOSITION A

POSITION A

POSITION B

POSITION B

POSITION C

POSITION C

POSITION D

POSITION D

POSITION E

POSITION E

Fig. 12. Successive Operations In Producing Part Shown at E

Fig. 13. Successive Operations In Producing Part Shown at E

lar forming cutter on the rear tool-arm further reduces the stock on the opposite side of the head to continue making the shank of the next piece. The thread of the shank is cut by a die-head mounted on the tool-head spindle opposite position *D*. In position *E*, the end of the shank is pointed by a tool in the tool-head spindle, while the projecting end of the work is again supported by a bushing, and the part is cut off by a tool mounted on the front tool-arm. This piece is produced at an average rate of 4 seconds.

Why are automatic screw machines equipped with special attachments for some classes of work?

The use of special attachments often makes it possible to finish a part which otherwise would require a second operation on some other machine. For example, one type of attachment is used for milling screwdriver slots across the heads of screws. After the screw is separated from the bar, it is transferred to the slotting attachment. Another type of attachment is used for drilling one or more holes radially through such parts as binding posts. A rear-end threading attachment is designed to thread the rear or cut off ends of pieces. A burring attachment may be used for light operations of countersinking or burring on the cut-off end, and various other attachments are applied to automatic screw machines.

Fig. 13 shows the sequence of the operations on a part which, after being cut off, is transferred automatically to a slotting attachment for milling a slot across the cut-off end. In position *A*, the outer end is turned down by a box-tool. After indexing to position *B*, the projecting end of the work is centered by a drill mounted in the tool-head spindle, while the round head of the large end and a recess at the left end of the thread are produced by a circular forming cutter mounted on the rear cross-slide. In position *C*, a hole is drilled through the shank and the end of the shank is faced. The thread is cut by employing a die-head on the tool-head spindle at position *D*. In position *E*, the piece is cut off by a tool mounted on the front tool-arm, but before this step is completed, the part is gripped in one cf the collets of a transfer spider which carries the cut-off piece to a slotting attachment on the front of the machine for milling the slot to produce a fork-shaped end. The time for producing this piece is 4 seconds.

When is a machine tool truly automatic?

The term "automatic," as applied by manufacturers to various classes of machine tools, does not always have the same meaning, and a machine which one manufacturer classifies as automatic would be considered semi-automatic by another. For instance, some machines which are designed to perform a certain cycle of operations, but are not capable of presenting unfinished parts to be operated upon to the tools, may be referred to as automatic machines. While such a machine is automatic or self-moving in that it controls the movements of the cutting tools, the attention of an operator is required every time a part is finished, so that such a machine is really semi-automatic. There are other types of machines which not only control all the movements of the cutting tools, but are equipped with work-feeding mechanisms so that, when one part has been finished, other duplicate parts may be produced automatically. The operation of such a machine is continuous until it needs to be supplied with raw material, which may either be in the form of bar stock, or separate castings or forgings, when a magazine feeding attachment is used. A machine of this type is automatic in the sense that it repeatedly performs all of the necessary operations, which include ejecting the finished work and presenting a new piece or length of stock to the tool. When a machine is capable of automatically producing duplicate parts repeatedly, it is universally referred to as automatic, whereas, if it simply performs a complete cycle of machining operations, but requires the attention of an operator each time a part is finished, it may be considered automatic by some, and semi-automatic by others. In some cases, a machine of the latter class is termed "automatic," while one that is capable of continuous operation is known as a "fully automatic." The term "automatic" is often used as a noun to indicate any kind of automatic turning machine, especially a screw machine or automatic chucking and turning machine of the turret lathe class. There are many different types of automatic turning machines.

Vertical Boring and Turning Machines

All the different types of turning machines now in use originated from the lathe. Many of these machine tools, however, do not resemble the lathe because, in the process of evolution, there have been many changes made in order to develop turning machines for handling certain classes of work to the best advantage. The vertical boring and turning machine or "mill" belongs to the lathe family, and is very useful for work within its range.

What are the chief features of a vertical boring and turning machine?

This type of machine tool, commonly referred to as a "boring mill," has a circular table which revolves about a vertical axis so that the work-holding surface is horizontal, thus making it comparatively easy to place in position and hold large circular castings such as flywheels, cast-iron covers, etc. This type of machine, in many respects, is like a lathe placed in a vertical position, the table of the mill corresponding to the faceplate or chuck of the lathe and the tool-head to the lathe carriage.

The part to be machined is held to the table either by clamps or in chuck jaws attached to the table. Special fixtures are also used. When the machine is in operation, the table revolves and the turning or boring tools remain stationary, except for the feeding movement. Very often more than one tool is used at a time (see Figs. 1 and 2). Each tool-head (consisting of a saddle and tool-bar) can be moved horizontally along cross-rail, and the tool-bars have a vertical feeding movement and angular adjustment. The feeding movements can be effected either by hand or power.

When a surface is turned parallel to the work table, the entire tool-head moves horizontally along the cross-rail (see right-hand tool in Fig. 2), but when a cylindrical sur-

Fig. 1. Turning Rim and Hub of Flywheel on Vertical
Boring and Turning Machine

Fig. 2. Turning Cast-steel Brake-drum on Vertical
Boring and Turning Machine

face is turned, the tool-bar moves vertically (see left-hand tool).

Vertical boring mills of medium and large sizes are equipped with two tool-heads, as shown, because a great deal of work done on a machine of this type can have two surfaces operated upon simultaneously. On the other hand, small mills have a single head, and ordinarily the tool-slide, instead of having a single tool-block, carries a turret in which different tools can be mounted. These tools are shifted to the working position as they are needed, by indexing the turret the same as on a regular turret lathe. Frequently, all the tools for machining a part can be held in the turret, so that little time is required for changing from one tool to the next. Some large machines equipped with two tool-heads have a turret on one head instead of the regular tool-block (see Fig. 1). The machine shown in Fig. 1 also has a side head which frequently can be used to advantage.

When both lathe and boring mill can be used in turning a part, what governs the selection?

Much of the work done by a vertical mill could also be machined in a lathe of equal size, but the former is more efficient for certain classes of work, especially when it is easier to clamp heavy parts to a horizontal table than to the vertical surface of a lathe faceplate. This advantage in mounting and clamping is especially true of the heavy parts for which the boring mill is principally used. The vertical boring and turning mill is designed for work which, generally speaking, is quite large in diameter in proportion to the width or height. The work varies greatly, especially in regard to its diameter, so that boring mills are built in a large range of sizes. The small and medium sizes will swing work varying from about 30 inches to 6 or 7 feet in diameter, whereas large machines, such as are used for turning very large flywheels, sheaves, etc., have a swing of 16 or 20 feet, and larger sizes are used in some shops. The size of a vertical boring and turning mill, like any other machine tool, should be somewhat in proportion to the size of the work for which it is intended, as a very large machine is unwieldy and, therefore, inefficient for machining comparatively small parts.

How are castings held on the table of a turning and boring mill?

There are three general methods of holding work to the table of a boring mill; namely, by the use of chucks, by ordinary bolts and clamps, or in special fixtures. When chucks are built into the table and have both universal and independent adjustments for the jaws, they can be used to advantage for holding castings that are either round or irregular in shape. The universal adjustment is used for cylindrical parts, such as disks, flywheels, gear blanks, etc., and the independent adjustment, for castings of irregular shape. Chucks which have either an independent or universal movement for the jaws are known as a "combination" type and usually have three jaws. There is also a four-jaw type which has the independent adjustment only. This style is preferable for work that is not cylindrical and which must be held very securely. Chuck jaws that do not form a part of the machine table, but are bolted to it in the required position, are also employed extensively (see Fig. 2).

Occasionally it is preferable to clamp a part directly to the table. This may be desirable because of the shape and size of the work, or because it is necessary to hold a previously machined surface directly against the table in order to secure greater accuracy. Sometimes a casting is held in the chuck for turning one side, and then the finished side is clamped against the table for turning the opposite side. Parts which are to be machined in large quantities are often held in special fixtures. This method is employed when it enables the work to be set up more quickly and, perhaps, more accurately than would be possible if regular clamps or chuck jaws were used.

In grinding tools for vertical boring and turning mills, what principles govern the shapes used?

The same principles that apply to lathe tools. The cutting end must have clearance, and the face against which the chips bear should have rake to increase the cutting efficiency. Rather short stocky tools generally are used on vertical boring and turning mills, to resist the heavy roughing cuts, especially when turning large castings. The set of turning tools shown in Fig. 3 can be used for a wide variety of ordinary turning operations. When a great many duplicate parts are to be machined, special tool equipment can often be used to advantage, but the form of this equipment depends upon the character of the work. The tool shown at A is a right-hand, roughing tool, and a left-hand tool of the same type is shown at B. Tool C is an offset or bent, left-hand round nose for roughing, and D is a right-hand offset roughing tool. A straight round nose is shown at E. Tool F has a flat, broad cutting edge and is used for finishing with coarse feeds. Left- and right-hand finishing tools of the offset type are shown at G and H, respectively. Tool I has a square end and is used for cutting grooves. Right- and left-hand parting tools are shown at J and K, and tool L is a form frequently used for rounding corners.

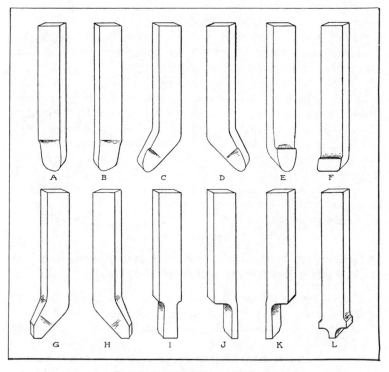

Fig. 3. Set of Boring-mill Tools

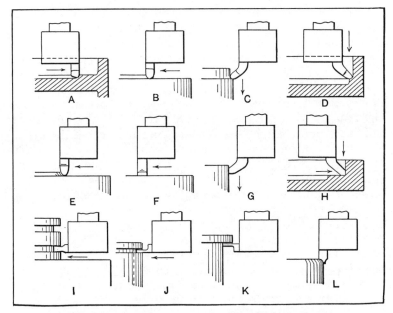

Fig. 4. Diagrams Illustrating Use of Different Forms of Tools

How are different types of tools applied to vertical boring mill operations?

The diagrams in Fig. 4 show, in a general way, how each of the tools illustrated in Fig. 3 are used, and correspond-ing tools are marked by the same reference letters in both of these illustrations. The right- and left-hand roughing tools A and B are for taking deep roughing cuts. One feeds away from the center of the table, or to the right (when held in the right-hand tool-block) and the other tool is ground to feed in the opposite direction. Ordinarily, when turning plain flat surfaces, the cut is started at the outside and the tool feeds toward the center, as at B, although it is some-times more convenient to feed in the opposite direction, as at A, especially when there is a rim or other projecting part at the outside edge. The tool shown at A could also be used for turning cylindrical surfaces, by clamping it in a hori-zontal position across the bottom of the tool-block. The feeding movement would then be downward or at right-angles to the work table.

The offset round-nose tools C and D are for turning exterior or interior cylinder surfaces. The shank of this tool is clamped in the tool-block in a vertical position and as the bent end extends below the tool-block, it can be fed down close to a shoulder. The straight type shown at E is commonly used for turning steel or iron, and when the point is drawn out narrower, it is also used for brass, although the front is then ground without rake. Tool F is for light finishing cuts and broad feeds. The amount of feed per revolution of the work should always be less than the width of the cutting edge as otherwise ridges will be left on the turned surface. The offset tools G and H are for finishing exterior and interior cylindrical surfaces. These tools also have both vertical and horizontal cutting edges and are sometimes used for first finishing a cylindrical and then a horizontal surface, or vice versa. Tool I is adapted to such work as cutting packing-ring grooves in engine pistons, forming square or rectangular grooves, and similar work. The parting tools J and K can also be used for forming narrow grooves or for cutting off rings, etc. The sketch K indicates how a tool of this kind might be used for squaring a corner under a shoulder. Tool L is frequently used on boring mills for rounding the corners of flywheel rims, in order to give them a more finished appearance. It has two cutting edges so that either side can be used as when rounding the inner and outer corners of a rim. These are typical turning operations.

In boring holes on a vertical type of mill, what tools are used?

There are several methods of machining holes when using a vertical boring mill. Ordinarily, small holes are cored in castings and it is simply necessary to finish the rough surface to the required diameter. Some of the tools used for boring and finishing comparatively small holes are shown in Fig. 5. Sketch A shows a boring tool consisting of a cutter c inserted in a shank, which, in turn, is held in the tool slide, or in a turret attached to the tool slide. The tool shown at B is a four-lipped drill which is used for drilling cored holes preparatory to finishing by a cutter or reamer. The tool illustrated at C has a double-ended flat cutter c.

which cuts on both sides. These cutters are often made in
sets for boring duplicate parts. Ordinarily, there are two
cutters in a set, one being used for roughing and the other
for finishing. The cutter passes through a rectangular slot
in the bar and this particular style is centrally located by
shoulders *s*, and is held by a taper pin *p*. Some cutter bars
have an extension end, or "pilot" as it is called, which
passes through a close-fitting bushing in the table to steady
the bar. Sketch *D* shows a finishing reamer. This tool takes
a very light cut and is intended to finish holes that have
been previously bored close to the required size. Sometimes
a flat cutter *C* is used for roughing and a reamer for finishing. The reamer is especially desirable for interchangeable
work, when all holes must have a smooth finish and be of

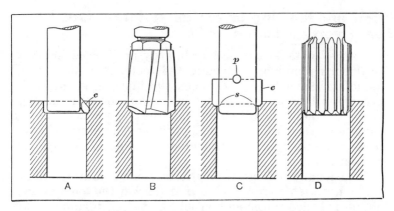

Fig. 5. Tools for Boring and Reaming Holes

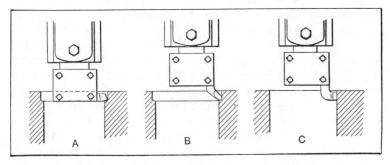

Fig. 6. Boring with Regular Turning Tools

the same diameter. When a reamer is held rigidly to a turret or tool-slide, it is liable to produce a hole that is either tapering or larger than the reamer diameter. To prevent this, the reamer should be held in a "floating" holder which, by means of a slight adjustment, allows the reamer to align itself with the hole. There are several methods of securing this "floating" movement. Large holes or interior cylindrical surfaces are bored by tools held in the regular tool-head. The tool is sometimes clamped in a horizontal position as shown at A, Fig. 6, or a bent type is used as at B. Cast iron is usually finished by a broad flat tool as at C, the same as when turning exterior surfaces. Obviously a hole that is bored in this way must be large enough to admit the tool-block.

How are tapering or conical surfaces turned on a vertical boring mill?

Conical or taper surfaces ordinarily are turned in a vertical boring mill by swiveling the tool-bar to the proper angle as shown in Fig. 7. When the taper is given in degrees, the tool-bar can be set by graduations on the edge of the circular base B, which show the angle a to which the bar is swiveled from a vertical position. The vertical power feed can be used for taper turning the same as for cylindrical work.

Occasionally it is necessary to machine a conical surface which has such a large included angle that the tool-bar cannot be swiveled far enough around to permit turning by the method illustrated in Fig. 7. Another method, which is sometimes resorted to for work of this class, is to use the combined vertical and horizontal feeds. (If the boring mill has the usual arrangement of one lever on the end of the cross-rail which selects either the bar or saddle feed, this prevents the engagement of both feeds at the same time, but the selecting lever can be disconnected and both feed clutches can be engaged by hand.)

The problem is to determine the angle x for the tool-slide (see Fig. 8) in order to turn to a given angle a.

Rule 1.—For equal rates of horizontal and vertical feed, the difference between 90 degrees and twice the angle a, equals angle x.

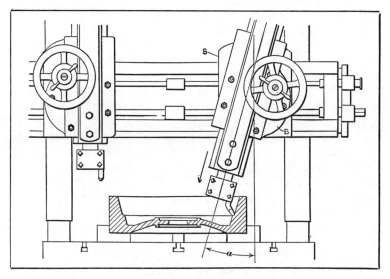

Fig. 7. Turning a Taper or Conical Surface by Inclining Tool-slide

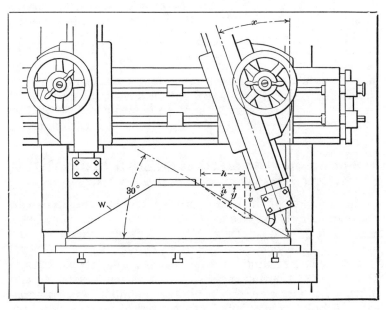

Fig. 8. Turning a Conical Surface by Using the Combined
Vertical and Horizontal Feeds

Example.—The required angle a is 32 degrees.

Angle $x = 90 - 64 = 26$ degrees.

When twice the required angle a is less than 90 degrees, the lower end of the bar is set to the right of its vertical position, and when twice the angle is greater than 90 degrees, the bar is set to the left.

Rule 2.—If the horizontal and vertical feeds are unequal, multiply the sine of angle a (Fig. 8) by the rate of horizontal feed movement h and divide product by the rate of vertical feed movement v, thus obtaining the sine of an angle. Find the angle equivalent to this sine, add it to angle a. The difference between the total angle thus obtained, and 90 degrees, equals the angle x for the tool-slide.

Example.—Angle a is 30 degrees. Horizontal feed rate is $\frac{1}{4}$ inch; vertical feed rate is 3/16 inch. Find angle x.

The sine of 30 degrees is 0.5; then $\dfrac{0.5 \times \dfrac{1}{4}}{\dfrac{3}{16}} = 0.6666$

which is the sine of 41 degrees 49 minutes, and angle x $= 90° - (30° + 41° 49') = 18$ degrees 11 minutes. Hence, to turn the casting to angle a in a boring mill having the horizontal and vertical feeds given, the tool-head would be set over from the vertical about 18 1/6 degrees. If the required angle a were greater than angle y obtained from the combined feeds with the tool-bar in a vertical position, it would then be necessary to swing the lower end of the bar to the left rather than to the right of a vertical plane.

In boring very large cylinders, is a horizontal or vertical type of machine preferable?

If the length of the bore is rather long as compared with the diameter, it may be necessary to use a horizontal machine, but if the length of the bore is not excessive, the vertical type of boring mill is often employed. As a general rule, very large cylinders, while being bored, should preferably be in the position they will occupy when assembled and in use. For instance, if a very large cylinder is to be vertical, it should be bored while in a vertical position, because if a horizontal boring machine is used, the cylinder may spring slightly to an oval shape while being bored, so that it will not be true after it is finished and placed in a vertical position. In setting a cylinder casting, it should be set true by the outside of the flange or by the outside of the cylinder body, so that the walls of the finished cylinder will be of uniform thickness. The finishing cut should also be a continuous one, because if the machine is stopped, even for a short time, the tool cools somewhat, and as the result of contraction a ridge will be left in the bore.

General Practice in Drilling and Reaming Holes

In the construction of practically all machinery, a great many holes must be drilled, owing to the extensive use of bolts, machine screws, and studs for holding the various parts together. The drilling machines or "drill presses," as they are often called, which are used for drilling these holes, are made in many different types, designed for handling different classes of work to the best advantage, and the various types are also built in a great variety of sizes, as the most efficient results can be obtained with a machine that is neither too small nor too large and unwieldy for the work which it performs. This section includes certain other operations which frequently are done on a drilling machine, such as counterboring and reaming. These operations are also performed on other types of machines such as lathes, turret lathes, boring mills, etc.

What are the common types of drilling machines?

Drilling machines are classified in various ways. The *upright drilling machine* is one type that is extensively used. As the name indicates, the general design of the machine is vertical, and the drill spindle is in a vertical position. All drilling machines, however, which have vertical spindles and are arranged vertically, are not classified as upright drills.

Radial Drilling Machine.—This is another very common design. It has a vertical spindle which is carried by an arm that may be swiveled about a vertical column. The distinguishing feature of this machine, however, is the radial adjustment of the arm about the column, which adjustment, in conjunction with the traversing motion of the drill-spindle head along the arm, makes it possible to readily locate the drill in any position within the range of the machine, which is a decided advantage when drilling heavy parts that can not be shifted easily. Machines of this class, therefore, are said to be of the radial type, because the radial or swiveling adjustment of the arm is the characteristic feature.

Sensitive Drill.—This is another vertical or upright design, but it is classified as sensitive because it is a comparatively small high-speed machine of light construction, which possesses sensitive qualities which are of value in drilling delicate work.

Multiple-spindle Type.—This type, which is built in both vertical and horizontal designs, is given a name that is self-explanatory. Some drilling machines equipped with multiple spindles are known as *gang drills*. The term *"gang drill"* is generally applied to a vertical design practically consisting of several machines combined in one unit, and with the spindles all in the same vertical plane. Machines of this general design are also referred to as multiple-spindle types, by some manufacturers. Drilling machines, however, having spindles which are arranged in a group so that they may be adjusted according to the respective positions of the holes, whether in a straight line, on a circle, or irregular as to location, are especially known as multiple-spindle types.

Drilling machines having more than one spindle may be named according to the number of spindles, as, for example, a four-spindle sensitive drilling machine, etc. In other cases, a special design of machine having several spindles is classified according to the work for which it is intended, as, for instance, a staybolt drilling machine, a locomotive frame drilling machine, a rail drilling machine, etc. Very heavy and powerful drilling machines of the vertical or upright type are also referred to as "high-duty" or "heavy-duty" type drilling machines, because they are capable of very rapid drilling.

Turret Type.—Some drilling machines are equipped with a turret which carries the necessary tools, and is indexed to locate these tools in the working position the same as the turret of a turret lathe. There are two general types of these machines: one has a turret which revolves about a horizontal axis with the tools in a vertical plane, and the other, a turret which revolves about a vertical axis. Machines of this type are adapted to work requiring successive operations, such as drilling, reaming, counterboring, etc.

What types of drills are used for drilling metals?

The most common type of drill for ordinary drilling in solid metal is the well-known twist drill. These drills, as designed for drilling in solid metal, are provided with two grooves or flutes as shown at *A*, Fig. 1. When a drilled,

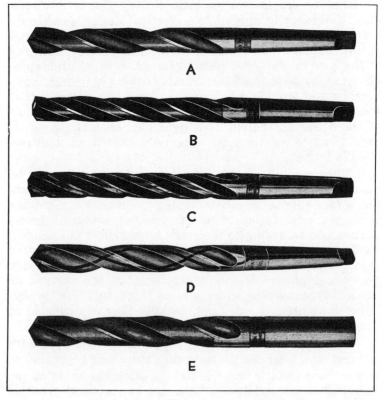

Fig. 1. Common Types of Twist Drills

cored or punched hole must be enlarged, a three-groove drill *B* or a four-groove drill *C* is commonly used. These three- and four-groove drills have flat ends and cannot be used for drilling in solid metal.

In drilling rather deep holes, it may be difficult to supply the point of the drill with the required amount of oil or cutting compound due to the tendency of the chips to carry the fluid back with them before it reaches the bottom of the hole. To overcome this difficulty, oil-hole drills may be used. This type, shown at *D*, is provided with internal holes or ducts through which the cutting fluid can be carried right to the drill point. The fluid and chips escape through the flutes of the drill in the usual manner.

What standard taper has been adopted for drill shanks?

The shank of a drill, or that part which is held in a socket, spindle or chuck, may be either straight (cylindrical) or tapered. If the shank is tapered, it conforms to the Morse standard. Drills *A*, *B*, *C* and *D*, Fig. 1, have taper shanks, and drill *E* a straight shank.

Morse standard tapers include eight different sizes ranging from No. 0 to 7. Five or six of these sizes are used for a range of taper shank drill diameters varying from ⅛ inch to 3 or 3½ inches, which is the usual commercial range. This means that each taper number includes quite a range of diameters. For example, one prominent twist drill manufacturer uses a No. 1 Morse taper for drill diameters ranging from ⅛ to 15/32 inch, inclusive; a No. 2 taper for diameters from 31/64 to 25/32 inch; a No. 3 taper for diameters from 51/64 to 1 1/16 inches; a No. 4 taper for diameters from 1 5/64 to 1 1/2 inches; a No. 5 taper for diameters from 1 33/64 to 3 inches; and a No. 6 taper for diameters from 3 1/16 to 3 1/2 inches.

In specifying a drill size, is the diameter always given?

There are three methods of designating the sizes of twist drills. In many cases, the actual diameter is given. Numbers are used to represent a certain range of small drill sizes, and a range of somewhat larger diameters is indicated by the letters of the alphabet. (See accompanying tables for the sizes equivalent to different numbers or letters.)

Twist drills in fractional sizes are made in a large range of sizes. To illustrate, one prominent manufacturer makes high-speed twist drills in sizes from ⅛ to 1¾ inches varying by 64ths, and by 32nds up to 2¼ inches and then by

Decimal Equivalents of Letter Size Drills

Letter	Size of Drill in Inches	Letter	Size of Drill in Inches	Letter	Size of Drill in Inches	Letter	Size of Drill in Inches
Z	0.413	S	0.348	L	0.290	E	0.250
Y	0.404	R	0.339	K	0.281	D	0.246
X	0.397	Q	0.332	J	0.277	C	0.242
W	0.386	P	0.323	I	0.272	B	0.238
V	0.377	O	0.316	H	0.266	A	0.234
U	0.368	N	0.302	G	0.261	....	......
T	0.358	M	0.295	F	0.257	....	......

Twist Drill and Steel Wire Gage
(Manufacturers' Standard)

No.	Size of Drill in Inches	No.	Size of Drill in Inches	No.	Size of Drill in Inches	No.	Size of Drill in Inches
1	0.2280	21	0.1590	41	0.0960	61	0.0390
2	0.2210	22	0.1570	42	0.0935	62	0.0380
3	0.2130	23	0.1540	43	0.0890	63	0.0370
4	0.2090	24	0.1520	44	0.0860	64	0.0360
5	0.2055	25	0.1495	45	0.0820	65	0.0350
6	0.2040	26	0.1470	46	0.0810	66	0.0330
7	0.2010	27	0.1440	47	0.0785	67	0.0320
8	0.1990	28	0.1405	48	0.0760	68	0.0310
9	0.1960	29	0.1360	49	0.0730	69	0.0292
10	0.1935	30	0.1285	50	0.0700	70	0.0280
11	0.1910	31	0.1200	51	0.0670	71	0.0260
12	0.1890	32	0.1160	52	0.0635	72	0.0250
13	0.1850	33	0.1130	53	0.0595	73	0.0240
14	0.1820	34	0.1110	54	0.0550	74	0.0225
15	0.1800	35	0.1100	55	0.0520	75	0.0210
16	0.1770	36	0.1065	56	0.0465	76	0.0200
17	0.1730	37	0.1040	57	0.0430	77	0.0180
18	0.1695	38	0.1015	58	0.0420	78	0.0160
19	0.1660	39	0.0995	59	0.0410	79	0.0145
20	0.1610	40	0.0980	60	0.0400	80	0.0135

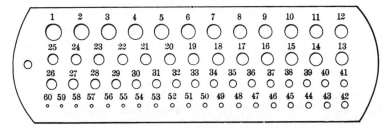

Fig. 2. Twist Drill and Steel Wire Gage

16ths up to 3½ inches. In the 26 letter size drills, size A is the smallest and represents a diameter of 0.234 inch. The largest size Z is equivalent to a diameter of 0.413 inch and the difference between consecutive sizes varies from 0.004 to 0.014 inch. In the numbered sizes, the No. 1 size equivalent to a diameter of 0.228 inch is the largest, and the No. 80 size equivalent to a diameter of 0.0135 inch is the smallest. One type of gage for measuring drills with numbered sizes has the number of the drill indicated by the number of the hole in which the drill fits. (Fig. 2.) The difference between the diameters of consecutive sizes represented by this gage only varies from 0.001 to 0.008 inch, so that almost any diameter between the smallest and largest size can be obtained. The decimal equivalents for each number are stamped on the back of the gage shown. Another common form of gage, known as the *jobbers' drill gage,* has a series of holes which vary in diameter from 1/16 to ½ inch, the diameters increasing successively by sixty-fourths. The sizes of the different holes are expressed by common fractions which are stamped on the gage.

Are straight shank twist drills made in the same sizes as taper shank drills?

There are, in general use, four different series of straight shank drills. One series is known as the *taper length* because these straight shank drills have the same total length as the taper shank drills. These straight shank sizes are the same as the taper shank sizes but the range of diameters is somewhat less and usually is from ⅛ to 2 inches.

Straight shank twist drills in the *jobbers length,* or short length, are a small series ranging from 1/64 or 1/32 up to ½ inch diameter. Straight shank twist drills are also made to conform to both the wire gage sizes and the letter sizes (see accompanying table). The letter sizes are also made with taper shanks.

How are drills held in the machine spindle?

There are three general methods of holding drills in the spindles of drilling machines and other tools that are used for drilling: 1. By inserting the drill shank directly into a hole in the machine spindle. 2. By inserting the drill shank in a socket or sleeve which is held by the drill spindle. 3. By using some form of drill chuck. Most drills have standard taper shanks and a flat tang at the end so that they may be driven either by the first or second method referred to. The size of the shank is the same on all drills up to a certain diameter, and then a larger shank is used for another range of sizes, and so on. If a drill is too small to permit inserting it directly in the spindle, a socket or sleeve is used which fits the spindle and has a taper hole corresponding to the size of the drill shank. The drill is caused to rotate with the spindle or socket, principally by the friction between the shank and the socket, and any slipping is prevented by a flat end or tang on the shank which engages a cross-slot at the end of the taper hole.

When are chucks used for holding drills?

Most drills, excepting small sizes, are driven by the engagement of the shank either with some form of socket or by insertion directly into the spindle. Drill chucks are used very extensively, especially for small drills. Ordinary drill chucks are adjustable so that one chuck may be used for holding any size of drill within the minimum and maximum capacity of the chuck. The use of a drill chuck is preferable, in many cases, to the socket method of holding drills. because when sockets are employed there must be one for each different size of drill shank. The drills used in chucks ordinarily have straight shanks instead of the taper form, although there is a type of chuck which may be used for holding either the straight or taper shank. There is an-

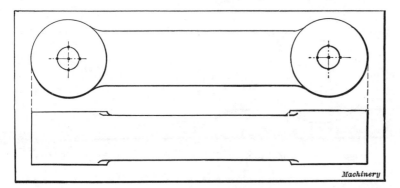

Fig. 3. Example of Drill-press Work

other class of drill chucks which is designed to enable drills, taps, and other tools to be quickly inserted or removed when drilling or tapping duplicate parts in quantity, without stopping the machine spindle. Manufacturers sometimes designate chucks of this class as the "automatic" type.

In drilling holes, how is the spacing or location controlled?

In machine-building practice, holes ordinarily must be located in certain positions or at given center distances within limits of accuracy which may vary considerably, depending upon the class of work. The simplest drilling job is that of drilling a single hole which need not be located accurately. A center punch mark may form a starting point for the drill and the hole is drilled approximately concentric with this punch mark. A slightly more difficult job would be to drill two holes at a given center-to-center distance within, possibly, 1/32 or 1/64 inch. The steel link shown in Fig. 3 is an example. If only one or possibly several of these links require drilling, the holes would first be laid out by making light punch marks at the required center distance; then dividers are used to draw circles slightly larger than the holes to be drilled. These circles serve as a guide in drilling. When the drill begins to cut, the location of the hole with reference to the scribed circle should be noted. If the hole starts off center, as at A, Fig. 4, a groove should be cut down that side which is farthest from

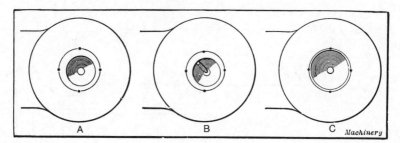

Fig. 4. Method of Starting Drill Concentric with Scribed Circle

the circle (see sketch *B*) by using a gouge and hammer, the proper depth of this groove depending on the amount that the hole is off center. The groove causes the drill to shift its position toward the grooved side. This operation is repeated, if necessary, so that the drill will finally be concentric with the circle (as at *C*) just before it begins to cut to the full diameter.

What are drill jigs and why are they used?

The drilling of holes by first laying them out as described in the preceding paragraph would be objectionable especially if a large number of duplicate parts had to be drilled accurately, as there is likely to be more or less variation in the location of the holes, and a certain amount of time is required for laying out these holes preparatory to drilling. The operator, in starting the drill, must also be careful to make it cut concentric with the scribed circle, which requires extra time, and there will necessarily be more or less variation. To overcome these objections, jigs are almost universally used for holding the work and guiding the drill or drills on a multiple type of machine, in drilling duplicate parts, especially when large quantities are required. As the number of differently shaped pieces which make up a single machine is often very large, and as most parts require more or less drilling, jigs are made in an almost endless variety of sizes and forms. The shape, in any case, depends upon the form of the work for which the jig is intended and also on the location of the holes to be drilled. A jig in its simplest form is merely a plate containing holes located so as to conform to the positions required for the drilled holes. Such a jig may simply be placed over the part to be drilled. It is located by some finished surface if possible and the drill is fed down through the different holes.

Fig. 5 shows how a ring-shaped jig is used for drilling equally spaced holes in a pipe fitting. The jig fits over an annular projection or raised face on the fitting and it is held by an ordinary clamp. This is one of the simplest types of jigs. Incidentally, the machine shown in Fig. 5 is a radial type.

A jig of simple design, for drilling a hole having two diameters, through the center of a steel ball, is shown in Fig. 6. The work, which is shown enlarged at *A*, is inserted while the cover is thrown back as indicated by the dotted lines. The cover is then closed and tightened by the cam-latch *D*, and the large part of the hole is drilled with the jig in the position shown. The jig is then turned over and a smaller drill of the correct size is fed through guide bushing *B* on the opposite side. The depth of the large hole

Fig. 5. Drilling Flange Holes in a Pipe Elbow with a Jig Plate Clamped to the Elbow Flange, Using Machine of Radial Type

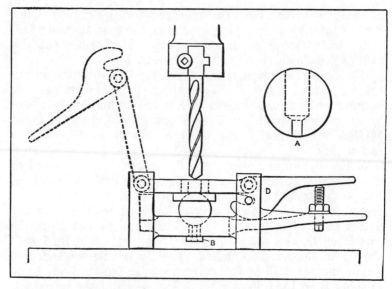

Fig. 6. Box Jig for Drilling Ball Shown Enlarged at A

could be gaged for each ball drilled, by feeding the drill
spindle down to a certain position as shown by graduation
or other marks, but if the spindle has an adjustable stop,
this should be used. The work is located in line with the
two guide bushings by spherical seats formed in the jig
body and in the upper bushing, as shown.

Why is the "box" type of jig used so extensively?

When the holes to be drilled are parallel, and especially
if they are in the same plane, a very simple form of flat jig
may be employed, but in many cases parts must be drilled
on different sides, and frequently castings or forgings are
very irregular in shape, so that a jig which is made somewhat in the form of a box and encloses the work is necessary, as it enables the guide bushings to be placed on all
sides and also makes it comparatively easy to locate and
securely clamp the part in the proper position for drilling.
A jig of this type is known as a "box jig." A typical box
jig is shown in Fig. 7. This jig is used for drilling several
holes in the part represented by heavy dot-and-dash lines.

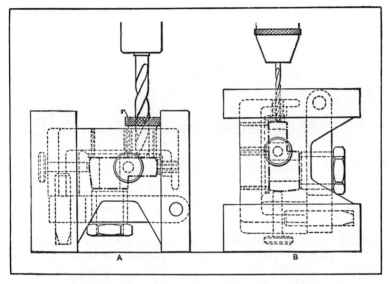

Fig. 7. Box Jig in Two Different Drilling Positions

For the drilling operation illustrated at *A,* the jig is placed with the cover side down, and the drill is guided by a removable bushing *r.* When the drilling is completed, the drill bushings are replaced by reamer bushings and each hole is finished by reaming. A small hole is drilled in the end of the casting by simply placing the jig on end as shown at *B.* This small drill might be in another spindle of a multiple-spindle machine; or a separate machine might be used. Box jigs which have to be placed in more than one position for drilling the different holes are usually provided with feet or extensions, as shown, which are accurately finished to align the guide bushings properly with the drill. These feet extend beyond any clamping screws, bolts, or bushings which may protrude from the sides of the jigs, and provide a solid support. When inserting work in a jig, care should be taken to remove all chips which might have fallen upon those surfaces against which the work is clamped and which determine its location.

The use of a jig not only saves time but also insures accurate and uniform work. As the result of this uniformity, corresponding parts can be drilled so nearly alike that they

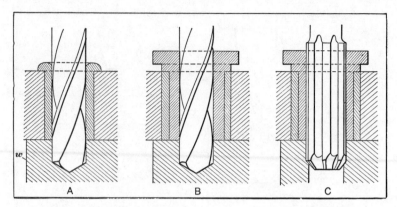

Fig. 8. Fixed and Removable Guide Bushings for Drill Jigs

will interchange, which is, of course, a great aid in assembling a machine and also makes it possible to easily replace a broken member.

Why are jigs provided with bushings of different kinds?

The holes in jigs are ordinarily lined with hardened steel bushings to eliminate wear. These guide bushings fit the drill closely and keep it in the proper position. Some jigs have fixed guide bushings and others removable bushings. A fixed bushing is shown by the sectional view at *A*, Fig. 8, which also indicates how the drill is guided while it is drill-

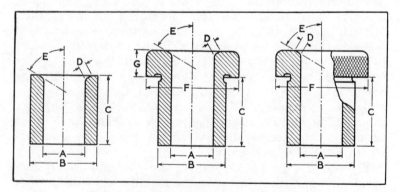

Fig. 9. Standard Forms of Jig Bushings

ing the work w. (The flanged top on this bushing is unnecessary and the flangeless form shown at the left in Fig. 9 is generally used.) Jigs are equipped with removable bushings when drills of a different size are to be used or when the drilled holes are to be finished by reaming. For example, if a hole is to be drilled and reamed, a removable bushing is used that fits the drill, as shown at B, and this is replaced by a bushing that fits the reamer, as shown at C.

Is there a standard for jig bushing dimensions?

The American standard covers the different types of jig bushings in common use. The standard dimensions are represented by the letters in Fig. 9. This standard includes a range of bushing sizes and also the following types of bushings:

Renewable Bushings.—Renewable wearing bushings to guide the tool are for use in liners which in turn are installed in the jig. They are used where the bushing will wear out or become obsolete before the jig or where several bushings are to be interchangeable in one hole. Renewable wearing bushings are divided into two classes, "Fixed" and "Slip." Fixed renewable bushings are installed in the liner with the intention of leaving them in place until worn out. Slip renewable bushings are interchangeable in a given size of liner and, to facilitate removal, they are usually made with a knurled head. (Standard dimensions of the various types of American Standard jig bushings are given in engineering handbooks.)

Press Fit Bushings.—Press fit wearing bushings to guide the tool are for installation directly in the jig without the use of a liner and are employed principally where the bushings are used for short production runs and will not require replacement. They are intended also for short center distances.

Liner Bushings.—Liner bushings are provided with and without heads and are permanently installed in a jig to receive the renewable wearing bushings. They are sometimes called "master bushings."

Jig Plate Thickness.—The American Standard lengths of jig bushings are based on standardized or uniform jig plate thicknesses of 5/16, ½, ¾, 1, 1⅜, and 1¾ inches.

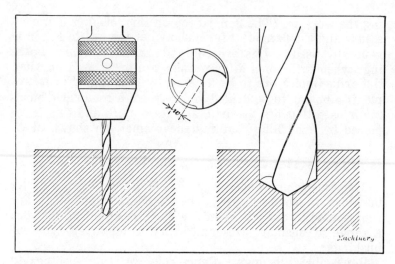

Fig. 10. A Small "Lead Hole" is Sometimes Used to Reduce Feeding
Pressure Required for Large Drill

In drilling large holes, how can the feeding pressure be reduced?

The feeding pressure required for a twist drill of, say, $1\frac{1}{2}$ inches diameter, may vary from 1500 to 3000 pounds, depending upon the kind of steel being drilled and the rate of feeding movement per drill revolution. The pressure can be greatly reduced and the drill be made to cut faster, by first drilling a small "lead hole," as shown in the view to the left, Fig. 10. The diameter of this lead hole should be as large as, or a little larger than, the width w of the drill point, because this point does not have the keenness of the cutting edges and merely scrapes the metal, so that the pressure necessary to force it downward is comparatively great. The lead hole relieves this excessive pressure and permits all the thrust to come directly on the cutting edges of the drill, as indicated by the sectional view to the right. The feeding pressure, in drilling "from the solid," depends partly upon the shape of the drill and thickness of the drill or web.

With the rigid and powerful machines now available, the lead-hole method ordinarily is not required. If the hole is exceptionally large, an approved method is to use two or more drills; the first is an ordinary two-groove drill and this is followed by one or more three- or four-groove drills.

What is the "step-by-step" method of drilling deep holes?

This method (as developed by the Leland-Gifford Co.) involves the use of a hydraulically operated head which automatically feeds the drill to a predetermined depth, withdraws it completely from the hole, and again advances it to a predetermined depth. This cycle is repeated until the hole has been drilled entirely through, or, in the case of a blind hole, to the required depth. With each withdrawal of the drill, the hole is cleared of chips and a copious stream of coolant fills the hole, cooling both tool and work. With this method, drills may be used that have flutes extending only a small fraction of their length and that have thicker web sections than standard drills, therefore possessing greater strength.

In order to analyze what occurs in drilling a deep hole with a continuous feed, let it be assumed that a 3/16-inch hole is to be drilled to a depth of 12 inches in S A E 1045 steel, using an ordinary two-fluted twist drill. With the long slender drill necessary for this operation, which can be supported at one end only, the cutting end is likely to become deflected if excessive end thrust or torsional strain is imposed on it. The drill will then deviate from its true path through the metal or break under the load. End thrusts or torsional strains are likely to be excessive with a continuous feed, because two-fluted drills must be made with a comparatively thin web, to permit the lubricant or coolant to be delivered to the drill point and the chips to escape from the hole. To meet these requirements, the cross-sectional area of the drill must be considerably less than the area of the hole itself. It thus becomes difficult for small-diameter drills to remain rigid under abnormal loads.

In the hydraulic step-by-step method of drilling deep holes, the depth to which the drill is fed into the work with each forward stroke of the hydraulic head is so controlled that the forward movement is completed before excessive thrusts occur and before the hole becomes clogged with

Fig. 11. Drilling Holes Only 0.006 Inch in Diameter through the Nozzle
of Fuel Injectors for Diesel Engines. The Hairlike Drill is
Flat on the Cutting End and is Run at a Speed of
30,000 Revolutions per Minute

chips. Only a small quantity of chips is produced at each forward drill movement, and it is for this reason that drills can be used having flutes extending only a fraction of their total length and with a thicker web than standard drills. The greater drill rigidity and strength provided by the larger cross-sectional area of the fluted end enables the drills to resist heavy thrusts in any direction.

Generally speaking, the practice is to drill to a depth equal to the drill diameter at each step. Thus, for example, in using a ¼-inch drill, stock to a depth of approximately ¼ inch would be removed with each forward stroke of the drill head. Accurate holes and long-life drill points are two important advantages of this controlled method of step-by-step drilling. For example, a 3/16-inch hole can be drilled 7 inches deep through alloy steel, straight within 0.010 inch. The time consumed in advancing and withdrawing the drills is negligible, because, with the hydraulic head used, these movements are speeded up much faster than the feed employed in the actual drilling. This hydraulic method of step-by-step drilling is applicable in the automotive industry for producing long holes of small diameter in crankshafts, connecting-rods, carburetor parts, etc.

How are holes drilled when the diameter is only 0.005 inch?

The atomizer nozzle of Diesel engines require very small holes. In some cases the diameter is only 0.005 or 0.006 inch. In using the machine shown in Fig. 11 the drill is operated on the step drilling principle, which means that it is reciprocated up and down during the operation to free the chips and enable lubricant to be applied until the nozzle section has been completely drilled through. The section of one nozzle is about 3/32 inch thick. The drill is flat on the end instead of being pointed, and has a flute that extends upward from the point for a distance of 7/16 inch. One of these fuel injection nozzles is mounted upon the index-head which is designed for any number of divisions required. Ten holes are generally drilled around a nozzle, the required spacing being readily obtained by means of the index-head. The angularity of the holes with respect to the center of the nozzle varies in different parts. The index-head is therefore of a design that can be accurately tilted into the required angular position. The nozzles are made of steel and are heat-treated after drilling.

The reciprocating movements of the drill are obtained by means of a ratchet mechanism which is driven separately from the main drive, by means of a small motor. The downward feed is obtained through the tension applied by a coil spring. Up-and-down movements of the drill spindle are effected every six seconds. Lubricant is brushed on the drill at each withdrawal from the hole. The drill spindle runs at about 30,000 revolutions per minute.

In another plant where Diesel engine atomizer nozzles are drilled, a speed of 5800 R.P.M. has proved satisfactory for drilling holes 0.010 inch in diameter. The nozzles are made of tough material to withstand the erosive action of the fuel oil under high pressure. Pivot drills are used. This is a flat-type used by jewelers. The fixture has a hinged leaf containing a bushing which is used to guide a prick-punch instead of the drill. This punch fits the bushing closely and it has an accurately ground conical point. By tapping the punch lightly, the location of the hole is marked; then the leaf is swung back so that the operator can see the drilling operation through magnifying glasses.

Why are small drills rotated at very high speeds?

Drills, like other metal-cutting tools, should be rotated as fast as possible without dulling them too quickly. It is evident that a small drill must run at a much higher speed than a large drill in order to obtain the same cutting speed in feet per minute. For example, a 1-inch drill rotating 300 R.P.M. would have about the same cutting speed as a 1/32-inch drill running 10,000 R.P.M. This explains why drilling machines for small hole drilling are designed to operate at very high speeds. The speed range varies according to the minimum and maximum drill sizes that the machine is designed to use; for example the maximum speeds of these machines may range from 5000 or 10,000 R.P.M. up to 30,000 or 40,000 R.P.M. In the manufacture of certain types of dies, carburetors, ejectors, electrical instruments, etc., extremely small holes are required, and one concern makes high-speed steel flat drills ranging in diameter from 0.100 inch down to only 0.002 inch.

How are multiple-spindle drilling machines applied?

Machines equipped with two or more drill spindles may be used (1) for drilling a number of holes simultaneously or (2) for a series of operations which can be performed to better advantage on a machine equipped with a spindle for each operation.

Multiple Drilling.—The arrangement of multiple-spindle machines is varied considerably to suit different kinds of work. Machines for drilling holes simultaneously may be divided into two general classes, namely, those having spindles which remain in the same plane, but can be adjusted for varying the center-to-center distance, and those having spindles which can be grouped in a circular, square, or irregular formation. The first class referred to is used for drilling rows of bolt or rivet holes in plates, etc., and the second type is adapted to the drilling of cylinder flanges, valve flanges or work requiring holes varying both in size and spacing.

Fig. 12 shows an example of multiple drilling. In this particular case, 36 holes are drilled in an airplane engine crankcase but only 9 are drilled simultaneously, the machine being equipped with a nine-spindle head. During the return upward movement, the work fixture is power-indexed to locate the work for drilling the next series of 9 holes. These holes are held to specified center distances within 0.002 inch. To expedite loading, the work fixture is slid on ways to the left-hand end of the machine base through the operation of an air cylinder.

Successive Operations.—A great many parts that have to be drilled require holes of different diameters, and other operations, such as counterboring, reaming, or counter-sinking, are frequently necessary. When work of this class is done in a machine having one spindle, considerable time is wasted in removing one drill and replacing it with a different size or with some other kind of tool. For this reason, drilling machines having several spindles are often used when the work requires a number of successive operations. The advantage of the multiple spindle or "gang" type is that all the different tools necessary can be inserted in the various spindles, and the drilling is done by passing the work from one spindle to the next. By this method, holes of different diameter can be drilled and counterboring or reaming operations performed without changing any tools. Multiple-spindle machines can also be used to advantage for other purposes.

Fig. 12. Drilling Thirty-six Breather Holes, Nine at a Time, in Crankcase Section

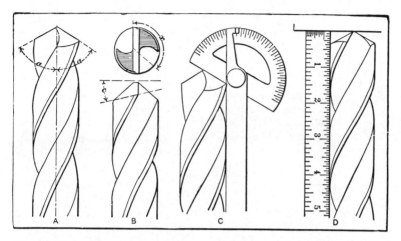

Fig. 13. Views Showing Angles to be Considered when Grinding Drills,
and Methods of Measuring Lip Angle and Clearance

In twist drill grinding, what are the requirements?

The point or cutting end of a drill should be ground carefully because a poorly formed drill affects the quality and
quantity of the work produced. It is difficult to grind drills
theoretically correct by hand, at least in a reasonable length
of time, and special grinders are often used for this purpose. Some shops, however, do not have such grinders, but
if the requirements of a correctly formed drill point are
known, it is possible, with practice, to grind a drill by the
"hand" method. The two cutting edges should incline at
the proper angle a with the axis, as shown at A in Fig. 13;
each edge should have the same inclination and be of the
same length; the angle of clearance c should be sufficient
to permit the drill to cut freely; the clearance should be the
same on both sides and increase toward the point of the drill.

To what angle should a drill point be ground?

As the angle between the cutting edges of a drill is decreased, the pressure required for feeding the drill downward through the metal becomes less, but the length of
each cutting edge is increased, with the result that more
power is required to turn the drill. Drills usually are
ground to an included angle of 118 degrees (an angle a,

Fig. 13, of 59 degrees between the cutting edge and axis).
This angle is believed to equalize the thrust and torsion to
the best advantage for average drilling. Diagram C shows
one method of checking the angle.

What clearance angle is required for drills?

Theoretically, the *clearance* of a drill should be just
enough to permit the drill to cut freely, because excessive
clearance weakens the cutting edges. The necessary clearance angle c at the periphery, Fig. 13, depends upon the
method of sharpening the drill. In any case, the clearance
angle should increase toward the center or point of the drill.
The reason why the clearance angle should vary will be
apparent when we consider that any given point on the cutting edge of a drill that is operating, follows a helical path.
The angle of the path traversed by any point is smallest at
the outer edge or circumference of the drill and this angle
increases for points nearer the center. This increase is due
to the fact that a point near the center advances at the same
rate as one on the outer edge; but the inner point rotates
around a path of smaller diameter, thus increasing the helix
angle or steepness of the path. The clearance angle should
preferably increase at the same rate toward the center, in
order to have sufficient clearance along the entire cutting
edge without *excessive* clearance at any point.

The clearance angle c often is about 12 degrees at the
circumference of the drill when the grinding is done by
hand and without a decided increase in clearance toward
the point. When soft metal is to be drilled and heavier feeds
are possible, the angle of clearance may be increased to
15 degrees, whereas for hard material, such as tool steel,
for example, the amount of clearance should be diminished,
as a fine feed must necessarily be used and a strong cutting
edge is required. These clearance angles of 12 or 15 degrees
are much larger than are required at the periphery, in order
to increase the angle adjacent to the point which otherwise
would have insufficient clearance. With one type of drill
grinder, the clearance angle at the periphery usually is
about 7 degrees, because special provision has been made
for increasing the angle toward the point, as explained
later in connection with the machine grinding of drills.

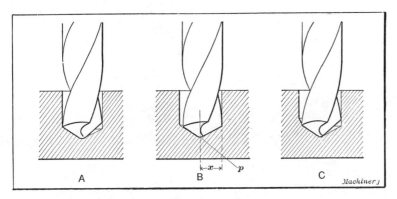

Fig. 14. Three Examples of Incorrect Drill Grinding

The clearance for each cutting edge may be tested by placing the drill point against a flat surface and then slowly revolving it close to a scale held in the position shown at *D*. If the clearances are not alike, this will be indicated by their relative positions to the graduation marks on the scale, as the drill is turned. The clearance is a very important feature in drill grinding, and the splitting of drills through the web is usually an indication either of incorrect clearance or excessive feed. If the end of a drill conforms exactly to the conical shape of the bottom of a hole, evidently it will not cut, because the lack of clearance would make it impossible to sink the cutting edges into the metal; therefore, when there is insufficient clearance for a given feed, the drill binds back of the cutting edges and is subjected to an excessive twisting strain. The clearance angle should increase gradually toward the center, until the line joining the two cutting edges makes an angle x somewhere between 125 and 135 degrees, as shown in the plan view at *B*.

What are the effects of incorrect drill grinding?

At *A* in Fig. 14 is shown the relation between a drill point and a hole when the cutting edges are not at the same angle with the axis. If both cutting edges are ground to the same angle, one edge counteracts the tendency of the other to spring away from the cut (provided the clearance is also

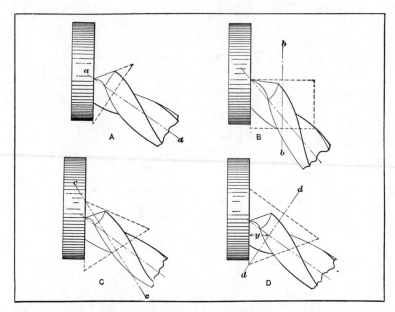

Fig. 15. Diagrams Illustrating Possible Methods of Grinding Drill Points

correct), but when these angles are different, as shown, one edge will do more work than the other, thus subjecting the drill to an unbalanced twisting or torsional strain. The drill will also be forced sidewise, which will result in an enlargement of the hole. The effect produced when the lengths of the cutting edges are unequal is illustrated at B. As the drill revolves about the center or point p, as it is fed into the metal, the horizontal distance x from this point to the side farthest away will equal the radius of the hole which will be larger than the drill diameter if the point is not central; therefore, each cutting edge should have the same length, as otherwise the drill will cut a hole larger than its diameter. At C a drill point is shown having cutting edges inclined at different angles to the axis and of different lengths, thus combining the disadvantages mentioned.

Why are machine-ground drills preferable?

While a skilled workman may be able to grind a drill very accurately by hand, the use of a drill grinder is preferable, as it not only saves time but insures uniform clearance angles and cutting edges of equal angles and lengths. Any appreciable deviation in the length of the cutting edges or an incorrect amount of clearance may impair the accuracy of the work or impose considerable stress upon the drill and the machine. In order to secure good results with twist drills, the two cutting edges should come into contact with the work throughout the entire length at the same time, and the clearance surface back of the cutting edge should vary uniformly from the point of the drill, where it is greatest, to the periphery, where it is the least acute.

When a drill is being ground, either by hand or in a regular drill grinding machine, it is held at an angle with the face of the grinding wheel and is turned so that the face of the wheel will come into contact with the entire surface back of each cutting edge. In grinding by hand, this turning movement of the drill is more or less irregular, depending upon the skill of the workmen. In the case of a machine, however, the rotation is mechanically controlled.

What motion is applied in machine-grinding a drill point?

The principle upon which drill grinders operate will be explained in connection with the diagrams, Fig. 15.

Rotation of Drill Around its Axis.—Diagram A represents a drill being ground on the plane surface of a grinding wheel by turning the drill around its own axis a-a, thus grinding the end to a conical form. With this method of grinding, there would be no clearance back of the cutting edges, and the drill would simply have a sharp point, so that there could be no cutting action.

Rotation Around Axis Parallel to Wheel-face.—The diagram B illustrates the grinding of a drill by turning it about an axis b-b, which is parallel to the face of the grinding wheel. If a drill was ground in this way, a cylindrical surface would be produced, which, in so far as its inclination to the cutting edge is concerned, would be uniform from the point or center of the drill to the periphery.

Rotation to Secure Variation in Clearance.—As already explained, the clearance should gradually increase from the outside circumference toward the point of the drill. One

method of obtaining this varying clearance, which has been
employed in connection with drill grinding machines, is
illustrated by diagram C. The rotation of the drill, when
grinding, is about an axis c-c which is inclined from the
face of the grinding wheel somewhat less than the axis of
the drill. When a drill is ground in this way, the end is
given a conical surface, the apex of the cone being above
the point of the drill, as indicated by the dotted lines.

The diagram shown at D indicates a method of grinding
a drill point by turning the drill about axis d-d. The apex
of the cone, in this case, is below the drill point, instead of
above it, as at C, and, consequently, the drill is not ground
to the correct form, because the clearance diminishes toward the center of the drill instead of increasing, as it
should.

Reduction in Both Clearance and Angle of Chisel Point.—
Unless special means are provided to obtain a decided
increase in the clearance angle toward the drill point, a
clearance of 12 degrees is required ordinarily, as previously
mentioned. With this amount of clearance, the angle x,
Fig. 13, of the "chisel point" on the drill will be 125 or 130
degrees, as required, to obtain the necessary point clearance.
The drill pointer or grinder shown in Fig. 16 (Oliver Instrument Co., Adrian, Mich.) is so designed that the maximum clearance at the circumference of the drill is only
about 7 degrees, and the angle x of the chisel point is only
about 110 degrees. The clearance toward the drill point
increases at such a rate that 7 degrees, or even less, at the
circumference is possible without interference anywhere
along the cutting edges when the drill feed per revolution
is at the maximum likely to be employed. The object is to
obtain maximum support or strength for the cutting edges
and also reduce the feeding pressure. The latter reductions
are said to amount to 25 or 30 per cent.

Operation of Drill Grinder, Fig. 16.—In grinding a drill on
the machine shown in Fig. 16, the drill rotates continuously
about its own axis at a constant rate of speed. The drill is
held in a two-jaw chuck which is rotated by gearing. This
chuck and the drill only have a rotary motion. The grinding
is done by the flat face of a ring-shaped wheel. The wheel-
spindle and wheel have a slight planetary or eccentric motion
which imparts to the wheel the equivalent of a traversing

movement. The wheel also has an endwise motion governed by a cam. This cam is so shaped and located that the inward motion of the wheel toward the drill starts when a drill lip is horizontal. As the wheel advances, it forms a helical clearance surface on the drill lips.

The continuous rotation of the drill causes each lip to be brought into contact with the wheel. The drill is so located in relation to the transverse motion that the wheel leaves the chisel point when it has been ground to an angle of 110 degrees. According to experiments of the Oliver Instrument Co., this angle proved to be the most efficient. Incidentally, if the wheel did not have a transverse motion, the chisel point would be ground at too great an angle and, consequently, would be too long for obtaining the best results. The continued advance of the wheel and the slowing up of the traversing movement at the end of its travel. causes the wheel to form a hollow or concave surface back

Fig. 16. Drill Pointer Designed to Grind Comparatively Small Clearance at Outer Edge with Increasing Clearance Toward the Center of the Drill

of the cutting edge adjacent to the point. The result is an increased rake at this part of the chisel point where there is slight cutting, thus reducing the end or feeding pressure. The clearance may be varied by a simple adjustment which reduces the amount of cam throw. The maximum angle of 7 degrees may be reduced to as low as 3 degrees. This change in clearance, however, affects only those surfaces of the drill which are immediately adjacent to the cutting edge.

Why are holes reamed?

Reamers are used for two main purposes: (1) for producing a hole that is smooth and true to size, and (2) for enlarging cored or drilled holes. Drilled holes are not always exactly round or straight and the diameters vary to some extent, especially when the drill used is sharpened by hand, so that, when accurate holes are required, the drilled hole is finished by reaming, to secure smooth straight holes of uniform diameter. Holes for bolts that must fit accurately are often finished in this way, although on some classes of work, which do not need accurately fitting bolts, a drill slightly larger than the bolt body is used and the reaming operation is omitted.

Drilled holes are, of course, somewhat larger than the actual drill diameter. If a drill is ground accurately, the hole usually is from 0.004 to 0.006 inch per inch of drill diameter larger than the actual drill diameter. For example, if the drill size is ½ inch, the hole might vary from 0.502 to 0.503 inch (0.500 × 0.004 + 0.500 = 0.502 inch).

What types of reamers are commonly used?

Reaming, like tapping, may be done by hand or in some type of machine tool. Two styles of hand reamers are shown at A and B, Fig. 17. Reamer A has straight flutes and reamer B helical or "spiral" flutes to give a shearing and smoother cut. When a very accurate hole is required, it is good practice to ream by hand. One method would be to first drill and possibly rough-ream the hole to within a few thousandths inch of the finished size, and then finish by using a hand reamer. In order to keep the reamer in alignment with the hole, especially when starting, the upper end is sometimes supported by a conical center which is inserted in the spindle. Hand reamers may be made either of carbon steel or high-speed steel. The diameters commonly range from ⅛ inch to 2 inches.

In machine reaming, what general types of reamers are used?

When reaming is done in some machine such as a lathe, turret lathe, or screw machine, two types of reamers that are extensively used are shown at *C* and *D*, Fig. 17. Reamer *C*, which is known as a fluted chucking reamer, has a taper shank similar to a drill shank, which is inserted in the spindle. This reamer will produce a smooth accurate hole, but it is not adapted to removing much metal, and the diameter of the drilled hole should not be more than 0.010 or

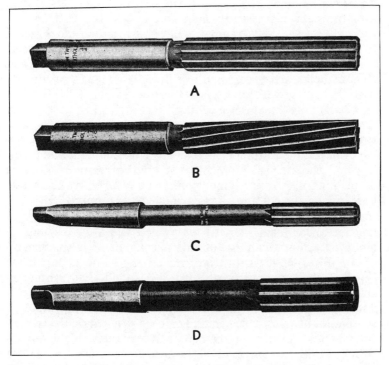

Fig. 17. Hand Reamers and Chucking Reamers

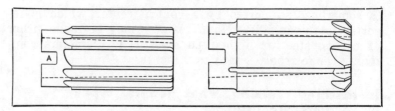

Fig. 18. Shell Reamers—Fluted and Rose Types

0.015 inch under the finished size. The speed for reaming should be much slower than for drilling, and a fluted reamer should not be forced too hard, as both the tool and work may be injured.

Rose Reamer.—The type of reamer shown at D is called a rose reamer. It differs from the fluted type in that the cutting is all done by the beveled edges at the end. The fluted cylindrical body, back of the cutting edges, fits closely into the partially reamed hole and guides the cutting end as it advances. This reamer will remove much more metal than the fluted type and it is used for enlarging holes, as well as for truing drilled holes. When very accurate and smooth holes are necessary, the fluted reamer is ordinarily used, but for general purposes the rose reamer is preferable, especially for "machine reaming" when jigs are used. If a fluted reamer is guided by a hardened jig bushing, the cutting edges along the body will be dulled more or less, depending on the alignment between the drilled hole and bushing and the resulting side thrust on the reamer. On the other hand, the rose reamer cannot be injured by the guide bushing, as the cutting edges are on the end only.

Shell Type.—The shell type of reamer shown in Fig. 18 has an arbor (not shown) on which the shell reamer is mounted. The advantage of this arrangement is that reamers of different sizes can be held on the same arbor. Two types of shell reamers are shown. A fluted shell reamer is shown at the left, and a rose shell reamer at the right. Some fluted reamers have left-hand helical or spiral teeth to give a shearing cut. Such reamers are particularly useful when a hole to be reamed is interrupted by openings which might interfere with the action of a straight-fluted reamer. If the teeth are helical, a right-hand reamer (or one that is turned to the right for reaming) is made with left-hand helical flutes, so that the cutting action will tend to force the reamer back instead of drawing it out of the holder. The arbors upon which shell reamers are mounted are made by small tool manufacturers with either straight shanks or Morse taper shanks. One arbor size can be used for a number of reamer sizes.

Jobber's Reamer.—For some machine-reaming operations, a reamer having longer cutting edges than the fluted design is preferred. The jobber's reamer is similar to a hand reamer, but it is provided with a taper shank so that it may be used for machine reaming. The shank is nearly always a Morse standard taper.

Adjustable-blade Reamers.—Hand, chucking, and shell reamers are made in adjustable-blade designs. These reamers are especially adapted to finish reaming. The radial adjustment of the blades is to compensate for wear or reduction in size by sharpening, so that a standard diameter can be maintained.

Why are some reamers held in a "floating" type of holder?

If a reamer is held rigidly, it is liable to produce a hole which tapers slightly or is too large. When a hole is bored with a single-point boring tool, it is concentric with the axis of rotation, and if a reamer that is aligned exactly with the bored hole is fed into the work, the finished hole should be cylindrical and of the correct size. It may be very difficult, however, to locate a reamer exactly in line with a bored hole, especially if there is imperfect alignment, or errors resulting from wear of the guiding ways or other important parts of the machine. To prevent inaccuracies due to this cause, reamers are often held in a "floating" holder. This type of holder is so arranged that the reamer, instead of being held rigidly, is allowed a slight free or floating movement so that it can adjust itself to a hole which has been bored true. In this way, the hole is reamed straight and to practically the same size as the reamer. There are many different designs of floating holders, but the general principle upon which they are based is illustrated by the different types to be described.

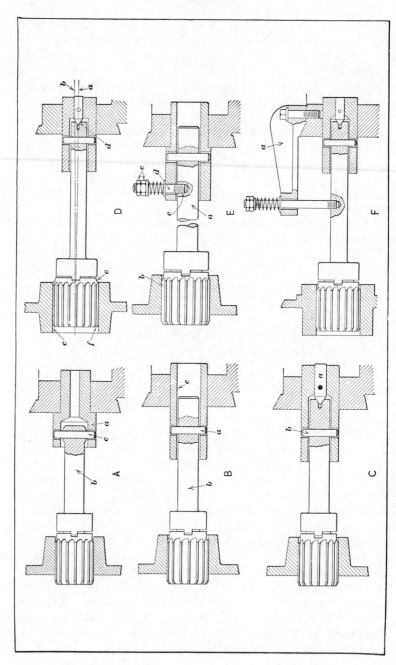

Fig. 19. Different Types of "Floating" Reamer Holders

How is the floating or self-adjusting type of holder arranged?

The types of floating reamer holders shown in Fig. 19 have been used on turret lathes but they might also be used on other machines. Type *A* consists of a body *a*, the shank of which fits the turret hole. Stem *b* has a spherical end through which passes the driving pin *c*. This pin also serves to take the thrust of the cut. The ball end allows a swivel action, but the reamer hangs so low that it must be started into the hole by hand.

Diagram *B* represents a type in which the driving pin *a* is sometimes a free fit in the body and in other cases loose in the shank. There should be a clearance between the shank *b* and the hole *c* of from 0.005 to 0.008 inch. An improved form of this holder is shown at *C*. A centering plug *a* has been added, which, in addition to centering the reamer, also takes the thrust. In certain cases, the use of this plug is a disadvantage, for if the turret does not index properly, the plug must obviously be off center, thus producing a like condition in the reamer itself. At *D* is shown such a condition in an exaggerated form. Suppose that the center of the turret hole *a* is 0.010 inch lower than the center of the spindle *b*, due to improper upkeep, excessive wear on the ways, etc. The hole *c* has been generated by a single-point boring tool and, therefore, should be symmetrical about the axis of rotation of the spindle. Assume that the reamer is 4 inches long and the distance from the forward end to the center of the plug *d* is 12 inches. If there is a back taper to this reamer of 0.001 inch per inch, it will be 0.004 inch smaller at *e* than at the forward end, or 0.002 inch on a side. The point *e*, then, will be 0.0013 inch lower than *f*, and, theoretically, will cut double this amount, *i.e.*, 0.0026 inch on the diameter.

A method of support by means of a spring is shown at *E*, the holder being of the same general type as the one shown at *B*. The reamer for this particular holder was 3½ inches in diameter and the shank *a* rather long. In testing the equipment, it was found impossible to obtain a correctly sized hole at the end *b*, where the reamer began to cut. It was bell-mouthed to the extent of from 0.003 to 0.005 inch, for about half an inch back, and the entire hole was in-

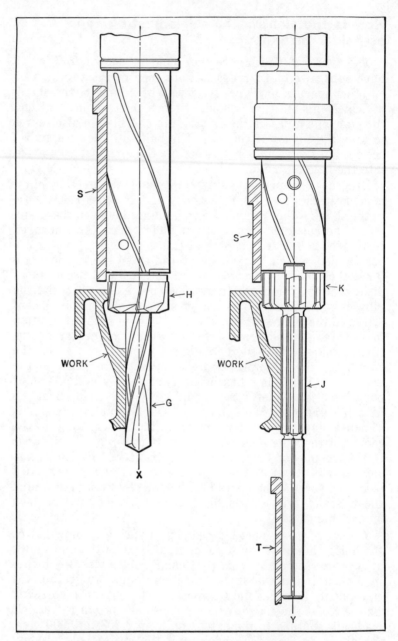

Fig. 20. Examples Showing Use of Multiple Tools

clined to be over-size. The weight of the reamer being considerable and the shank rather long caused a "drag" in entering the hole. The shank was drilled and tapped at c for a ½-inch stud, and a ⅝-inch clearance hole was provided in the holder directly above it at d. The check-nuts e were used to compress the spring shown until the weight of the reamer was properly balanced. This arrangement was found to correct the trouble and the hole obtained was sized properly. At F is shown a similar holder; the reamer was still longer and heavier, but in this instance the supporting bracket a was fastened to the turret itself.

Why are combination drilling and reaming tools used for certain operations?

For certain operations on duplicate parts, especially if manufactured in large quantities, a drill and reamer may be combined in tandem form; hence both tools may operate simultaneously during all or part of the time. There are many different types of multiple or combination tools, and their use not only saves time but insures concentricity or alignment of different surfaces.

The two multiple tools shown in Fig. 20 are merely to illustrate the principle involved. The one shown at the left consists of a drill G followed by a core drill H. (A core drill or shell drill is used for enlarging cored or other holes and is not adapted to drilling holes in solid metal.) The multiple tool shown at the right has a straight-fluted reamer J, a larger reamer K, and at the lower end a pilot that enters bushing T to insure accurate alignment. There is also a guiding surface above reamer K which fits into sleeve S. In machine-building practice, holes, counterbores or other machined surfaces of varying diameters, frequently have a common center line, and tools of the multiple type are applicable. Such tools are more or less special and are only used when their cost is justified by the saving in time, as in the manufacture of duplicate parts in quantity.

What is the difference between boring and reaming?

When a hole is enlarged, the operation is sometimes classed as boring; but holes are also enlarged by reaming.

When a single-point tool is used to enlarge a hole, as on a lathe, the operation is called boring; but tools for enlarging holes often have two or more cutters or cutting edges and the application of such tools may or may not be classed as boring. Cylinders frequently are bored by using a cutter-head containing several single-point tools or cutters to distribute the work of cutting and some tools of the multiple-cutter type resemble reamers but are classed as boring tools. What, then, is the difference between boring and reaming?

If a tool of either the single- or multiple-cutter type is supported independently of the work, as by a bar or holder, and the hole is generated by the rotation of the work and feeding movement of the tool, the operation may properly be classed as boring. The term reaming generally applies to tools which are guided in varying degree by a machined hole. This guiding surface in the hole may be cut by the reamer itself; for example, when a hole is enlarged by a rose reamer, it cuts at the leading end and fits into the hole thus formed as it advances. While the rose reamer is only partially supported by the work, the operation differs in principle from that of generating a hole by boring with a tool that is supported entirely by a bar or holder.

What is "counterboring"?

While drilling machines are intended primarily for drilling holes in solid metal, they are generally used for other operations also, such as counterboring, countersinking, spot-facing, reaming and tapping. When a hole is enlarged for part of its length, thus forming a shoulder at the end of the enlarged portion, this operation is usually known as counterboring. Counterbores are frequently used for enlarging holes to form seats for the heads of machine screws. A machine screw of the fillister-head type and a method of enlarging a hole which has been previously drilled for the body of the screw are indicated at A, Fig. 21. The upper view shows the screw-head in position and the lower view the cutting end of a counterbore after it has been fed to the proper depth. Counterbores are often used for facing a spot around a hole, as indicated at B, to provide a true bearing surface for a bolt head.

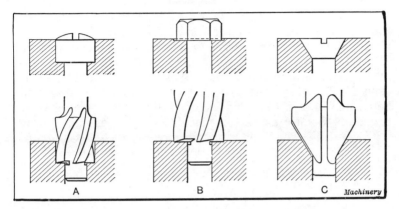

Fig. 21. Use of Counterbore and Countersink

Shanks.—Counterbores are generally provided with a long neck between the shank and the cutting portion so as to enable deep holes to be counterbored. The shank may be either straight or provided with a Morse taper.

Clearance.—Clearance is provided on the end of the cutting teeth only and not on the cylindrical surface, because all cutting is done at the end. To facilitate the relieving process, a small neck is turned between the guide and the body for clearance. The amount of clearance on the end of the cutting edges is, for general work, from 4 to 5 degrees.

Counterbores for Screws.—Counterbores for screw-holes are generally made in sets. Each set contains three counterbores: one with the body of the size of the screw-head and the pilot the size of the hole to admit the body of the screw; one with the body the size of the head of the screw and the pilot the size of the tap drill; and the third with the body the size of the body of the screw and the pilot the size of the tap drill.

What is "countersinking"?

On some classes of work, screws having heads that are conical on the under side are used. Forming a conical seat for a head of this shape is known as *countersinking*. The operation is similar to counterboring, except that a tool for forming a conical seat is used, as indicated at *C*, Fig. 21.

The form of countersink shown is used after the hole for the screw-body has been drilled. Countersinks are also used which have a drill of the proper size at the end, instead of a pilot, so that the straight and conical parts of the hole are finished in one operation. This type of countersink is used for forming centers in the ends of parts that are to be turned in a lathe. The included angle in this case is 60 degrees. Countersinks for machine screws or cap screws with conical-shaped heads should have an included angle of 82 degrees, as this is the American standard.

Precision Methods of Spacing or Locating Holes

The degree of accuracy required in the construction of certain classes of machinery and tools has made it necessary to employ various precise methods and appliances for locating holes or finished surfaces within the prescribed limits of accuracy. Approved methods of locating work, such as are used more particularly in tool-rooms will be explained. The methods described may not be the best under all conditions, because the best way may be dependent upon the element of accuracy with little regard for the time required to do the work, or time may be an important factor. Any one method is seldom, if ever, the best under all circumstances, and it is necessary to consider the conditions in each case and be guided by judgment and experience in determining just how the work should be done.

The methods here described are utilized when locating holes in jigs, dies, special gages, and many other classes of precision work. These methods, however, require more or less adjusting and repeated measuring; consequently, considerable time is required in some cases. When a precision jig boring machine is available, holes may be located very accurately to given dimensions without preliminary laying out or measuring. Machines of this type are included in the section on "Cylinder Boring and Precision Jig Boring."

How are gage-blocks used for accurate adjustment of work on a lathe faceplate?

The gage-block method of locating a jig-plate or other part, in different positions on a lathe faceplate, for boring holes accurately at given center-to-center distances, is illustrated in Fig. 1. The way the size blocks are used in this particular instance is as follows: A pair of accurate parallels are attached to a faceplate at right angles to each other

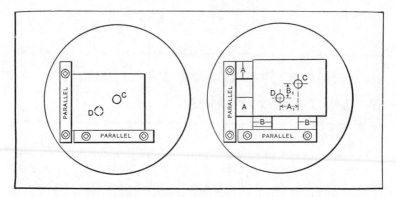

Fig. 1.   Method of Setting Work on Faceplate by using
Precision Gage Blocks

and they are so located that the center of one of the holes
to be bored will coincide with the lathe spindle. The hole
which is aligned in this way should be that one on the work
which is nearest the outer corner, so that the remaining
holes can be set in a central position by adjusting the work
away from the parallels. After the first hole is bored, the
work is located for boring each additional hole by placing
size blocks of the required width between the edges of the
work and the parallels. For instance, to set the plate for
boring hole D, size blocks (or a combination of blocks or
gages) equal in width to dimension A_1 would be inserted
at A, and other blocks equal in width to dimension B_1 beneath the work as at B. The dimensions of these blocks
equal the horizontal and vertical distances between holes C
and D. With the use of other combinations of gage-blocks,
any additional holes that might be required are located in
the central position. While only two holes are shown in this
case, it will be understood that the plate could be located
accurately for boring almost any number of holes.

This method usually is applied to work having accurately
machined edges, although a part having edges which are
of a rough or irregular shape can be located, if it is mounted
on an auxiliary plate having accurately finished square
edges. For instance, if holes were to be bored in the casting
for a jig templet which had simply been planed on the top
and bottom, the casting could be bolted to a finished plate

having square edges and the latter be set in the different positions required by means of size blocks. Comparatively large jig-plates are sometimes located for boring in this way and the milling machine is often used instead of a lathe.

What is the principle of a compound slide as applied to precision hole boring?

A compound slide for precision hole boring consists of two slides located at 90 degrees to each other and arranged for right-angle adjustments. These movements at right angles make it possible to locate the upper or work-holding slide in position for boring any hole within the extreme limits of the adjustments. To illustrate, assume that a vertical milling machine is to be used for drilling and boring several holes in a plate attached to the upper slide. The entire fixture is mounted on the milling machine table and each slide is adjusted longitudinally and laterally to suit corresponding dimensions between the holes. When a compound slide is to be used for precision hole boring, the dimensions on the drawing should be given so that any hole can be placed in the boring position by means of longitudinal or lateral adjustments (or both) corresponding to the given dimensions.

The exact distance that each slide is moved may be determined by means of gage-blocks or by micrometer gages forming part of the compound slide fixture. Some compound slides merely have contact points between which gage-blocks are inserted to obtain a given adjustment. Compound slides are especially useful in boring holes in jig plates, dies, etc. The principle of the compound slide is illustrated by the preceding method of using gage-blocks for setting precision work on a lathe faceplate by making right-angle adjustments.

How is the compound slide principle applied in locating work on an angle plate?

If a compound slide is not available, jig plates, etc., may be located in different positions on an angle-plate, as shown in Fig. 2. The angle-plate is set at right angles to the spindle of the machine and depth gages and size blocks are

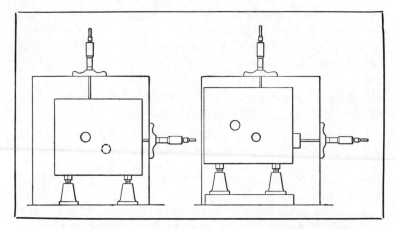

Fig. 2. Locating Work from Edges of Angle-plate by Means of Depth Gages and Gage Blocks

used for measuring directly the amount of adjustment. Both the angle-plate and the work should have finished surfaces on two sides at right angles to each other, from which measurements can be taken. After the first hole has been bored, the plate is adjusted the required distance both horizontally and vertically, by using micrometer depth gages, which should preferably be clamped to the angle-plate. If the capacity of the gages is exceeded, measurements may be taken by using standard size blocks in conjunction with the depth gages.

It is frequently necessary to bore holes in cast jig-plates or machine parts, which either have irregularly-shaped or unfinished edges. A method of locating such work is illustrated in Fig. 3. The part to be bored is attached to an auxiliary plate A which should have parallel sides and at least two edges which are straight and at right angles to each other. This auxiliary plate with the work is clamped against an accurate angle-plate B, which should be set square with the axis of the machine spindle. A parallel strip is bolted to the angle-plate and the inner edge is set square with the machine table. After the first hole is bored, the work is located for boring the other holes, by taking vertical measurements x from the table to the edge of the auxiliary plate, and horizontal measurements y between the parallel and the plate. These measurements, if quite large, might be taken with micrometer gages, whereas, for comparatively small adjustments, size blocks might be more convenient.

How are holes accurately located by the "button method"?

If a precision jig-boring machine is not available, holes in jig plates, dies, etc., are often located by the so-called "button method." This method is commonly employed by toolmakers for accurately locating work on the faceplate cf a lathe. The "button method" is so named because cylindrical bushings or buttons are attached to the work in positions corresponding to the holes to be bored, after which they are used in locating the work (see diagram, Fig. 4). These buttons, which are ordinarily about 0.300 to 0.500 inch in diameter, are all ground and lapped to the same size, and the ends are finished perfectly square. The outside diameter should preferably be such that the radius can easily be determined, and the hole through the center should be about $\frac{1}{8}$ inch larger than the retaining screw so that the button can be adjusted laterally.

In the practical application of the button method, the

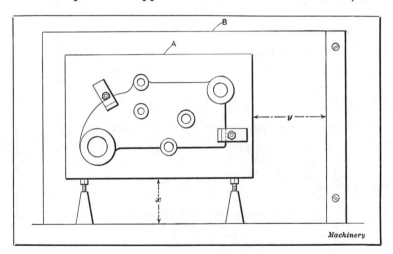

Fig. 3.   Method of Holding and Locating Casting of Irregular Shape for Boring Holes

general procedure is as follows: First the centers of all holes to be bored are laid out by the usual method. Holes are drilled at these points and tapped for the machine screws which are used to clamp the buttons. After the buttons are clamped lightly in place they are set in correct relation with each other. The proper location of the buttons is very important, as their positions largely determine the accuracy of the work. The best method of locating a number of buttons depends somewhat upon their relative positions, the instruments available, and the accuracy required. When buttons must be located at given distances from the finished sides of a jig, a surface plate and vernier height-gage are often used. The method is to place that side from which the button is to be set, upon an accurate surface plate and then set the button by means of the height-gage, allowance being made, of course, for the radius of the button. The center-to-center distance between the different buttons can afterwards be verified by taking direct measurements with a

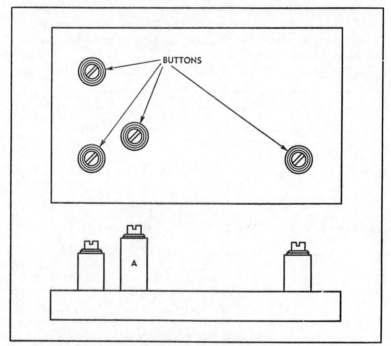

Fig. 4. Diagram Illustrating Button Method of Locating Holes

micrometer by measuring the overall distance and deducting the diameter of one button, assuming that the dimensions are within the measuring range of a micrometer.

After the buttons have been set and the screws are tightened, all measurements should be carefully checked. The work is then mounted on the faceplate of the lathe and one of the buttons is set true or in line with the axis of the lathe spindle, by the use of a test indicator. When the dial of the indicator ceases to fluctuate, thus showing that the button runs true, the latter should be removed so that the hole can be drilled and bored to the required size. In a similar manner other buttons are indicated and the holes bored, one at a time. It is evident that if each button is correctly located and set perfectly true in the lathe, the various holes will be located the required distance apart within very close limits. If one hole is close to another, a long button may be used, as shown at A, Fig. 4, to provide room at the outer end for the indicator point.

When it is necessary to make duplicate parts having a number of holes located in exactly the same relative positions, the usual practice is to first produce a "master plate" by the button method; this master plate is then used in machining the duplicate plates as explained later.

What is the plug-and-sleeve method of aligning buttons for precision hole boring?

In boring jig plates, etc., on a milling machine, one method of locating the work is illustrated in Fig. 5, where a jig-plate is shown set-up for boring. The jig, with buttons B accurately located in positions corresponding to the holes to be bored, is clamped to the angle-plate A that is set at right angles to the spindle. There is a plug P inserted in the spindle, the end of which is ground to the exact size of the indicating buttons. A sliding sleeve S is accurately fitted to this plug and, when the work is to be set for boring a hole, the table and knee of the machine are adjusted until the sleeve S will pass over the button representing the location of the hole, which brings the button and spindle into alignment.

When setting the button in alignment, all lost motion or backlash should be taken up in the feed-screws. For in-

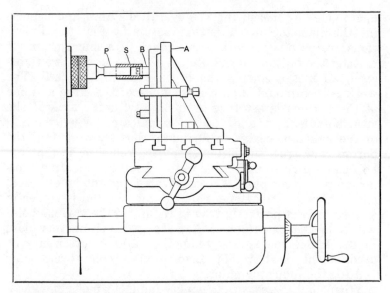

Fig. 5. Plug-and-sleeve Method of Aligning Spindle of Milling Machine
with Button on Jig Plate

stance, if the button on the jig should be a little higher
than the plug in the spindle, do not lower the knee until
the bushing slips over the button, but lower the knee more
than is required and then raise it until the bushing will
pass over the button. This same rule should be followed for
longitudinal adjustments. After the button is set by this
method, it is removed and the plug in the spindle is replaced
by a drill and then by a boring tool or reamer for finishing
the hole to size. In a similar manner, the work is set for
the remaining holes. The plug P for the spindle must be
accurately made so that the outer end is concentric with
the shank, and the latter should always be inserted in the
spindle in the same relative position. With a reasonable
degree of care, work can be set with considerable precision
by this method, providing the buttons are properly set.
Some toolmakers use, instead of the plug and sleeve referred
to, a test indicator for setting the buttons concentric with
the machine spindle. This indicator is attached to, and revolves with, the spindle, while the point is brought into
contact with the button to be set. The difficulty of seeing

the pointer as it turns is a disadvantage, but, with care, accurate results can be obtained.

How are equally-spaced holes drilled by the two-disk method?

This simple method of spacing holes that are to be drilled in a straight line is illustrated in Fig. 6. Two disks are made, each having a diameter equal to the center-to-center distance required between the holes. These disks must also have holes which are central with the outside to act as a guide for the drill or reamer. The first two holes are drilled in the work while the disks are clamped so that they are in contact with each other and also with the straightedge as shown. One disk is then placed on the opposite side of the other, as indicated by the dotted line, and a third hole is drilled; this process of setting one disk against the opposite side of the other is continued until all the holes are drilled. When it is necessary to drill a parallel row of "staggered" holes, the second row can be located by placing disks of the proper size in contact with the disks used for the first row.

How are equally-spaced holes drilled by successively locating a jig from the last hole drilled?

The adjustable jig for accurately spacing small holes (shown in Fig. 7) is especially useful in locating a number of equally-spaced holes between two previously drilled or bored holes. The accuracy of this method lies in the fact that a slight error in the original spacing of the guide bushing is multiplied, and, therefore, easily detected. There are two of these guide bushings A and B which are carried by independent slides. These slides can be shifted along a dovetail groove after loosening the screws of clam-gib C. To illustrate the method of using this jig, suppose five equally-spaced holes are to be located between two holes that are 12 inches apart. As the center-to-center distance between adjacent holes is 2 inches, slides A and B would be set so that the dimension x equals 2 inches plus the radii of the bushings. A straightedge is then clamped to the work in such position that a close-fitting plug can be inserted through the end holes which were previously drilled or

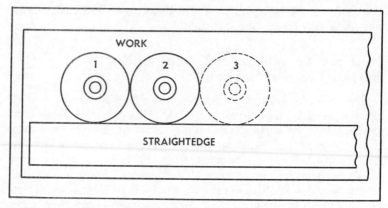

Fig. 6. Locating Equi-distant Holes in a Straight Line by Means
of Disks and Straightedge

bored. Then with a plug inserted through, say, bushing *B*
and one of the end holes, the first of the series of five holes
is drilled and reamed through bushing *A;* the jig is then
shifted to the left until the plug in *B* enters the hole just
made. The second hole is then drilled and reamed through
bushing *A* and this drilling and shifting of the jig is continued until the last hole is finished. The distance between
the last hole and the original end hole at the left is next
tested by attempting to insert close-fitting plugs through
both bushings. Evidently, if there were any inaccuracy in
tl e spacing of the bushings, this would be multiplied as
many times as the jig was shifted, the error being accumu-

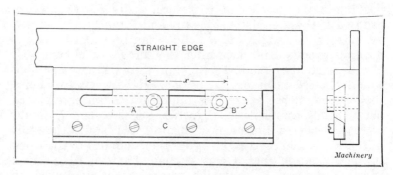

Fig. 7. Adjustable Jig for Accurate Hole Spacing

lative. To illustrate how the error accumulates, suppose that the bushings were 0.001 inch too far apart; then the distance to the first hole would be 2.001 inch, to the second hole, 4.002 inch, and finally the distance from the first to the sixth hole would be 10.005 inches; consequently, the distance between the sixth and seventh holes would equal 12 — 10.005 = 1.995 inch, or 0.005 inch less than the required spacing, assuming, for the sake of illustration, that the first and last holes were exactly 12 inches apart. In case of an error of 0.005 inch, the bushings would be set closer together an amount equal to one-fifth of this error, as near as could be determined with a micrometer, and all of the holes would then be re-reamed.

In precision work, how are holes equally spaced around a circle?

The method depends upon the degree of accuracy required. The methods to be described are intended for very precise work. Assume that it is necessary to machine a number of holes in a plate so that all the holes are on a circle or equi-distant from a central point, and also the same distance apart, within very small limits. A simple method of spacing holes equally is illustrated at A, Fig. 8. A number of buttons equal to the number of holes required are ground and lapped to exactly the same diameter, preferably by mounting them all on an arbor and finishing them at the same time. The ends should also be made square with the cylindrical surface of the button. When these buttons are finished, the diameter is carefully measured and this dimension is subtracted from the diameter of the circle on which the holes are to be located in order to obtain the diameter d. A narrow shoulder is then turned on the plate to be bored, the diameter being made exactly equal to dimension d. By placing the buttons in contact with this shoulder, they are accurately located radially and can then be set equi-distant from each other by the use of a micrometer. In this particular case, it would be advisable to begin by setting the four buttons which are 90 degrees apart and then the remaining four. The buttons are next used for setting the work preparatory to boring as described previously in connection with the "button method."

How are circular spacing errors corrected by the split-ring method?

The split-ring method of securing equal spacing for holes in indexing wheels, etc., is illustrated at *B*, Fig. 8. This method is not to be recommended if the diameter of the circle on which the holes are to be located must be very accurate. The disk or ring in which the holes are required is formed of two sections *e* and *f*, instead of being one solid piece. The centers for the holes are first laid out as accurately as possible on ring *e*. Parts *e* and *f* are then clamped together and the holes are drilled through these two sections. If there is error in the spacing, all of the holes will not match, except when plate *e* is in the position it occupied when being drilled. Whatever errors may exist in the spacing can be eliminated, however, by successively shifting plate *e* to different positions and re-reaming the holes for each position. A taper reamer is used and two pins should

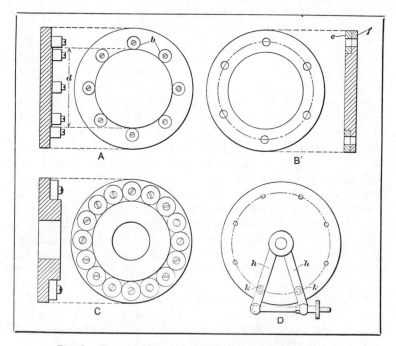

Fig. 8.   Four Methods of Accurately Dividing a Circle

be provided having the same taper as the reamer. Ring *e* is first located so that a hole is aligned quite accurately with one in the lower plate. The ring is then clamped and the hole is partly reamed, the reamer being inserted far enough to finish the hole in plate *e* and also cut clear around in the upper part of plate *f*. One of the taper pins is then driven into this hole and then a hole on the opposite side is partly reamed, after which the other pin is inserted. The remaining holes are now reamed in the same way, and the reamer should be fed in to the same depth n each case. If a pair of holes is considerably out of alignment, it may be necessary to run the reamer in to a greater depth than was required for the first pair reamed, and in such a case all the holes should be re-reamed to secure a uniform size.

The next step in this operation is to remove the taper pins and clamps, turn index plate *e* one hole and again clamp it in position. The reaming process just described is then repeated; the holes on opposite sides of the plate are re-reamed somewhat deeper, the taper pins are inserted, and then all of the remaining holes are re-reamed to secure perfect alignment for the new position of the plate. By repeating this process of shifting plate *e* and re-reaming the holes, whatever error that may have existed originally in the spacing of the holes will practically be eliminated.

How is a circle equally divided by contact of uniform disks?

When an accurate indexing or dividing wheel is required on a machine, the method of securing accurate divisions of the circle illustrated at *C*, Fig. 8, is sometimes employed. There is a series of circular disks or bushings equal in number to the divisions required, and these disks are all in contact with each other and with a circular boss or shoulder on the plate to which they are attached. The spaces between adjacent disks are used to accurately locate the dividing wheel, by the successive engagement of each space with a suitable latch or indexing device. When making a dividing wheel of this kind, all of the disks are ground and lapped to the same diameter and then the diameter of the central boss or plate is gradually reduced until all of the disks are in contact with each other and with the boss.

How are holes equally spaced by correcting cumulative errors?

The indexing method of spacing holes equi-distantly, illustrated by the diagram at D, Fig. 8, is based upon the cumulative error principle. An accurately fitting plug is inserted in the central hole of the plate in which holes are required. Two arms h are closely fitted to this plug, but are free to rotate and are provided with a fine-pitch screw and nut at the outer ends for adjusting the distance between the arms. Each arm contains an accurately-made, hardened steel bushing k located at the same radial distance from the center of the plate. These bushings are used as a guide for the drill and reamer when machining the holes in the plate.

Rule.—To determine the center-to-center distance between the bushings, divide 180 by the number of holes required; find the sine corresponding to the angle thus obtained, and multiply it by the diameter of the circle upon which the holes are located.

Example.—If there were to be eleven holes on a circle 8 inches in diameter, the distance between the centers of the bushings would equal $\frac{180}{11}$ = 16.36 degrees. The sine of 16.36 degrees is 0.28167; 8 × 0.28167 = 2.2534 inches. The arms are adjusted to locate the centers of the bushings this distance apart by placing closely fitting plugs in the bushings and measuring from one plug to another with a micrometer or vernier caliper. Of course, when taking this measurement, allowance is made for the diameter of the plugs.

After the arms are set, a hole is drilled and reamed; an accurately fitting plug is then inserted through the bushing and hole to secure the arms when drilling and reaming the adjacent hole. The radial arms are then indexed one hole so that the plug can be inserted through one of the arms and the last hole reamed. The third hole is then drilled and reamed, and this operation is repeated for all of the holes. Evidently, if the center-to-center distance between the bushings is not exactly right, the error will be indicated by the position of the arms relative to the last hole and the first one reamed; moreover, this error will be multiplied as many times as there are holes. The arms should be re-adjusted

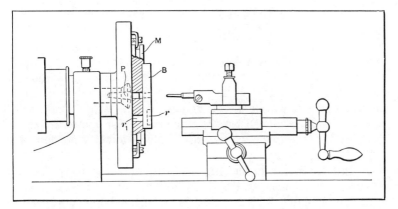

Fig. 9.   Master Plate Applied to a Bench Lathe Faceplate

accordingly and larger bushings inserted in the arms. Then the holes are re-reamed and this operation is repeated until the holes are all equi-distant.

The value of this method lies in the fact that it shows the cumulative error. Thus, if the arms were 0.0005 inch too far apart, the difference between the first and eleventh hole would equal $11 \times 0.0005 = 0.0055$ inch. This same principle of dividing can be applied in various ways. For instance, the radial arms, if slightly modified, could be used for drilling equally-spaced holes in the periphery of a plate or disk, or, if a suitable marking device were attached, a device of this kind could be used for accurately dividing circular parts.

How is a "master-plate" used for accurately boring duplicate sets of holes in two or more plates?

When it is necessary to bore holes in two or more plates so that they are duplicates as to the location of the holes, circular recesses, etc., what is known as a master-plate is often used for locating the work on the lathe faceplate. This master-plate M (see Fig. 9) contains holes which correspond to those wanted in the work, and which accurately fit a central plug P in the lathe spindle, so that by engaging first one hole and then another with the plug, the work is accurately positioned for the various operations.

When making the master-plate, great care should be taken to have the sides parallel and the holes at right angles to the sides, as well as accurately located with reference to one another. The various holes may be located with considerable precision by the use of buttons as previously described. Of course, it is necessary to have a hole in the master-plate for each different position in which the work will have to be placed on the faceplate; for example, if a circular recess r were required, a hole r_1 exactly concentric with it would be needed in the master-plate. The method of holding the work and locating it with reference to the holes in the master-plate will depend largely on its shape. The cylindrical blank B illustrated is positioned by a recess in the master-plate in which it fits. The work is commonly held to the master-plate by means of clamps and tap bolts or by screws which pass through the work and into the master-plate. Solder is sometimes used when it is not convenient to hold the work by clamps or screws.

The plug P which locates the master-plate is first turned to fit the spindle or collet of the lathe, and the outer or projecting end is rough-turned for the holes in the master-plate, which should all be finished to exactly the same diameter. The plug is then inserted in the spindle and ground and lapped to a close fit for the holes in the master-plate. The latter, with the work attached to it, is next clamped to the faceplate by the straps shown, which engage a groove around the edge of the master-plate. The work is accurately located for machining each hole by loosening the master-plate and engaging the proper hole in it with the central plug. It is apparent that by the use of this same master-plate, a number of pieces B could be made which would be practically duplicates.

The master-plate method of locating work can be applied in many different ways. It is used for making duplicate dies, for accurately locating the various holes in watch movements, and for many other operations requiring great precision. Master-plates are quite frequently used by tool-makers when it is necessary to produce a number of drill jigs which are to be used for drilling holes in different parts having the same relative locations, thus requiring jigs that are duplicates within very close limits.

Cylinder Boring and Precision Jig Boring

Machines which are especially adapted to the boring of cylindrical surfaces may or may not be designed exclusively for boring. For example, the horizontal type of machine which is found in many shops, see Fig. 1, is primarily a boring machine, but it is frequently used for other operations, such as drilling, milling, and flange or other facing. For this reason, such machines are generally called "horizontal boring, drilling, and milling machines." The "vertical boring mill" is very generally used for turning cylindrical, flat, and tapering surfaces as explained previously. In fact, this type of machine is used more for turning than for boring in most shops, and it is generally referred to by the manufacturer as a "vertical boring and turning machine." In the manufacture of automobile engines and in certain other plants where a large amount of duplicate boring is done, special types of boring machines are used. Some of these are designed expressly for a given class of work and are arranged to bore, simultaneously, all of the holes in an engine cylinder block or other part.

What are the general methods of machining the bores of cylinders and similar parts?

The type of machine used and the method of boring and finishing the interior of cylindrical surfaces depends upon the size, accuracy, and finish required. For example, a method representing approved practice in the case of a large engine, pump or compressor cylinder would not be suitable for the cylinder of an automobile or airplane motor. In general, the methods of machining cylinders or other bores of various types may be classified broadly as

345

(1) boring with single-point tool; (2) boring with single-point tool and then reaming, provided the diameter is not too large for reaming; (3) boring with single-point tool and grinding; (4) boring with single-point tool and honing. Many cylindrical parts are bored on standard machine tools such as engine lathes, turret lathes, etc., but the extensive use of cylinders in automobile production and in certain other lines of manufacture has led to the development of special machines and tools designed exclusively for cylinder work. The design and size of the cylinder may affect the method of machining and the quantity required in a given time may also have a decided bearing upon the type of equipment used.

Fig. 1. Horizontal Boring, Drilling and Milling Machine

In boring large cylinders, what type of machine is used?

Cylinders such as are used on steam engines, pumps, air compressors, etc., and many other cylindrical parts, are bored ordinarily on a horizontal type of machine that is especially adapted for boring operations. These machines, however, as mentioned previously, frequently are used for other operations such as flange facing, drilling, and milling, particularly when these additional operations will permit finishing a cylinder casting or other part in connection with boring and without changing the position of the work. This not only saves time, but insures accuracy between the different surfaces. A horizontal type of boring, drilling and milling machine of the general type shown in Fig. 1 has a horizontal spindle which holds and rotates the boring-bar. This bar is supported at its outer end for most boring operations.

The *floor type* of horizontal boring, drilling, and milling machine is intended for boring very heavy parts such as the cylinders of large engines or pumps, the bearings of heavy machine beds, and similar work. This design is ordinarily referred to as the "floor type," because the work table or floor plate is low for accommodating large heavy castings. The spindle which drives the boring-bar, and the spindle feeding mechanism, are carried by a saddle. This saddle is free to move vertically on the face of a column which is mounted on transverse ways extending across the end of the main bed. This construction permits the spindle to move vertically or laterally (by transversing the column) either for adjusting it to the required position or for milling operations. The spindle also has a longitudinal movement for boring. There is usually an outer bearing for supporting the boring-bar. This type of machine can also be used for drilling and milling, although it is intended primarily for boring, and the other operations are usually secondary.

What types of tools or cutters are used on boring machines?

Single-point boring tools may be used on a machine of this type, but frequently the cutter-head on the boring-bar is provided with two or more single-point tools or cutting ends in order to distribute the work and also equalize the thrust of the cuts.

There are various methods of attaching cutters to boring-bars and the cutters used vary for different classes of work. A simple style of cutter which is used widely for boring small holes is shown at A in Fig. 2. The cutter c is made from flat stock and the cutting is done by the front edges e and e_1 which are beveled in opposite directions to provide rake. The cutter is held in the bar by a taper wedge w and it is centered by shoulders at s, so that the diameter of the hole will equal the length across the cutter. The outer corners at the front should be slightly rounded, as a sharp corner would be dulled quickly. These cutters are made in different sizes and also in sets for roughing and finishing. The roughing cutter bores holes to within about 1/32 inch of the finish size and it is then replaced by the finishing

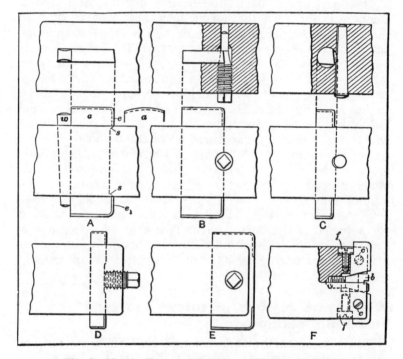

Fig. 2. Simple Types of Double-end Boring Cutters

cutter. A cutter having rounded ends, as shown by the detail sketch *a*, is sometimes used for light finishing cuts. These rounded ends form the cutting edges and give a smooth finish.

Another method of holding a flat cutter is shown at *B*. The conical end of a screw bears against a conical seat in the cutter, thus binding the latter in its slot. The conical seat also centers the cutter. A very simple and inexpensive form of cutter is shown at *C*. This is made from a piece of round steel, and it is held in the bar by a taper pin which bears against a circular recess in the side of the cutter. This form has the advantage of only requiring a hole through the boring-bar, whereas it is necessary to cut a rectangular slot for the flat cutter.

For some work, a short bar is inserted in the spindle and holds a cutter at the outer end. An inexpensive method of holding a cutter at the end of a bar is shown at *D*. The cutter passes through a slot and is clamped by a bolt as shown. When it is necessary to bore holes that are "blind" or closed at the bottom, a long boring-bar which passes through the work cannot, of course, be used. Sometimes it is necessary to have a cutter mounted at the extreme end of a bar in order to bore close to a shoulder or the bottom of a hole. One method of holding a cutter so that it projects beyond the end of a bar is indicated at *E*. A screw similar to the one shown at *B* is used, and the conical end bears in a conical hole in the cutter. This hole should be slightly offset so that the cutter will be forced back against its seat. The tool shown at *F* has adjustable cutters. The inner end of each cutter is tapering and bears against a conical-headed screw *b* which gives the required outward adjustment. The cutters are held against the central bolt by fillister-head screws *f* and they are clamped by the screws *c*. Boring tools are made in many different designs and the number and form of the cutters is varied somewhat for different kinds of work.

When are cutter-heads with two or more tools used for boring?

When large holes are to be bored, the cutters are usually held in a cast-iron head which is mounted on the bor-

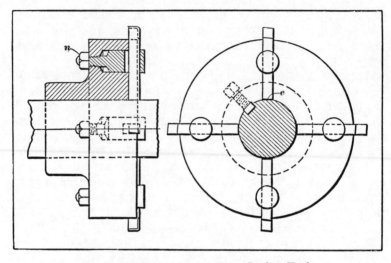

Fig. 3.   Cutter-head with Four Boring Tools

ing-bar. The number of cutters used in a cutter-head varies. By having several cutters, the work of removing a given amount of metal in boring is distributed, and holes can be bored more quickly with a multiple cutter-head, although more power is required to drive the boring-bar. The boring-bar is also steadied by a multiple cutter-head, because the tendency of any one cutter to deflect the bar is counteracted by the cutters on the opposite side.

A disk-shaped head having four cutters is illustrated in Fig. 3. The cutters are inserted in slots or grooves in the face of the disk and they are held by slotted clamping posts. The shape of these posts is shown by the sectional view. The tool passes through an elongated slot and it is tightly clamped against the disk by tightening nut n. This head is also driven by a key which engages a keyway in the boring-bar.

Two other designs of cutter-heads are shown in Fig. 4. The one illustrated at A has cutters which are held in an inclined position. The cutters are clamped by screws c and they can be adjusted within certain limits by screws s. The cutters are placed at an angle so that they will extend beyond the front of the head, thus permitting the latter to be moved up close to a shoulder. The cutter-head shown in

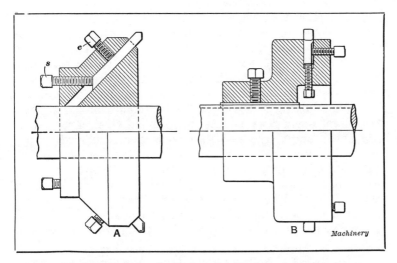

Fig. 4. Cutter-heads Equipped with Adjustable Tools

Fig. 3 can also be moved up close to a shoulder if bent cutters are used. The idea in bending the cutters is to bring the cutting edges in advance of the clamping posts so that they will reach a shoulder before the binding posts strike it. The arrangement of cutter-head *B* (Fig. 4) is clearly shown by the illustration.

Cutter-heads are often provided with two sets of cutters, one set being used for roughing and the other for finishing. It is a good plan to make these cutters so that the ends *e* (Fig. 3) will rest against the bar or bottom of the slot, when the cutting edge is set to the required radius. The cutters can then be easily set for boring duplicate work. One method of making cutters in sets is to clamp the annealed stock in the cutter-head and then turn the ends to the required radius by placing the head in the lathe. After both sets of cutters have been turned in this way they are ground to shape and then hardened.

What is diamond or precision boring?

The expression "diamond boring" or "precision boring" is applied particularly to the boring of holes on machines designed for high speeds and the use of carbide or diamond boring tools. Diamonds have long been used for machining materials that were too hard to yield to the cutting edges of steel tools, but their use for machining the softer materials requiring an extremely hard tool is a later development. After carbide tools became available, they were used in place of diamond tools for most precision boring operations. The carbide boring tools are used in the form of small cutting tips, brazed into toolholders. The term "diamond boring" is often applied even when carbide tools are used. Light cuts and fine feeds are employed in precision boring and to obtain the best results, the cutting edge must be lapped to a high polish, so that there will be no grinding marks on the cutting edge. A high degree of accuracy is obtained in boring holes in parts made of bronze, aluminum, fiber, Bakelite, copper, hard rubber, and various other materials, by the application of diamond and carbide tools.

Both carbide, and diamond tools, must be used where vibration is reduced to a minimum. If there is any considerable amount of vibration, the keen hard cutting edge of the carbide or diamond will be destroyed. Carbide tools are more uniform and dependable than diamond, and they are not so likely to chip. Moreover, the cutting face and edge desired can be more readily obtained when sharpening carbide tools.

Carbide tools are made in different grades which vary in regard to hardness, shock resistance, and other properties. Some grades are preferable for cutting steel and others give better results in machining cast iron, brass, and nonmetallic materials. See also page 475 of Volume 2.

How is diamond or precision boring applied to cylinders?

Various methods have been employed to secure the accuracy that is essential for automobile and airplane engine cylinders. Formerly, it was the practice to bore a cylinder and then finish it either by reaming or grinding. At the present time, the general practice is to precision-bore a cylinder and then finish it by honing. When a bored cylinder is finished by honing, a very smooth and accurate surface must first be obtained by the boring operation. This is accomplished by the use of modern precision boring machines that are designed primarily for such work. These machines use single-point boring tools made of tungsten carbide which is almost as hard as the diamond, and, consequently, is capable of retaining a keen cutting edge even at relatively high cutting speeds. A fine feed is used and a very accurate cylindrical surface is left by the boring tool.

In boring with tungsten-carbide tools try the following speeds: For cast iron, 200 to 250 feet per minute; brass, 300 to 400 feet per minute; bronze, 250 to 350 feet per minute; aluminum, 1500 feet per minute.

Precision boring machines may have either vertical or horizontal spindles. In automotive cylinder boring, the general practice is to use a machine having parallel spindles equaling the number of "bores" in the cylinder casting. These spindles are fixed at the required center distance and all of the holes are bored simultaneously. A horizontal type of machine having eight spindles is shown in Fig. 5. The table holding the cylinder block is moved hydraulically for the feeding and return movements. Cylin-

Fig. 5. Precision Boring of Automobile Cylinder Blocks

ders of the V-type are bored on machines having two groups
of spindles inclined to suit the bores in each V-section.

What type of machine is designed for boring holes in jigs or other parts requiring accurate spacing?

The jig-boring machine is designed expressly for jig
boring or similar work and is so arranged that either the
part to be bored, or the boring spindle or spindles (or both
work and spindles) can be adjusted to accurately locate
the holes at given center-to-center distances without preliminary measurements or laying out.   One design of jig-
boring machine has a single spindle adjustable on a cross-
rail located above a horizontal work-table, which may be
adjusted along its bed in a direction at right angles to the
cross-rail. With this machine, the work is located in the
required position by moving the horizontal work-table
lengthwise and the vertical spindle laterally along its
cross-rail.   Another type of jig-boring machine which is
extensively used is so designed that adjustments for locating various holes to be bored are obtained by lengthwise
and lateral or cross-adjustments of the work-holding table.
A compound table type of machine is shown in Fig. 6.

What types of measuring devices are used on jig-boring machines?

Jig-boring machines are equipped with accurate means
of measuring the longitudinal and lateral adjustments for
boring various holes to given dimensions within close limits.
Some machines have precision lead-screws with micrometer dials.   Another type of measuring device consists of
vernier scales which show the lengthwise and lateral measurements.   A third method consists in using end-measuring rods and micrometers between adjustable stops. To
obtain greater refinement and insure uniform measuring
pressure for all measurements, contact at one end may be
with a dial gage. Linear scales may be used in conjunction with the end-measuring micrometers, for approximate
adjustments.

The machine shown in Fig. 6 has a built-in measuring
device for each slide, holes being located by two dimensions
at right angles. The first hole is located either by measur-

ing from a finished edge or by the most convenient and accurate method for a given job. After the spindle is in position for boring the first hole, the table is locked and the "zero point" for the entire job is established by two dial indicators which serve as pressure gages. In adjusting for boring the next hole, end measures are used to obtain the even inches and inside micrometers graduated to 0.0001 inch for the fractional measurements. When the end measure and micrometer are set for the exact dimension required, the slow-motion adjustment of the table is used to move the table until the dial indicator for that particular slide registers the zero point. These indicators are only for establishing and maintaining this zero point whenever an adjustment is made and they are not used for obtaining any part of the required dimension but only as means of obtaining constant measuring pressure that is not dependent upon the workmen's sense of touch.

Fig. 6. Precision Jig-boring Machine

The dimensions on the drawing should be such that the machine can be set directly by them. For example, in boring several holes in a jig plate, the zero point is established for the first hole and then successive positions for the other holes are obtained by right-angle adjustments of the compound table conforming to similar measurements on the drawing. This applies, of course, to work which does not require circular dividing or angular measurements.

How are holes finished to size on jig-boring machines?

After a hole has been drilled, it may be finished either by boring with a single-point tool or by the use of an end-

Fig. 7. Precision Jig-boring Machine Finishing the Holes in a Drill Jig

mill type of reamer which enlarges the hole chiefly by end-cutting and finishes it by the reaming action of the helical teeth along the body of the mill or reamer. These end-mills or end reamers provide a rapid method of finishing holes but they are not as accurate as a single-point boring tool. End mills may be used for holes conforming to certain standard or commonly used sizes, assuming that the required degree of accuracy is obtained. They may also be used when holes are to be finished in a jig-grinding machine. Single-point boring tools of the adjustable or offset type are used either for holes of special size, to obtain greater accuracy than by end reaming, or when suitable end reamers are not at hand. These adjustable boring tools consist of a taper shank that fits into the machine spindle, and means of adjusting the tool radially for controlling the diameter of the hole to be bored. Non-adjustable boring bars are also used. These have taper shanks which fit directly into the machine spindle.

How is circular indexing or dividing done on a jig-boring machine?

Precision jig borers are equipped with circular or rotary tables for precision circular indexing. Fig. 7 shows the application of a rotary table for boring the holes in a drill jig. The outer edge of the table is graduated in degrees for setting it approximately to the required angle. A rapid-traversing handwheel is used for this approximate adjustment. A smaller slow-motion handwheel is used to obtain the exact position. A large dial is graduated in minutes and a vernier subdivides the reading to five seconds. A tilting rotary table may be used when holes must be bored at an angle.

What are the advantages in using jig-boring and jig-grinding machines?

Jig-boring machines are widely used at the present time because they make it possible to bore holes rapidly and accurately to given center distances. While such machines are designed primarily for boring holes in jigs, they are also used for various other classes of precision hole boring. Prior to the introduction of these machines, slower precision methods were required. (See section on Precision Methods of Spacing or Locating Holes.) While these precision methods are still employed, especially where jig-boring machines are not available, they usually require much more time.

In many cases, a jig borer is a "jig eliminator." In other words, such a machine may be used instead of a jig either when the quantity of work is not large enough to warrant making a jig or when there is insufficient time for jig making. These machines are also useful in making parts for the first model of a machine or other device.

In the practical application of jig-boring machines, the drawings should be so dimensioned that every hole required can be readily located from the longitudinal and lateral dimensions given on the drawing.

The jig grinder is an economical machine for finishing holes in hardened parts. The holes in such parts should preferably be end reamed or bored prior to the hardening operation, in a jig-boring machine, to reduce as far as possible the errors and grinding allowances.

Controlling Degree of Accuracy in Interchangeable Manufacture

In manufacturing duplicate machines or other mechanisms, two general methods of procedure are possible. One method is to build each machine independently of the others in obtaining the necessary fits between the different parts. For instance, in manufacturing a given lot of machines, some part such as a bearing, for example, might be fitted to its shaft in order to obtain the quality of fit required. Let us assume that this same individual fitting job is done on each machine and without attempting to use bearings or shafts sufficiently uniform to make them interchangeable on any of the various machines in a given lot. If this practice were followed, each bearing would be suitable for its own particular shaft and machine, and it could not be placed on another machine unless it happened, by chance, to be the right size. In other words, in manufacturing duplicate machines according to this plan, the various parts would be fitted together on an individual basis and more or less by cut-and-try methods. But if this were done, both manufacturing and maintenance costs might be increased considerably. The accuracy of different parts or fittings would also vary more or less and depend somewhat upon the judgment or skill of different workmen, especially if dimensions were given on drawings without any indication as to the accuracy required.

What is interchangeable manufacture?

Another method of manufacture makes it possible to finish duplicate parts in lots and without individual fitting to any particular machine. This is possible because the parts are sufficiently accurate to assemble properly in any machine of a given lot or series. This is known as *interchangeable manufacture*. In producing a machine, the degree of accuracy that is essential for the different parts

359

varies considerably. Furthermore, one type of machine or mechanism requires for certain parts, or perhaps throughout its construction, much greater accuracy than certain other types. When the interchangeable plan of manufacture is adopted, it is evident that there must be some method of establishing the accuracy required for different parts, and then means must be provided to insure adhering to whatever limits of accuracy have been prescribed.

The interchangeable method of manufacture is especially applicable in the production of duplicate machines or other mechanical devices, particularly when the quantity is large. The term "interchangeable" implies that the various parts of a mechanism are accurate enough to function properly and sufficiently uniform in size and shape to fit or assemble in any of the machines of a lot or series for which the part is intended. In other words, the parts are theoretically, at least, interchangeable. Limits of accuracy are established for the individual parts and also for groups of assembled parts; then manufacturing and gaging equipment is used to obtain and check the established limits.

Who originated the interchangeable system of manufacture?

It is interesting to note, in passing, that the importance of establishing some method of insuring a reasonable degree of accuracy or uniformity in the manufacture of duplicate parts was realized back in 1798 by Eli Whitney, inventor of the cotton gin. He obtained a contract from the government for 10,000 muskets, built a shop in the outskirts of New Haven, and there laid the foundations of the interchangeable system of manufacture. Using limit-gages, milling machines, and rude jigs, he demonstrated that guns could be manufactured by machine tools, not only interchangeably but cheaper than by the old hand methods.

Are machine parts always made as accurately as possible?

No, this would be bad manufacturing practice, although there is no objection to accuracy that does not increase production costs. Extreme or unnecessary accuracy may increase greatly the manufacturing cost. While it would be possible to finish parts to given dimensions within 0.0001 inch or even less, such extreme accuracy in most cases would serve no useful purpose, but it would require, in addition to precise finishing processes, very accurate gaging or inspection. With the modern machine tools and other manufacturing equipment now available, many machine parts in the regular course of manufacture may be produced more accurately than they need to be to serve properly the intended purpose. In such cases, the unnecessary accuracy is, of course, on the safe side and desirable. But if unnecessary accuracy greatly increases the production costs and does not improve the functioning of a part, increase its durability, or result in some other desirable condition, then it is evident that any increase in manufacturing cost to secure such accuracy is unwarranted. For example, let us assume that many thousands of small pins are required in connection with the production of a certain mechanical device. If these pins, when made approximately ½ inch in diameter, will serve as well as pins that are almost exactly ½ inch, there would be no point in using the extremely accurate pins, especially if this required a much slower method of producing them. This leads up to one of the most important principles in present-day manufacturing methods. It is the principle of controlling accuracy and establishing it for any part or group of machine parts *with reference to their function*. In order to produce parts according to this principle, it is evident that there must be some method or plan for indicating definitely just what degree of accuracy is required for any given dimension and that is the basis for interchangeable manufacture.

Are there different degrees of interchangeability?

There are several degrees of interchangeability in machinery manufacture. Strictly speaking, interchangeability consists in making the different parts of a mechanism so uniform in size and contour that each part of a certain model will fit any mating part of the same model, regardless of the lot to which it belongs or when it was made. However, as often defined, interchangeability consists in making each part fit any mating part in a certain series;

that is, the interchangeability exists only in the same series. Selective assembly is sometimes termed interchangeability, but is merely assembly without fitting. It will be noted that the strict definition of interchangeability does not imply that the parts must always be assembled without hand work, although that is usually considered desirable. It does mean, however, that when the mating parts are finished, by whatever process, they must assemble and function properly, without fitting individual parts one to the other.

When a machine has been installed possibly at some distant point, a broken part can readily be replaced by a new one sent by the manufacturer, but this feature is secondary as compared with the increased efficiency in manufacturing on an interchangeable basis. In order to make parts interchangeable, it is necessary to use gages and measuring tools, to provide some system of inspection, and to adopt suitable tolerances or allowable variations from the basic dimensions. Whether absolute interchangeability is practicable or not may depend upon the tolerances adopted, the relation between the different parts, and their form. Parts will always interchange if the tolerances are large enough, and the maximum sizes of members such as shafts, etc., do not exceed the minimum sizes of holes which receive them when the machine is assembled; but if the tolerances are too large, the parts may be useless.

Should the interchangeable system be applied to all mechanical products?

Interchangeable manufacturing should only be applied where it is economical. In general, the *principle* of controlled accuracy is desirable even in very small shops or manufacturing plants, but it does not follow that there should be complete interchangeability in all cases. In fact, there are many exceptions. For example, where the production of duplicate machines or other devices is small, strict interchangeability or a system approaching it might be too costly. This applies particularly to shops or plants turning out a miscellaneous class of work or where special machines are built without even a single duplicate machine in some cases. There should be a sensible balance between manufacturing and assembling costs, and savings in assembling would in many shops be much more than offset by the increased manufacturing cost resulting from interchangeable manufacture on a small scale.

In some lines, the question of service costs is also important, or costs in connection with future repairs and replacement of parts. The use of interchangeable parts is, of course, very important in this connection, but the extent of such replacements varies widely in different lines of manufacture. It is not a question of having strict interchangeability or none at all. The problem, in general, is to determine how far the principle of interchangeable manufacture can be applied profitably in any shop or plant.

What are basic dimensions and why are they very important in machine construction?

A basic dimension is the theoretical or nominal size, which, for practical reasons, is only approximated; or, it is the dimension which would be obtained if perfection were possible and did not result in increased manufacturing costs. However, since perfection is impossible and also unnecessary, so far as the dimensions of machine parts are concerned, it is general practice to give a base or *basic dimension* and then indicate by supplementary "tolerance" dimensions just how much the actual dimension can vary from the basic without causing trouble; or, to put it another way, how much *inaccuracy* is allowable without causing a part to fit or function improperly.

Anyone at all familiar with mechanical devices knows that there are wide variations in the accuracy required for different parts. Some, for example, might need to be within 0.001 or 0.002 inch, or less, of a given or basic size, whereas other parts might function perfectly if within, say, 0.010 to 0.020 inch of this basic dimension. To illustrate further, suppose that a hole (which is to receive a stud) requires a diameter of about 1.250 inch (see Fig. 1); but assume that the actual diameter may vary from this 1.250 inch size as much as 0.005 inch oversize without too much play between the hole and stud. In this case, 1.250 inch is the basic dimension or the dimension aimed at. In producing such holes, some might happen to have a diameter of

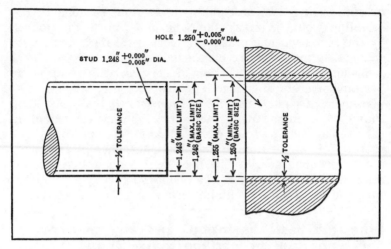

Fig. 1. Graphic Illustration of the Meaning of the Terms Limit and Tolerance

exactly 1.250 inch, whereas the diameters of other holes would be up to the maximum of 1.255 inch and yet serve equally well. Since, as a general rule, approximate dimensions are easier to obtain and maintain than very accurate ones, *unnecessary* accuracy is avoided unless it is obtained without extra effort or cost.

How is a basic dimension established?

A basic dimension, as a general rule, represents the most important dimension or one that would cause the most trouble if not sufficiently accurate. To illustrate, the stud shown in Fig. 1 is to fit into a hole and some clearance is required. The stud diameter is 1.248 + 0.000 — 0.005 inch; the hole is 1.250 + 0.005 — 0.000. With these dimensions, the minimum clearance obtained when a maximum stud enters a minimum hole equals 1.250 — 1.248 = 0.002 inch. If a stud is made larger than the maximum dimension given, proper assembly might be difficult or impossible; but these studs may be 0.005 under this maximum size. Hence, in this case and as a general rule, the basic diameter of a stud, shaft or any other male part is the maximum diameter and the tolerance is minus.

If the hole in the preceding case is less than 1.250 inch, proper assembly may again be difficult or impossible, but the hole may be 0.005 inch over size; hence, in this case and as a general rule, the basic diameter of a hole is the minimum limit with a plus tolerance.

When a plug or shaft is larger than the hole in the hub in order to obtain a forced fit, the preceding general rules are reversed. In the case of forced fits, the minimum fit allowance represents the most critical point; hence, for force fits the basic dimension of the shaft is the minimum limit requiring a plus tolerance, while the basic dimension of the hole is the maximum limit requiring a minus tolerance.

When dimensions are given to locate two or more holes, such as center-to-center distances, the basic dimension should represent the danger point or that dimension which should be aimed for to avoid trouble.

What is a tolerance and how is it related to a basic dimension?

Tolerance is the amount that the dimension of a machine part may vary from the basic dimension. The use of tolerances is to insure *controlling* the accuracy of machine parts. In other words, since perfection is practically impossible, the imperfections or inaccuracies are definitely specified by giving the tolerances on the drawings; then the parts are checked by the use of proper gaging equipment to safeguard against inaccuracies of such magnitude that they would interfere with the functioning of a part or group of assembled parts. Suppose the diameter of a pin is given on a drawing as ¾ inch and without a tolerance. While this might be done in repair shops or in small plants making special equipment and not concerned particularly with interchangeable manufacture, in the larger plants and especially where many duplicate machines or other devices are produced, dimensions are accompanied by tolerance figures. Without these indications of required accuracy, the shop man would be in doubt as to just what degree of accuracy is needed to insure proper functioning of the part; so he would rely upon judgment or experience—and these might or might not be dependable.

It would be possible in any well-equipped shop to make a ¾-inch pin or other part within, say, 0.0005 inch of a given diameter or even more accurate than this; but why waste time in securing a high degree of accuracy when an approximate diameter would serve just as well? This explains why basic dimensions are accompanied by tolerances on many drawings.

When is a tolerance "unilateral" and when is it "bilateral"?

The term *unilateral tolerance* means that the total tolerance, as related to a basic dimension, is in *one* direction

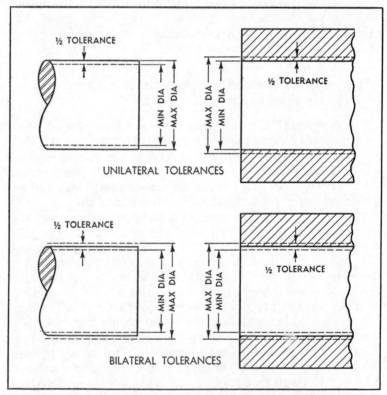

Fig. 2. Diagrams Illustrating Unilateral and Bilateral Tolerances. Full Lines Show Basic Diameters and Dotted Lines Allowable Variations

only. For example, if the basic dimension were 1 inch and a tolerance of 0.002 inch were expressed as 1.00 — 0.002, or as 1.00 + 0.002, these would be unilateral tolerances, since the total tolerance in each case is in one direction. On the contrary, if the tolerance were divided, so as to be partly plus and partly minus, it would be classed as *bilateral*.

Thus, $1.00 \begin{smallmatrix} + & 0.001 \\ - & 0.001 \end{smallmatrix}$ is an example of bilateral tolerance, because the total tolerance of 0.002 is given in two directions — plus and minus. (See diagrams, Fig. 2.)

There are different ways of expressing tolerances or of giving allowable dimensions. These different methods should be understood in order to properly "read" or interpret the dimensions on a drawing. When tolerances are unilateral, one of the three following methods should be used to express them:

(1) Specify limiting dimensions only as
    Diameter of hole: 2.250, 2.252
    Diameter of shaft: 2.249, 2.247

(2) One limiting size may be specified with its tolerances as
    Diameter of hole: 2.250 + 0.002, — 0.000
    Diameter of shaft: 2.249 + 0.000, — 0.002

(3) The nominal size may be specified for both parts, with a notation showing both allowance and tolerance, as
    Diameter of hole: 2¼ + 0.002, — 0.000
    Diameter of shaft: 2¼ — 0.001, — 0.003

Bilateral tolerances usually have plus and minus tolerances of equal amount. An example of the expression of bilateral tolerances follows:

$$2 \pm 0.001 \text{ or } 2 \begin{smallmatrix} + & 0.001 \\ - & 0.001 \end{smallmatrix}$$

Bilateral tolerances are not always divided equally as in the preceding example. To illustrate, if the total tolerance is 0.003 inch, it might be given as plus 0.001 and minus 0.002, in which case it would be written as follows:

$$2 \begin{smallmatrix} + & 0.001 \\ - & 0.002 \end{smallmatrix}$$

In general, if a greater tolerance is permissible in one direction than in the other, this may indicate that the tolerance should be unilateral instead of bilateral.

In which direction should a unilateral tolerance be applied?

A unilateral or one-direction tolerance should be applied in whichever direction is not likely to cause trouble. For example, if a shaft having a basic diameter of 2 inches would cause trouble in an assembled machine if over 2 inches but work satisfactorily if slightly under 2 inches, then the tolerance should be minus. If an excessive variation in either direction from the basic dimension is equally objectionable, then the tolerance should be bilateral or divided so as to be plus and minus relative to the basic dimension. Where tolerances are required on the distances between holes, usually they should be bilateral, as variation in either direction is usually equally dangerous. The variation in the distance between shafts carrying gears, however, should always be unilateral and plus; otherwise the gears might run too tight. A slight increase in the backlash between gears is seldom of much importance.

Is a dimension representing a tolerance the same as one representing a limit?

These terms, *tolerance* and *limit,* are often used interchangeably or as though they had exactly the same meaning; however, according to strict usage of the terms, there is a decided difference. The term limit should preferably be applied to indicate a limiting dimension. To illustrate, the maximum major diameter of a 2-inch American Standard screw thread is 2 inches. This is the *maximum limit* or limiting dimension for the major diameter. The minimum major diameter is 1.9746 inches. This is the *minimum limit.* If this minimum limit is subtracted from the maximum limit, the difference of 0.0254 inch represents the *tolerance* for this particular dimension; hence, tolerance is the difference between maximum and minimum limiting dimensions. The diagram, Fig. 1, shows a hole having a maximum limit of 1.255 inch, a minimum limit of 1.250 inch and a tolerance of 1.255 — 1.250 = 0.005 inch.

What is the difference between a tolerance and an allowance?

The terms "allowance," and "tolerance" are often used interchangeably in connection with the fitting of machine parts, but, according to common usage, there is the following distinction: *Allowance* is the amount required (either above or below a nominal or basic size) in order to secure a certain class of fitting between different parts. For instance, if the hole in a crank disk is 3 inches in diameter and the shaft is made 3.005 inches in diameter, in order to secure a forced fit, the 0.005 inch would represent the *allowance* for that part.

The dimensions for obtaining a certain allowance and class of fit may also have tolerances to insure obtaining an allowance that is within a certain desired minimum and maximum. To illustrate, suppose a cylindrical part such as a shaft is to fit snugly in the hub of a pulley. Assembly is to be by hand or possibly by the application of light pressure in some cases. According to the American Standard for a "snug fit" and a 4-inch nominal diameter, the shaft should be 4.00 + 0.000 — 0.0006 and the hole should be 4.00 + 0.001 — 0.000. When shafts and holes are made according to these tolerances, the maximum allowance (which represents a clearance) equals 4.001 — 3.9994 = 0.0016 inch. The minimum allowance is zero.

What is the "selective assembly" of machine parts?

Selective assembly consists of selecting by trial mating members of a mechanism that will give the desired fit at assembly, with little or no further machining or fitting. Companion parts made to the extreme limits are not supposed to interchange. For instance, a shaft or pin of maximum size may not assemble with a mating part of minimum size, although the maximum shaft and maximum hole and also the minimum shaft and hole must interchange. A good example of this selective method of assembling is found in the production of ball bearings. The balls are sorted into groups, according to their size, to facilitate the assembly of any bearing with balls of uniform size. Nearly every so-called "interchangeable" mechanism represents a combination of interchangeable and selective methods of quantity production.

The matter of clearances and tolerances, when manufacturing on an interchangeable basis, is quite different from manufacturing on the basis of selective assembly. In interchangeable manufacturing, the minimum clearances should be as small as the assembling of the parts and their proper operation under service conditions will allow. The maximum clearances should be as great as the functioning of the mechanism permits. The difference between the maximum and minimum clearances establishes the sum of the tolerances on the companion surfaces. When this allowable difference is smaller than normal manufacturing conditions will permit, however, parts cannot be economically manufactured on an interchangeable basis. In such cases one of two courses is open. First, excess metal may be left on one part which is fitted at assembly (this usually proves an expensive process) ; or second, tolerances can be established which enable the parts to be manufactured economically and then sorted and assembled according to their size. This second method is known as selective assembly manufacturing.

Different Classes of Fits for Assembled Machine Parts

There are many different classes of fits between parts that must be assembled together. For some parts, considerable clearance either is required or is preferable, whereas other parts must have no play or clearance whatever. There are also many parts which must fit together very tightly; in fact, when the fit is between cylindrical parts, the inner member or plug may be somewhat larger than the hole which receives it, as, for example, when a crankpin is forced ino a crank disk to obtain a very rigid permanent assembly. In between the loose fits or those having considerable clearance, and very tight fits, there are numerous others varying from loose to tight. For example, a shaft that revolves in a bearing must be slightly smaller than the bearing to provide room for a film of lubricant and prevent seizure in case the shaft expands more than the surrounding bearing as the temperature rises due to friction; but the amount of clearance varies considerably and depends upon such factors as the size of the journal, the type of machine and the general quality of the construction or the need for accurate fits.

How is the class or quality of fit determined for any machine part?

The kind or quality of fit for different machine parts should, as far as possible, be based upon actual experience with whatever mechanism the parts are intended for. Since machines and other mechanical devices are built in an endless variety of types and sizes, and for a wide range of purposes, it is evident that the degree of accuracy and quality of fits essential for one class of equipment may differ considerably from that required for some other class. For this reason, it is impracticable to establish general rules for governing the kind or quality of the fittings needed throughout the mechanical industries. It is possible, however, to give the average tolerances and allowances needed for certain grades of fits as they apply to very common machine parts or elements, such as plain cylindrical parts and threaded parts.

How are different classes of fits designated?

There are two general methods of indicating the kind or quality of a fit. One is by using a name which indicates the class of fit in a general way; the other is by giving the actual tolerances and allowances required for a given fit, or possibly a symbol designating such tolerances and allowances.

The names of fits include such terms as *clearance fits, running fits, sliding fits, push fits, driving fits, forced fits* and *shrinkage fits*. While these terms are more or less self-explanatory, they are, of course, very general and do not definitely indicate the exact quality of the fit.

What are "clearance" or "free fits" and the usual allowances for obtaining them?

This term might be applied to any fit having a clearance space between the internal and external members. Some clearance is always required for rotating shafts, sliding parts, or wherever there must be room either for a film of lubricant or to provide for expansion which might cause the parts to bind, thus breaking down the oil film and resulting in seizure between the parts. The amount of clearance allowed for a running shaft depends upon the general quality of workmanship required and the diameter of the shaft.

Clearance Fit Allowances.—The following figures are given merely as a general indication of probable allowances. Running or free fit allowances usually range from a minimum of 1 or 2 thousandths up to 4 or 5 thousandths. For example, if a shaft diameter is approximately 1 to 2 inches, the allowance usually ranges from a minimum of 0.001 to 0.0015 inch up to a maximum of 0.002 or 0.003 inch. If the diameter is, say, 4 or 5 inches, the minimum usually ranges from 0.0025 to 0.003 up to a maximum of 0.004 to 0.006 inch

What is a "push fit" and how much is allowed to obtain fits of this class?

The term "push fit," which may also be called a "snug fit," represents the closest fit that permits assembling parts by hand. In other words, anything closer would, in many cases, at least, require greater force than can be exerted by hand in assembling the parts. With a push fit, there should be no perceptible play between the parts, which means that the difference between the internal and external members is very slight. In fact, the diameter of the hole and plug may be practically the same. If the diameter of the two is *exactly* the same, there are differences of opinion about assembly by hand; but opinions on this point may be misleading for the simple reason that the *exact* measurements of plug and hole usually would not be known, since knowing the *exact* dimension requires means of determining it within millionths of an inch.

Allowances for Push Fits.—The allowances for fits of the push or snug class may vary from practically nothing up to 0.001 or 0.002 inch, depending upon the diameter and quality of the finish.

What is a "driving fit"?

When a plug or a shaft is made slightly larger than the hole into which it is to be inserted and the allowance is such that the parts can be assembled by driving, this is known as a *driving fit*. Obviously, such fits are employed when the parts are to remain in a fixed position relative to each other.

Before assembling parts with a driving fit, the bearing surfaces should be oiled. For assembling, a hydraulic press usually is preferable. A hammer or sledge may be used for light work, or a ram for comparatively large pieces. This ram consists either of a heavy steel bar or wooden beam which is supported by a rope or chain in a horizontal position and level with the work. In using the ram, it is drawn back and then pushed forward so that the end strikes the part being assembled. When it is difficult to drive a plug or a shaft into the hole, the operation of driving can be assisted greatly by the use of clamps and bolts. The clamp is placed across the end of the plug or shaft and is tightened by the bolts, thus subjecting the plug to a pressure. By continuing to tighten the clamp between successive blows of the ram, the parts can be readily assembled, provided the fit allowance is not excessive.

Allowances for Driving Fits.—The allowance for a driving fit depends upon the length of the bearing surface, the diameter, the smoothness of the surfaces and the thickness and kind of metal surrounding the hole. When the bearing surface of the hole is long, a smaller allowance is required for a driving fit than for a comparatively short hole. The total allowance also increases with the diameter and depends largely upon the condition of the surfaces. For diameters from 1 to 2 inches, the common allowance would be from 0.0005 to 0.0015 inch. For diameters from 2 to 3 inches, the allowance might range from 0.0015 to 0.0025 inch. Larger diameters requiring tight fits ordinarily would be assembled by using a hydraulic or other form of press. If the allowance for a 2-inch diameter is, say, 0.002 inch, this means that the internal part is 0.002 inch larger than the hole.

What is a "forced" or "pressed fit"?

"Forced" or "pressed fit" is the term used when a pin, shaft, or other cylindrical part is forced into a hole of slightly smaller diameter, ordinarily by the use of a hydraulic press or some other type of press capable of exerting considerable pressure. A forced fit has a larger allowance than a driving fit, and therefore requires greater pressure for assembling. As a rule, forced fits are restricted to parts of small and medium size, while shrinkage fits have no such limitations and are especially applicable when a maximum "grip" is desired, or when (as in the construction of ordnance) accurate results as to the intensity of stresses in the assembled parts are required.

The proper allowance for a forced fit depends upon the mass of metal surrounding the hole, the size of the work, the kind and quality of the material of which the parts are composed, and the smoothness and accuracy of the pin and bore. When a pin or other part is pressed into a hole a second time, the allowance for a given tonnage should be diminished somewhat because the surface of the bore is smoother and the metal more compact. Hence, data and formulas for forced fit allowances must be general in their application.

Crankpins, car-wheel axles, and similar parts which must be held very securely, are given forced or pressed fits rather than driving fits. The allowance per inch of diameter usually is about 0.001 to 0.0015 for diameters up to 4 or 5 inches. The allowance per inch tends to decrease as the diameter increases because of the increase in area; thus the total allowance for a diameter of 2 inches might be 0.004 inch, whereas, for a diameter of 8 inches, the total allowance might not be over 0.003 to 0.005 inch. In some shops, the allowance is made practically the same for all diameters, the increased surface area of the larger sizes giving sufficient increase in pressure. See accompanying "Record of Assembling Pressures for Forced Fits."

How much pressure is required for assembling parts when forced fits are employed?

The pressure required for assembling cylindrical parts depends not only upon the allowance for the fit, but also upon the area of the fitted surfaces, the smoothness of the surfaces, and the mass and kind of metal surrounding the hole. In making a pressed fit, the pressure at which the parts should be assembled is based upon the size and character of the work and the degree of tightness desired. If the assembling pressure is determined first, the next step is to estimate the probable allowance, that is, how much larger the fitted part should be than the hole into which it is forced, in order to enter at approximately the required pressure. In plants where a special line of machinery is regularly manufactured, and the same parts are continually made, work to be assembled in this way is machined to dimensions which are known to be right from previous experience.

Record of Assembling Pressures for Forced Fits—1

Diameter of Shaft, Inches	Diameter of Bore, Inches	Length of Hub, Inches	Diameter of Hub, Inches	Hub Material in	Allowance, Inches	Pressure, Tons
3.504	3.500	6	5	Steel	0.004	30
3.504	3.500	6	5	Steel	0.004	45
4.004	4.000	6	6¼	Steel	0.004	35
4.004	4.000	6	6¼	Steel	0.004	40
4.003	4.000	8	5½	Steel	0.003	30
4.004	4.000	6	6¼	Steel	0.004	35
4.004	4.000	8	5½	Steel	0.004	40
4.004	4.000	6	7¼	Steel	0.004	50
4.004	4.000	6	6¼	Steel	0.004	45
4.054	4.051	6	6¼	Steel	0.003	40
4.5035	4.500	8	6½	Steel	0.0035	45
4.505	4.503	6½	5¾	Cast Iron	0.002	20
4.503	4.500	6	10	Cast Iron	0.003	30
4.503	4.500	8	6½	Steel	0.003	40
4.880	4.875	7	7½	Steel	0.005	48
4.880	4.875	6	7¼	Steel	0.005	45
4.880	4.875	7	8	Steel	0.005	40
4.880	4.875	6	7¼	Steel	0.005	50
4.880	4.875	6	7¼	Steel	0.005	50
4.880	4.875	7	8	Steel	0.005	55
4.880	4.875	6	7½	Steel	0.005	45
4.880	4.875	6	7½	Steel	0.005	45
4.880	4.875	7	8	Steel	0.005	55
5.003	5.000	8	10	Cast Iron	0.003	20
5.002	5.000	5½	7¾	Steel	0.002	50
5.502	5.500	8½	13	Cast Iron	0.002	25
5.630	5.625	7	13	Cast Iron	0.005	30
5.629	5.625	8¼	8¼	Steel	0.004	65
5.630	5.625	7	8	Steel	0.005	45
5.630	5.625	7	8½	Steel	0.005	55
5.630	5.625	7	9¼	Steel	0.005	48
5.630	5.625	8	8	Steel	0.005	55
5.752	5.750	8	12¾	Cast Iron	0.002	20
6.005	6.000	8	9	Steel	0.005	70
6.005	6.000	8	9	Cast Iron	0.005	30
6.003	6.000	8	14½	Cast Iron	0.003	40
6.130	6.125	7	8¼	Steel	0.005	65
6.253	6.250	9	11½	Steel	0.003	60
6.2735	6.273	9	11½	Steel	0.0005	15
6.503	6.500	6	12	Cast Iron	0.003	40
6.502	6.500	8	13	Cast Iron	0.002	25
6.503	6.500	8	14¾	Cast Iron	0.003	35
6.502	6.500	12	10	Cast Iron	0.002	50
6.610	6.605	11	14	Steel	0.003	60

Record of Assembling Pressures for Forced Fits—2

Diameter of Shaft, Inches	Diameter of Bore, Inches	Length of Hub, Inches	Diameter of Hub, Inches	Material in Hub	Allowance, Inches	Pressure, Tons
6.939	7.000	8	11	Cast Iron	0.002	17
7.002	6.937	10	12	Steel	0.002	75
7.002	7.000	9	17	Cast Iron	0.002	50
7.003	7.000	10	13	Steel	0.003	85
7.003	7.000	9	16¾	Cast Iron	0.003	40
7.003	7.000	8	12¾	Cast Iron	0.003	35
7.003	7.000	10	13	Steel	0.003	50
7.003	7.000	9	17	Cast Iron	0.003	50
7.034	7.031	8	10½	Steel	0.003	75
7.2525	7.2495	9	16¾	Cast Iron	0.003	35
7.502	7.499	8	12¾	Cast Iron	0.003	55
7.5027	7.500	8	14½	Cast Iron	0.0027	20
7.534	7.531	10	12	Steel	0.003	50
8.002	8.000	9½	13¾	Steel	0.002	60
8.002	8.000	9½	13¾	Steel	0.002	60
8.002	8.000	16	14	Steel	0.002	110
8.003	8.000	9	17	Cast Iron	0.003	50
8.503	8.500	8	14½	Cast Iron	0.003	45
8.503	8.500	9	15	Cast Iron	0.003	40
8.507	8.504	9	11	Cast Iron	0.003	40
8.939	8.937	8	13	Cast Iron	0.002	20
9.002	8.999	12	20½	Cast Iron	0.003	65
9.0025	8.999	12	20½	Cast Iron	0.0035	75
9.002	9.000	10	14	Steel	0.002	75
9.003	9.000	12	21	Cast Iron	0.003	70
9.003	9.000	12	14¾	Cast Iron	0.003	85
9.003	9.000	10	18⅜	Steel	0.003	80
9.003	9.000	9	17	Cast Iron	0.003	45
9.939	9.937	7½	13	Cast Iron	0.002	25
10.003	10.000	9	16¾	Cast Iron	0.003	40
10.0035	10.000	14	21	Cast Iron	0.0035	80
10.502	10.500	8	13	Cast Iron	0.002	16
11.005	10.9997	14	20¾	Cast Iron	0.0053	38
11.002	11.000	12¾	18	Steel	0.002	85
11.002	11.000	13	18	Steel	0.002	90
11.0035	11.000	10	17½	Cast Iron	0.0035	60
12.003	12.000	13	20½	Cast Iron	0.003	70
13.003	13.000	14	22	Cast Iron	0.003	85
13.0045	13.000	12	22	Cast Iron	0.0045	90
13.004	13.000	13	26	Cast Iron	0.004	100
13.003	13.000	12¾	21	Steel	0.003	125
14.033	14.031	14	21	Steel	0.002	100
16.004	16.000	14	25½	Cast Iron	0.004	120
20.002	20.000	20	28⅞	Steel	0.002	160

The accompanying illustration shows the assembling of piston-pins into automobile engine pistons. The arbor press used is equipped with a small hydraulic cylinder and an oil pressure gage which shows the number of pounds required to force the pin into the piston. The sizes of the pin-holes and of the pins are marked so that the assembler can, by selection, obtain the allowance which experience has

Piston-pins are Assembled in the Pistons within Predetermined Pressure Limits by Means of an Arbor Press

shown will give the required assembling pressure. The pressure, in this case, must not be less than 175 pounds to force the pin through the first boss and not more than 350 pounds to force it through the second boss. The crank-pins of locomotives may require assembling pressures ranging from 25 to 50 tons.

What is a shrinkage fit?

A shrinkage or shrink fit is one obtained by making the internal member, such as a shaft or plug, slightly larger than the hole in the external member, the same as for force fits. In the case of a shrinkage fit, however, pressure is not required in assembling the parts, since the external member is heated and expanded sufficiently to permit inserting the internal part easily. Then, as the external part cools or is cooled by applying water, it shrinks tightly around the inner part.

When are shrinkage fits used in preference to forced fits?

Whether parts are to be assembled by forced or shrinkage fits depends upon conditions. For example, to press the steel tire of a locomotive over its wheel center, without heating, would ordinarily be a rather awkward and difficult job. On the other hand, pins, etc., are easily and quickly forced into place with a hydraulic press and there is the additional advantage of knowing the exact pressure required in assembling, whereas there is more or less uncertainty connected with a shrinkage fit, unless the stresses are calculated.

General practice seems to favor a smaller allowance for shrinkage fits than for forced fits, although in many shops the allowances are practically the same in each case, and for some classes of work, shrinkage allowances exceed those for forced fits. In any case, the shrinkage allowance varies to a great extent with the form and construction of the part which has to be shrunk into place. The thickness or amount of metal around the hole is the most important factor. The way in which the metal is distributed also has an influence on the results.

Tests to determine the difference in the quality of shrinkage and forced fits showed that the resistance of a shrinkage fit to slippage was, for an axial pull, 3.66 times greater than that of a forced fit, and, in rotation or torsion, 3.2 times greater. In each comparative test, the dimensions and allowances were the same. The most important point to consider in establishing allowances for shrinkage fits is the stress in the hub at the bore, which depends chiefly upon the shrinkage allowance. If the allowance is excessive, the elastic limit of the material will be exceeded and permanent set will occur, or, in extreme cases, the ultimate strength of the metal will be exceeded and the hub will burst.

How are very low temperatures used for obtaining expansion fits or the reverse of shrinkage fits?

The term "shrink" or "shrinkage" fit commonly is used when a ring-shaped outer member is heated and expanded in order to obtain a very tight fit between the outer and inner parts as the outer member shrinks around the hub or inner member. For some classes of work this process is reversed—that is, the inner part is *contracted* by using dry ice to lower its temperature; then a tight fit is obtained as the inner part expands in the outer member. The temperature of dry ice is about 109 degrees F. below zero; consequently, it may be used for contracting metal parts before inserting them into the holes or recesses. For example, this method has been applied in assembling cast-iron sleeves or liners into engine cylinder block castings. The liners are ground to a diameter that will provide a tight fit when they expand into the cylinder bores. They are placed in a dry ice refrigerator for 16 minutes, during which time they shrink about 0.006 inch in diameter. They are then inserted quickly into the cylinder bores and soon expand to provide a tight fit.

To cite another example, dry ice has been used in assembling alloy valve seat rings into cylinder blocks. The rings remain in the dry ice refrigerator from 6 to 12 minutes and attain a temperature of at least 90 degrees F. below zero. The resulting shrinkage makes it possible to insert them readily into the recessed holes of the cylinder block.

Is it practicable to always obtain fits of exactly the same quality?

No, there is always more or less variation in the kind or quality of a fit between mating parts, even though the allowance is supposed to be the same. Such variations, however, may not be great enough to be important. They are due to the fact that the actual dimensions of shafts, holes, etc., as produced under practical working conditions, are never absolutely uniform. To illustrate, if the diameter of a hole in a certain part happens to be down to the minimum limit, and the diameter of a shaft or pin assembled with it happens to be up to the maximum limit, the smallest clearance or tightest fit, as the case may be, would then be obtained. Now, if this order is reversed, and a minimum shaft happens to be assembled in a maximum hole, then the largest clearance (or smallest allowance in case of a forced fit) will be obtained. Such variations ordinarily are very small and the intention is to establish tolerances that will not result in variations large enough to make any practical difference or interfere with the usefulness of the parts. In some cases, however, when the fit allowance happens to represent one of these extreme conditions, the assembled parts may not function satisfactorily. If some clearance is required, the minimum clearance should be as small as will permit the ready assembly and operation of the parts, while the maximum clearance should be as great as the functioning of the mechanism will allow.

What standards apply to different classes of fits for cylindrical parts?

American-British-Canadian conferences held in 1952 and 1953 resulted in a draft proposal for an ABC system of limits and fits. The effect of this proposal was to provide a unified basis for each of the three countries' national standards on limits and fits. It was not intended that this document would be used in the form presented but rather that each country would republish it in its usual national form, without, however, altering the technical contents.

The American Standard for Preferred Limits and Fits for Cylindrical Parts (ASA B4.1-1955) is in accord with the recommendations contained in the ABC agreements and in addition has been extended to cover other areas considered important to American industry, mainly sizes above 20 inches.

In the American standard, fits are designated by means of the following symbols which facilitate reference to classes of fit for educational purposes. The symbols are not intended to be shown on manufacturing drawings; instead, sizes should be specified on drawings.

The letter symbols used are as follows:

RC   Running or Sliding Fit
LC   Locational Clearance Fit
LT   Locational Transition Fit
LN   Locational Interference Fit
FN   Force or Shrink Fit

These letter symbols are used in conjunction with numbers representing the class of fit; thus FN4 represents a Class 4, force fit.

Each of these symbols (two letters and a number) represents a complete fit for which the minimum and maximum clearance or interference and the limits of size for the mating parts are given directly in tables (see MACHINERY'S HANDBOOK).

Description of Fits.—The classes of fits are arranged in three general groups: running and sliding fits, locational fits, and force fits.

Running and Sliding Fits (RC).—Running and sliding fits, for which limits of clearance are given in Table 2, are intended to provide a similar running performance, with suitable lubrication allowance, throughout the range of sizes. The clearances for the first two classes, used chiefly as slide fits, increase more slowly with the diameter than for the other classes, so that accurate location is maintained even at the expense of free relative motion.

Locational Fits (LC, LT, and LN).—Locational fits are fits intended to determine only the location of the mating parts; they may provide rigid or accurate location as with interference fits, or provide some freedom of location, as with clearance fits. Accordingly, they are divided into three groups: clearance fits (LC), transition fits (LT), and interference fits (LN).

Force Fits (FN).—Force or shrink fits constitute a special type of interference fit, normally characterized by maintenance of constant bore pressures throughout the range of sizes. The interference therefore varies almost directly with diameter, and the difference between its minimum and maximum value is small, to maintain the resulting pressures within reasonable limits.

Graphical Representation of Limits and Fits.—A visual comparison of the hole and shaft tolerances and the clearances or interferences provided by the various types and classes of fits can be obtained from the diagrams in MACHINERY'S HANDBOOK. These diagrams have been drawn to scale for a nominal diameter of 1 inch.

How are different classes of screw thread fits provided for in the American Standard?

The American Standard includes a system of limits for both screws and nuts. The different classes of limits listed below conform to the American Standard as revised in 1949 and later. There are three new series designated by symbols 1A, 2A, and 3A for *external* threads and 1B, 2B, and 3B for *internal* threads.

Classes 1A and 1B.—These classes replace Class 1 of the former American Standard. They might be specified where a little looseness or play is not objectionable and when rapid assembly is essential.

Classes 2A and 2B.—These classes are the recognized standard for the normal production of screws, bolts, nuts, and for many other applications.

Classes 3A and 3B.—The pitch diameter tolerances in this classification are 75 per cent of those allowed for 2A and 2B. In other words, this classification calls for a higher degree of accuracy than 2A and 2B.

Classes 2 and 3.—These two classes have the same limiting dimensions as Classes 2 and 3 of the former American Standard. They are not included in the Unified Series. Maximum external and minimum internal thread dimensions are basic. Tolerances for Class 3 are approximately 70 per cent of Class 2 tolerances.

Data for Classes 2 and 3 are now only included for reference purposes in the American Standard since these threads have been replaced almost completely by Unified classes 2A, 2B, 3A, and 3B.

Tables giving standard limits for both screws and nuts will be found in engineering handbooks.

Calipers, Micrometers and Other Measuring Instruments

The measuring tools used in machine construction to secure the required degree of accuracy, include tools for measurements of length, tools for the measurement of tapers or angles, gages for screw threads, etc. In these general classes of measuring and gaging tools, there are many different types and designs. For instance, there is the adjustable type, which is graduated and is used for taking direct measurements in inches or degrees; then, there is the gage type which is fixed and cannot be used for determining various sizes or angles, but simply for gaging or testing one particular size. There are also tools for taking approximate measurements and others designed for very accurate or precise measurements.

When are ordinary calipers used for checking measurements?

Calipers are used principally for external and internal measurements not requiring great accuracy, and are made in a variety of designs. Sketch A, Fig. 1, shows outside calipers and indicates how they are used for testing the size of a cylindrical part. Inside calipers for testing the diameter of a hole are shown at B, and sketch C illustrates how the outside calipers are set by comparison with the inside pair, or vice versa.

Most calipers are either of the firm joint or the spring type; the former type, which is shown at A and B, simply has a friction joint between the two "legs," whereas the spring type (illustrated at D and E) is provided with an adjusting screw and nut, and the two members are forced together against the tension of the curved spring at the upper or pivot end. These are merely constructional features and have nothing to do with the use of the calipers. Spring calipers are not made in large sizes like the friction-joint type.

The spring type of calipers shown at D and E are used for measuring the diameters of threads. Caliper D is for testing the outside diameter. It has broad ends which span two or more threads so that the diameter across the tops of the threads can easily be obtained by first adjusting the caliper to just touch the threads and then measuring the distance between the ends with a machinist's rule. Caliper E is for testing the diameter at the bottom or root of the thread. The ends are V-shaped so that the points will bear at the bottom of the thread groove. For accurate measurements, a thread micrometer or the 3-wire method should be used.

The caliper illustrated at F is half caliper and half divider. This form is often used for drawing a line parallel to a finished edge or for locating a central point on the end of a shaft by setting the caliper to the radius of the shaft, as near as can be judged, and then scribing arcs which, at the point of intersection, indicate the center.

The special form of caliper shown at G is useful either for testing the distance from the end of a shaft or rod to a shoulder, or the distance from one shoulder to another.

How are calipers "set" or adjusted to a given size or dimension?

Outside calipers are commonly set to a given dimension in inches, by holding one end against the end of a scale and adjusting the other end until it coincides with the graduation line representing the required size. A more accurate and positive method is to use a standard plug or disk gage of the required diameter, if one is available. When setting inside calipers with a scale, the end of the latter should be placed squarely against some true surface; then one end of the caliper is held against this same surface, thus aligning it with the end of the scale, while the other end is adjusted to the required measurement. To insure a square end against which to place a scale and caliper, hold the scale on the blade of a square with one end resting against the beam or stock. Standard ring gages or an outside

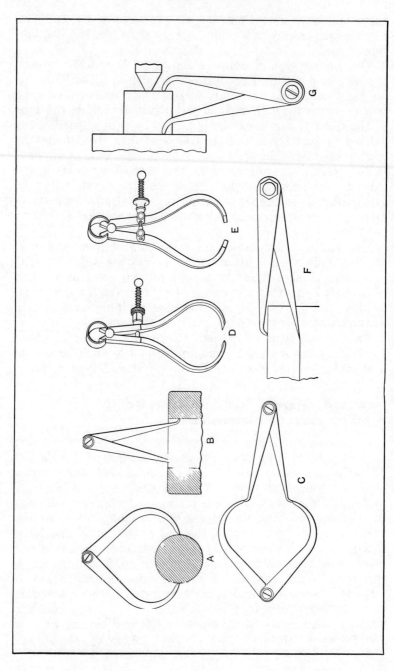

Fig. 1. Different Types of Calipers for Machine Shop Work

micrometer are preferable for setting inside calipers. When using a micrometer, it is first set to the size required; then the ends of the caliper are adjusted to just touch the parallel faces of the anvil and spindle of the micrometer. When an attempt is made to set inside calipers to a given measurement, by first setting outside calipers with a scale and then transferring the size to the inside caliper, obviously, several chances of error are introduced.

If the shaft at A, Fig. 1, were being fitted to the hole B, the calipers would be set as follows: First the inside pair would be adjusted to just touch both sides of the hole, when held as shown. The outside calipers would then be set to just touch the ends of the inside calipers so that the outside pair, practically speaking, would represent the hole and could be used for testing the size of the shaft. If a rather heavy pressure were required to force the outside calipers over the shaft, this would indicate that the diameter was too large, unless a forced fit was wanted. If the pressure were the same as between the two pairs of calipers, the shaft would fit tightly; whereas, if the calipers passed over easily and without perceptible pressure, a close sliding fit should be obtained.

Is it practicable to estimate a fit allowance from the side play of an inside caliper?

Judging a fit allowance by the amount of side play that inside calipers have in a hole is not very reliable, especially when considerable accuracy is necessary. The following rule may be used to determine the allowance for a given amount of side play, or, in other words, the difference between the diameter of the hole and the dimensions to which the caliper is set or the length of a standard end-measuring rod.

Rule.—Determine the amount of side play in sixteenths of an inch or the number of sixteenths; square this number and divide the result by twice the caliper setting or length of the end-measuring rod. The quotient represents the allowance or difference in thousandths of an inch.

Example. — Suppose a standard end-measuring rod, 6 inches long, had a side play of $\frac{1}{4}$ inch in a bored hole. What is the difference between the length of the rod and the diameter of the hole?

In ¼ inch, there are 4 sixteenths; hence, the allowance or difference $=\dfrac{4 \times 4}{2 \times 6} = \dfrac{16}{12} = 1.3$ thousandths or 0.0013 in.

While this method does not give results which are absolutely accurate, the error is so small, especially when the amount of side play is small, that it can usually be disregarded. Judging an allowance for a fit in this way would be unnecessary in most shops, owing to the gages and micrometers for both external and internal measurements which are now in common use and give direct measurements.

Why are micrometers used so extensively?

In measuring or testing sizes by means of calipers, the degree of accuracy attained depends largely upon the skill, judgment, and experience of the one who sets and uses the calipers. Some machinists and toolmakers can work within very close limits, while others lack the delicate sense of touch that is necessary. In order to largely reduce this personal factor, micrometers are extensively used, especially by toolmakers, in order to obtain direct measurements and secure different classes of fits by a definite allowance in thousandths of an inch instead of by judging the allowance from the pressure or side play of ordinary calipers.

Micrometer calipers are precision measuring instruments that are equipped with a screw of fine pitch and graduations which show very minute movements of the screw so that very accurate measurements can be taken. A small size for external measurements is shown at A, Fig. 2. The part to be measured is placed against the anvil a and the adjustable spindle b is then screwed in until it bears lightly against the work, by turning the thimble or sleeve c; the size is then determined by referring to the micrometer graduations. Most micrometers are graduated to read to thousandths of an inch, although some have an auxiliary vernier scale which enables readings to within 0.0001 inch to be taken.

What is the "ratchet stop" of a micrometer?

Many micrometers have what is called a ratchet stop d, Fig. 2, at the end of the barrel or thimble. If this is used when adjusting the measuring point against the work, it

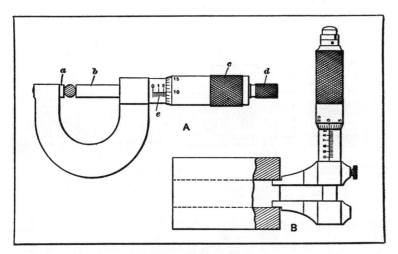

Fig. 2. Outside and Inside Micrometers

will slip when the point bears lightly, and thus prevent excessive pressure. This slipping will be indicated by the "click" of the ratchet. The advantage of securing a uniform contact or degree of pressure is that uniform readings are then obtained. Obviously, a difference in pressure will give a different reading and might result in a serious error.

What is the principle of the micrometer and the general rule for "reading" it?

The pitch of the thread on the spindle b (Fig. 2) of an ordinary micrometer is $\frac{1}{40}$ of an inch. Along the frame at e (see also detail sketch A, Fig. 3), there are graduations which are $\frac{1}{40}$ inch apart; therefore, when thimble c and the measuring spindle are turned one complete revolution, they move in or out a distance equal to one of the graduations or $\frac{1}{40}$ inch, which equals $\frac{25}{1000}$ inch. Now instead of turning the thimble one complete revolution, suppose it is turned say $\frac{1}{25}$ of a revolution; then the distance between the anvil

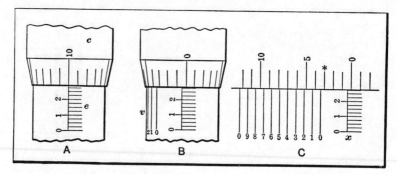

Fig. 3. Micrometer Graduations

and the end of the spindle will be increased or diminished $\frac{1}{25}$ of $\frac{25}{1000}$ of an inch, or one thousandth inch. This is why the beveled edge of a micrometer spindle has twenty-five graduations, each of which represents 0.001 inch. Following is a general rule for reading a micrometer:

Rule.—Count the number of whole divisions that are visible on the scale of the frame, multiply this number by 25 (the number of thousandths of an inch that each division represents) and add to the product the number of that division on the thimble which coincides with the axial zero line on the frame. The result will be the diameter expressed in thousandths of an inch.

As the numbers 1, 2, 3, etc., opposite every fourth subdivision on the frame indicate hundreds of thousandths, the reading can easily be taken mentally. Suppose the thimble is screwed out so that graduation 2, and three additional subdivisions are visible (as shown at A, Fig. 3), and that graduation 10 on the thimble coincided with the axial line on the frame. The reading then would be 0.200 + 0.075 + 0.010, or 0.285 inch.

If the micrometer has a vernier, how is the measurement or reading determined?

Some micrometers have a vernier scale v on the frame (see sketch B, Fig. 3), in addition to the regular graduations, so that measurements within 0.0001 inch can be taken. Micrometers of this type are read as follows:

Rule.—First determine the number of thousandths, as with an ordinary micrometer, and then find a line on the vernier scale that exactly coincides with one on the thimble; the number of this line represents the number of ten-thousandths to be added to the number of thousandths obtained by the regular graduations.

The relation between the graduations of the vernier and those on the thimble is more clearly shown by diagram *C*. The vernier has ten divisions which occupy the same space as nine divisions on the thimble, and for convenience in reading are numbered as shown. The difference between the width of a vernier division and one on the thimble is equal to one-tenth of a space on the thimble. Therefore a movement of the thimble equal to this difference between the vernier and thimble graduations represents 0.0001 inch. When the thimble zero coincides with the line *x* on the frame, the zero of the vernier coincides with the third line to the left (marked with an asterisk). Now when the thimble zero (or any other graduation line on the thimble) has passed line *x*, the number of ten-thousandths to add to the regular reading is equal to the number of that line on the vernier which exactly coincides with a line on the thimble. Thus the reading shown at *C* is 0.275 + 0.0004 = 0.2754 inch.

What types of micrometers are used for internal measurements and for large diameters?

One type of micrometer for measuring the diameters of holes or for taking other internal dimensions is shown at *B*, Fig. 2. The measuring surfaces are hardened and ground to a radius to secure accurate measurements and to avoid cramping when measuring the distances between parallel surfaces. The movable jaw has a clamp screw that is tightened when it is desired to retain the setting of the calipers. Another form of inside micrometer is shown in Fig. 4. This particular size can be used for measurements varying from 2 to 12 inches. When testing the diameter of a comparatively small hole, when there is not sufficient room for the hand, an auxiliary handle *a* is screwed into the micrometer head as shown in the illustration. The micrometer screw has a movement of one-half inch and by inserting extension rods of different lengths in the head at *b*, any dimension up

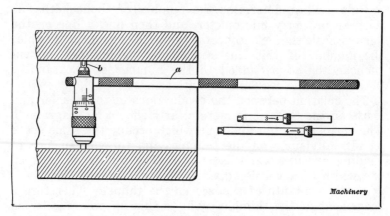

Fig. 4. Inside Micrometer Equipped with Extension Rods

to 12 inches can be obtained. Two of these extension rods are shown to the right. They are provided with collars which serve to locate them accurately in the micrometer head.

An inside micrometer gage that is especially adapted for large internal measurements is shown at *A*, Fig. 5. This gage consists of a holder equipped with a micrometer screw with graduations reading to 0.001 inch, and into this holder is inserted an adjustable rod. This rod also has graduations in the form of a series of annular grooves of a form and depth that allow clamping fingers on the holder to spring into them, thus making it possible to shift the rod in or out to the required length. Gages of this type usually have a series of rods so that a wide range of sizes can be measured. They are not only used for internal measurements but for setting calipers and for similar work.

A micrometer caliper for large external measurements is shown at *B*, Fig. 5. The micrometer screw has an adjustment of one inch and is graduated to read to 0.001 inch. When measuring small sizes, the long anvil or spindle *s* is used, whereas, for larger sizes, one of the shorter spindles is inserted. The sides of the steel frame are covered with hard rubber to prevent inaccuracies in the measurements as the result of expansion from the heat of the hands. As will be noted, this micrometer has a ratchet stop to insure uniform pressure when measuring.

What is a vernier and why is it used?

The vernier is an auxiliary scale that is attached to
vernier calipers, height gages, depth gages, protractors, etc.,
for obtaining the fractional parts of the subdivisions of the
true scale of the instrument. For example, the true or regular scale of the vernier caliper shown in Fig. 6 is graduated
in fortieths of an inch, but by means of the vernier scale V,
which is attached to the sliding jaw of the instrument,
measurements within one-thousandth of an inch can be
taken. In other words, the vernier, in this case, makes it
possible to divide each fortieth of an inch on the true scale
into twenty-five parts. The distance that the vernier scale
zero has moved to the right of the zero mark on the true
scale (which equals diameter D) may be read directly in
thousandths of an inch, by calling each tenth on the true
scale that has been passed by the vernier zero, one hundred
thousandths, and each fortieth, twenty-five thousandths,
and adding to this number as many thousandths as are indicated by the vernier. The vernier zero in the illustration is
slightly beyond the five-tenths division; hence, the reading
is 0.500 plus the number of thousandths indicated by that
line on the vernier that exactly coincides with one on the

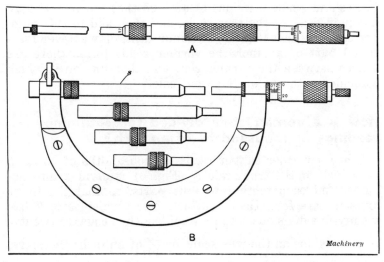

Fig. 5. (A) Inside Micrometer Gage for Large Holes.
(B) Large Outside Micrometer

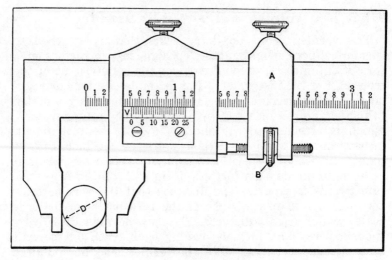

Fig. 6. Vernier Caliper

scale which, in this case, is line 15, making the reading 0.500 + 0.015 = 0.515 inch.

How to Read a Vernier.—The following is a general rule for taking readings with a vernier: Note the number of inches and whole divisions of an inch that the vernier zero has moved along the true scale, and then add to this number as many thousandths, or hundredths, or whatever fractional part of an inch the vernier reads to, as there are spaces between the vernier zero and that line on it which coincides with one on the true scale.

How is a vernier scale divided for obtaining readings in thousandths of an inch?

When a vernier caliper reads to thousandths of an inch, each inch of the true scale S (Fig. 7) is divided into ten parts, and each tenth into four parts, so that the finest divisions are fortieths of an inch. The vernier scale V has twenty-five divisions, and its total length is equal to twenty-four divisions on the true scale, or $\frac{24}{40}$ of an inch; therefore, each division on the vernier equals $\frac{1}{25}$ of $\frac{24}{40}$ or $\frac{24}{1000}$ inch.

Now, as $\dfrac{1}{40}$ equals $\dfrac{25}{1000}$ we see that the vernier divisions

are $\dfrac{1}{1000}$ inch shorter than those on the true scale. There-

fore if the zero marks of both scales were exactly in line,

the first two lines to the right would be $\dfrac{1}{1000}$ inch apart;

the next two $\dfrac{2}{1000}$, etc. It is evident, then, that if the

vernier were moved to the right until, say, the tenth line
from the zero mark exactly coincides with one on the true
scale, as shown at A, the movement would be equal to
0.010 inch, since this line was 0.010 inch to the left of the
mark with which it now coincides, when the zero lines of
both scales were together. If the vernier were moved along
to the position shown by the next diagram B, the true scale
would indicate directly that the reading was slightly over
0.500 inch, and the coincidence of the graduation line 15 on
the vernier with a line on the true scale would show the
exact reading to be $0.500 + 0.015 = 0.515$ inch.

The true scale S, shown at C, is graduated into sixteenths
of an inch, and the vernier V has eight divisions with a

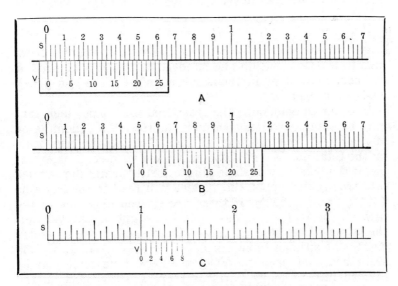

Fig. 7. Scales with Verniers Set in Different Positions

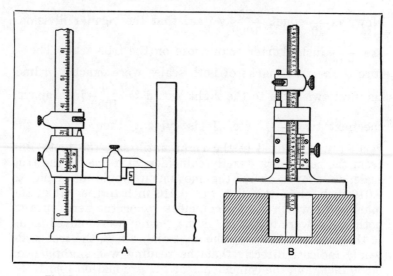

Fig. 8. (A) Vernier Height Gage. (B) Vernier Depth Gage

total length equal to seven divisions on the true scale, or
$\frac{7}{16}$ of an inch; therefore, each division on the vernier is
$\frac{1}{8}$ of $\frac{1}{16}$, or $\frac{1}{128}$ inch shorter than the divisions on the true
scale; so we see that in this case the vernier enables read-
ings to be taken within one hundred and twenty-eighths of
an inch, instead of in thousandths as with the one previously described.

In order to determine the fractional part of an inch that
may be obtained by any vernier, multiply the denominator
of the finest subdivision of an inch given on the true scale
by the total number of divisions on the vernier. For example, if the true scale is divided into fortieths and the vernier
into twenty-five parts, the vernier will read to thousandths
$(40 \times 25 = 1000)$. If there are sixteen divisions to the
inch on the true scale and a total of eight on the vernier,
the latter will enable readings within one hundred twenty-
eighths of an inch to be taken $(16 \times 8 = 128)$. It will be
seen then that each subdivision on the true scale can be
divided into as many parts as there are divisions on the
vernier.

What is a vernier height gage?

The vernier height gage, shown at *A*, Fig. 8, is used for locating jig buttons, measuring the vertical distance from one plane surface to another, etc. It is similar to a vernier caliper, except that there is a rather heavy base which allows the gage to stand upright. The movable jaw of this gage has a projection or extension which is beveled to a sharp edge for scribing lines at any required height. This extension may also be used for height measurements. The illustration shows how it might be used for testing the height of a button attached to a jig plate. The gage is graduated to read to thousandths, by means of a vernier scale on the sliding jaw. There are graduations on both sides, giving readings on one side for outside or height measurements and on the other side for inside measurements between the jaws.

Fig. 9. Testing Position of Machine Vise with Dial Gage

What is a vernier depth gage?

Illustration *B*, Fig. 8, shows a depth gage for measuring the depths of holes, recesses in dies, etc. The vertical blade or scale is graduated and by means of a vernier gives readings to thousandths of an inch. Height and depth gages are also made on the micrometer principle; that is, instead of having a scale and vernier, the adjustments are effected by a micrometer screw, graduated to read to thousandths.

What is a dial test indicator and how is it used?

The dial test indicator (see Fig. 9) is a form of gage having a graduated dial and a hand which is connected to a test-point by a system of multiplying levers, so that a very slight movement of the test-point is greatly magnified by the indicating hand. This test-point is placed in contact with the part to be tested, and variations, either in size, alignment, or concentricity, depending upon how the gage is used, are shown by the movements of the hand relative to the dial, which is graduated to read to thousandths of an inch. Dial indicators are used in combination with many different forms of gaging devices.

This type of gage is extensively used in connection with the erection of machinery, for detecting any lack of parallelism between surfaces, in inspection departments, in tool-making or other precision work, and for testing the accuracy of rotating parts such as spindles or arbors. In testing rotating parts, the slightest deviation or eccentricity is shown by fluctuations of the dial hand, which is so connected with the contact point that any motion of the latter is magnified a number of times. The graduated dial face is adjustable so that it can be turned to locate the zero mark directly under the hand, after the contact point has been adjusted against the work. The graduations then give a direct reading for any deviation from the central or zero position.

The dial indicator is often attached to a surface gage, in place of the pointer or scriber (see Fig. 10), for testing the parallelism of a surface, especially when it is desirable to know the exact amount of inaccuracy. A dial indicator may have a "hole attachment" consisting of an extension lever

Fig. 10. Dial Gage Attached to Surface Gage for Checking
Accuracy of Crankshaft

for entering a hole. This might be used, for example, in testing the accuracy or concentricity of a hole or other internal
surface (one form of attachment is shown in Fig. 11).

For what purpose is a center indicator used?

The center indicator or lathe test indicator is used to set
any point or punch mark in line with the axis of a lathe
spindle preparatory to boring a hole. The plan view, Fig. 12,
shows how the indicator is used. It has a pointer A, the
end of which is conical and enters the punch mark to be
centered. This pointer is held by shank B which is fastened
in the toolpost of the lathe. The joint C, by means of which
the pointer is held to the shank, is universal; that is, it
allows the pointer to move in any direction. When the part
being tested is rotated by running the lathe, if the center
punch mark is not in line with the axis of the lathe spindle,
obviously, the outer end of pointer A will vibrate, and as
the joint C is quite close to the inner end, a very slight
error in the location of the center punch mark will cause a

perceptible movement of the outer end, as indicated by the dotted lines. When the work has been adjusted until the pointer remains practically stationary, the punch mark is in line with the axis of the lathe spindle. When two holes are being bored to a given center-to-center distance, by first laying out the centers and then indicating them true in this way, the accuracy depends largely upon the location of the center punch marks.

What are straightedges and why are different forms used?

Straightedges are used to test flat surfaces for determining whether or not they are true planes, and also for test-

Fig. 11. Dial Gage Equipped with Attachment for Checking
Holes or Internal Surfaces

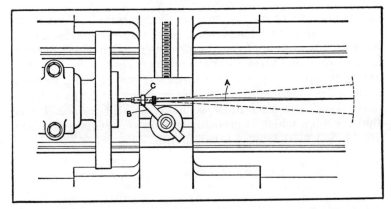

Fig. 12. Plan View Illustrating Use of Center Indicator

ing round parts for bends, or curvatures in a lengthwise direction. Straightedges are also used in "laying out" certain classes of work. A common form of machinists' straightedge is of rectangular section, as shown at *A*, Fig. 13. In order to increase the sensitiveness of a straight-

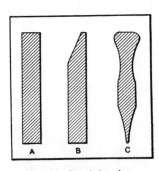

Fig. 13. Straightedges

edge for showing minute deviations or curvatures, the testing edge may be made narrower by beveling one side as shown at *B*, thus decreasing the width to about 1/16 inch. For work requiring extreme accuracy, the type of straightedge shown at *C* is commonly used. This form is usually known as a *knife-edge* straightedge. The testing edge is very narrow and is of semi-circular cross-section so that a line contact is obtained instead of a surface contact. This line contact shows any minute curvature which may exist, and as the edge is curved, the accuracy of the test will not be affected if the straightedge is not held exactly at right angles to the surface being tested. When using a straightedge having plane or flat surfaces, it should be held square with the work, because, if canted so that only one edge is in contact, any inaccuracy along this edge would appear as an inaccuracy in the surface being tested. When comparing a surface with a straightedge, there should be a good light on the side opposite the observer, so that any irregularities or curvatures in the work can readily be detected. Straightedges are made in a large variety of sizes, varying from a few inches up to 10 feet or more in length. Obviously, the large sizes must be made as stiff as possible so that the edge which is used for testing will remain true and not be deflected from a straight line.

Fixed Gages for Checking the Sizes of Duplicate Parts

The term "gage" is generally applied to that type of size-checking tool which conforms to a fixed dimension and is used for testing sizes but is not provided with graduated adjustable members for measuring various lengths or angles. There are exceptions, however, to this general classification. Measuring instruments, such as the micrometer and vernier caliper, are indispensable because they can be used for determining actual dimensions, and may be adjusted to cover quite a range of sizes. These adjustable measuring tools, however, have certain disadvantages for such work as testing the sizes of duplicate parts, especially when such tests must be made repeatedly, and solid or fixed gages are commonly used. There is less chance of inaccuracy with a fixed gage and it is more convenient to use than a tool which must be adjusted for each measurement; but a set of gages covering a wide range of sizes is costly, and fixed gages are used more particularly for testing large numbers of duplicate parts in connection with interchangeable manufacture. The term "fixed gage," as here used, is not intended to imply that the gage cannot be adjusted at all. Many gages which are fixed while in use, are so designed that the measuring points can be adjusted sufficiently to compensate for wear whenever this is necessary.

What is a limit gage?

With the modern system of interchangeable manufacture, machine parts are made to a definite size within certain minimum and maximum limits which are varied according to the accuracy required, which, in turn, depends upon the nature of the work. In order to insure having all parts of a given size or class, within the prescribed limits, so that

403

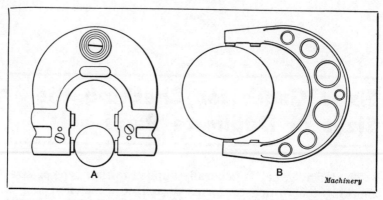

Fig. 1. (A) Adjustable Limit Gage. (B) Limit Gage with Fixed Points

they can readily be assembled without extra and unnecessary fitting, what are known as "limit gages" are used. One form of limit gage for external measurement is shown at A, Fig. 1. This general form is called a "snap gage." It has two sets of measuring plugs. The lower set forms the "go" end and the upper set the "not go" end. The distance between the plug faces of the "go" end is the maximum allowable diameter. When the work has been turned or ground to the correct diameter it will pass between the "go" plugs but not between the inner set of plugs, without exerting greater pressure than should be applied in gaging. The plugs are adjustable so that when the gage becomes inaccurate, as the result of wear, the plugs can easily be reset, a standard reference gage being used to determine the distance between them. The plugs are plain cylinders of hardened steel and are lapped to a snug sliding fit in the hole of the gage body. The ends are square and bear against adjusting screws, the forward ends of which are also lapped square. Another snap gage of the limit type is shown at B. This gage has fixed non-adjustable points which can be renewed in case of wear.

What are the common forms of snap gages?

One type of snap gage, which is shown at A in Fig. 2, is known as a *standard* or *reference* gage. This gage is not provided with any working limit and is made to standard size, being used for reference purposes only. It is usually made from a high-carbon steel forging, carefully hardened, seasoned, ground on the measuring faces, and lapped.

A type which is a combination of snap and plug gages for external and internal checking is shown at *B*. At *C* is shown a common type of limit snap gage which is made from sheet steel, varying in thickness from ¼ to ½ inch, depending upon the diameter and character of the work being gaged. Snap gages of this type should have as wide a bearing surface as possible, as this greatly increases their life.

Another type of limit snap gage which is usually made from a forging, although sometimes from a malleable casting, is shown at *D*. This gage is made in two principal forms, one being shown by the full outline and the other by the dotted outline *a*. The dotted outline type of gage is used to reduce the weight, when the diameter to be measured is greater than 1 inch.

A single-ended type of limit gage is illustrated at *E*. This is provided with one plain jaw and one stepped form for the tolerance. Gages of this kind are usually made from drop-forgings and hardened. At *F* is shown a limit snap gage in which the body is made from cast iron with solid measuring points inserted. This gage is not provided with any adjustment, and it is necessary to renew the points when they become worn. This type is used only on very large work.

Limit gage *G* has one plain jaw and two adjustable pins opposite. The adjustable pins are prevented from turning in the holder by means of screws, as shown, the pins having a flat side against which the heads of the screws rest. The pins or anvils are adjusted in and out by means of headless screws and are clamped by the screws passing through at right angles to the axis of the anvils. The forward faces of these anvils are beveled to prevent marring the work. Another type of adjustable measuring gage, in which all four measuring pins are adjustable, is shown at *H*. The frame is provided with an insulated rubber grip to prevent the heat of the hand from affecting the accuracy of the gage.

In using double-ended limit gages of the type shown at *D*,

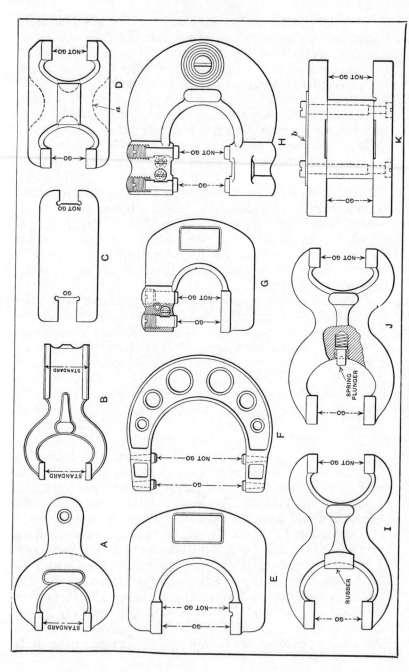

Fig. 2. Types of Snap Gages

where the "go" end passes over the work, the gage will soon become inaccurate unless handled carefully, owing to the hammer effect on the throat of the gage when it hits the work. This causes a peening action which gradually opens the jaws. Different devices have been used for overcoming this. One, which is shown at *I*, consists in using a rubber pad fastened to the throat of the gage, as indicated. This takes the shock of impact of the gage on the work and prevents the peening action. Another method is shown at *J*, which consists of inserting a spring plunger in the throat of the "go" end of the gage. The "not go" end need not be made in this manner, as it is not supposed to pass over the work.

How is a "built-up" type of snap gage constructed?

The built-up type of snap gage (one form of which is shown at *K* in Fig. 2) consists of three members—one center spacing block and two measuring blocks. The form in which these measuring blocks are made differs in various plants. In some cases, one of the measuring blocks is split in half and the limit provided by grinding down half the center block the required amount for the "not go" end. The other method, which is shown at *K*, consists in having the limits on one of the measuring blocks. This type of gage is comparatively cheap to manufacture, as it can be finished complete on the surface grinder and is easily built up and it is only necessary to change the center block and the tolerance on one of the side blocks to adapt it for different sizes. A brass plate *b* is fastened under the head of the screws to carry the job number and any other necessary data. It is the practice in some plants to put the "go" and "not go" dimensions on this piece, so that the operator knows what dimensions he is working to.

Is there a standard design for adjustable snap gages?

The American gage design standard includes four designs of adjustable snap gages. These are designated as Models *A*, *B*, *C*, and *MC*. Model *A* (Fig. 3) has four gag-

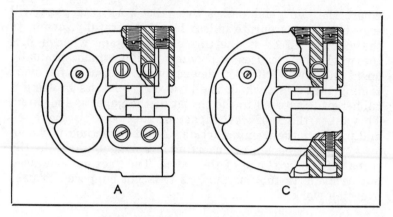

Fig. 3. Snap Gage of Standard Design

ing pins. Model *B* is like *A*, excepting the pins or "buttons" which have flanged or enlarged gaging ends. Model *C* (Fig. 3) has two flanged gaging buttons and a single block anvil opposite. Model *MC* is a miniature snap gage with two gaging buttons and a single block anvil.

In establishing this American Standard, the intention was to embody the most desirable features of gages previously manufactured. The gaging pins or buttons are adjustable and have an approved type of locking device which has stood the test of time. Model *A* is for all diameters up to 12 inches inclusive; Model *B* is for all diameters from

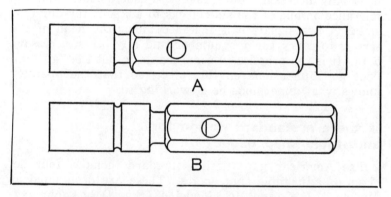

Fig. 4. Taper-lock Plug Gages of Standard Design

½ to 11¼ inches inclusive; Model *C* is for all diameters up to 11⅝ inches inclusive; and Model *MC*, which is made in two sizes only, is for diameters up to 0.760 inch only.

What type of limit gage is commonly used for gaging small holes?

The type of limit gage shown at *A*, Fig. 4, is very generally used. The "go" end at the left is longer than the "not go" end at the right so that the user can readily distinguish between the two. Each gaging end has a taper shank which fits into a taper hole in the gage handle. This is known as the *taper lock* design, and it has the rigidity of a solid gage. According to the American Standard, the taper lock design is used for plain plug gages in diameters ranging from above 0.059 to and including 1.510 inches. The use of this design for larger diameters up to about 2.5 inches is optional. When the gages become worn, new ones may be inserted in the handle.

What is a progressive plug gage?

The name "progressive" is applied to a plug gage which has the "go" and "not go" gaging sections combined in a single unit. A gage of this type is shown at *B*, Fig. 4. The minimum allowable diameter is followed by the "not go" end. The American Standard progressive types of plug gages are for diameters from 0.240 to 2.510 inches.

Why are some plug gages provided with reversible gaging ends?

The reversible type of plug gage is to permit reversing the position of the plug when one end is worn, thus increasing the life of the gage. A reversible plug gage having one gaging member is shown at *A*, Fig. 5. This reversible design has three wedge-shaped locking prongs on the handle which engage locking grooves in the gaging member. The handle and gaging end are held together by a screw. According to the American Standard, the reversible design is for all plain and thread plug gages in diameters above 1.510 to and including 8.010 inches, with the exception of

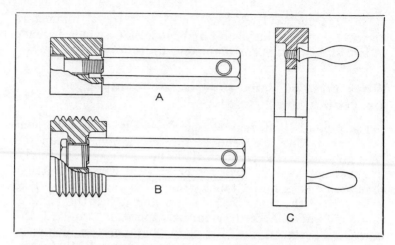

Fig. 5. (A and B) Gages of Reversible Design; (C) Annular Design
for the Larger Diameters

pipe thread plug gages for which the reversible design is
standard from 2- to 6-inches, nominal pipe sizes.

What is the annular type of plug gage?

The annular design is in the form of a ring, as shown
at *C*, Fig. 5. This design is intended for comparatively
large diameters ranging from about 8 to 12 inches, according to the American Standard. Ordinary plug gages for
such large diameters would, of course, be heavy and difficult to handle. The annular type has two handles for
convenience in holding the gage when checking the size of
a hole.

Are plug gages used for checking
the sizes of threaded holes?

Yes, this type is very generally used. Thread plug gages
for the smaller diameters have the taper lock construction
and are similar to the plain plug gage *A*, Fig. 4, excepting
that the plugs are threaded to whatever "go" and "not go"
pitch diameters are required. According to the American
Standard, the taper lock design of thread plug gages are

used for diameters from ¼ to 1½ inches, and the reversible design (shown at *B*, Fig. 5), from 1½ to 8 inches. Thread plug gages for diameters from 8 to 12 inches are similar to the annular design of plain plug gage *C*, Fig. 5, except that the outer surface of the rim is threaded.

What is a "ring gage"?

This gage, as the name implies, is in the form of a ring and it is used for checking shafts, plugs, or other external diameters. The American gage design standard includes plain ring gages in sizes above 0.059 to and including 12.260 inches. Diameters up to and including 0.510 inch consist of a hardened bushing that is pressed into a soft gage body (see upper illustration, Fig. 6). Solid or one-piece ring gages are used for sizes above 0.510; but diameters above 1.510 are flanged to reduce the weight and

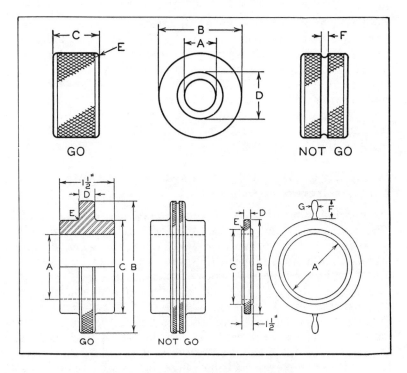

Fig. 6. Ring Gages of Standard Design

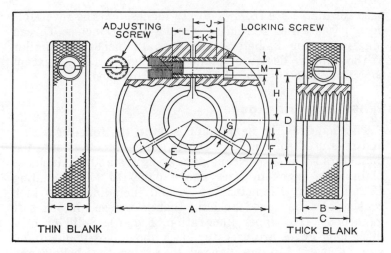

Fig. 7. Standard Ring Gage for Screw Threads

facilitate handling (see lower illustration). The "not go" gages are distinguished from the "go" gages by an annular groove cut into the surface of the flange. Ring gages for diameters from 5.510 to 12.26 inches are provided with two handles, as shown by the illustration in the lower right-hand corner. The American Standard for gages applies to the various dimensions indicated by the letters on the illustrations. Tables giving these dimensions will be found in engineering handbooks.

Is the ring type of gage used for checking external screw threads?

The ring type of gage is widely used for this purpose. The hole in the gage is threaded and a limited amount of adjustment is provided. The American gage design standard is shown in Fig. 7. There is an adjusting screw and a locking screw which provides a positive lock without introducing stresses in the gage body which might tend to cause distortion. In making a gage of this type or in adjusting it, it is not practicable to determine the actual gage size by direct measurement. It can, however, be tested or set readily by means of a threaded plug of the right size; hence, these so-called "setting plugs" are used. Some com-

mercial setting plugs have a threaded end for checking the
pitch diameter and a cylindrical or plain plug gage at the
opposite end for checking the minor diameter.

For what purpose are master gages used?

Master gages are used only for verifying inspection gages,
or for checking the product in case a disagreement arises
between the manufacturer and the purchaser. Under the
heading "master gages" are included various gages known
as "checks," "masters," and "reference gages." Master
gages should, if possible, be of the same design and construction as the inspection gages, but should have practically no allowance for wear. In some cases, checks or
masters are made which are complements or the reverse
of the inspection and working gages, as, for example, thread
ring gages which are used for plug thread gages. Master
gages are of double importance to the manufacturer who
has part of his product made outside of his plant, because
his own inspectors may reject work that the outside manufacturer claims to be correct. To prevent such disputes one
set of masters should be kept at the outside manufacturer's
plant and one at the home plant.

At what standard temperature should
precision gages be checked for size?

Inasmuch as the length of a gage varies somewhat with
temperature changes, it is evident that the length should be
based upon some standard temperature. In the standardization of precision gages for industrial use, 68 degrees F.
has been adopted generally in the United States during re-
cent years as the standard temperature, because it is the
common or average working temperature to which gages
are ordinarily subjected in practice.

Formerly 62 degrees F. was the temperature used for
precision gage standardization, as this is the temperature,
approximately, at which the standard yard bar is at the
correct length; but a temperature of 68 degrees F. is the
generally used working standard for the calibration of industrial gages. This temperature not only conforms to average working temperatures, but it has been widely employed

for many other physical tests, and moreover, it is the exact equivalent of 20 degrees C.

This same temperature of 20 degrees C., or 68 degrees F., has been adopted as the standard for gage work and other industrial measuring instruments, by engineering standardization bodies in Germany, Holland, Sweden, and Switzerland. In the United Kingdom the temperature of 62 degrees F., applies to the fundamental standard yard bar, but 68 degrees is the standard for industrial gage and instrument calibration.

What system of checking sizes is designed to reduce spoilage and improve quality?

The inspection system designed to minimize defective work and also improve the average of quality is known as "statistical quality control" or merely as "quality control." In plants where there is interchangeable manufacturing, in is the general practice to employ inspectors whose job is to check the sizes of finished parts. This inspection as applied in most plants is merely to determine if the dimensions are within the allowable maximum and minimum limits—a method which meets requirements in many plants. To illustrate, assume that the center-to-center distance between two holes must be $4 \pm .003$ inches. This dimension indicates that a center distance of 4 inches is desirable but any dimension between 4.003 and 3.997 will pass inspection and be acceptable. But suppose that the center distance of many parts happens to be very close to one of the limiting dimensions. In that case, they would pass the ordinary system of inspection but, obviously, there would be greater danger of exceeding the limit than if most of the center distances were close to the intermediate value of 4 inches. The "quality control" system is designed to show definite trends toward the dividing line between acceptable and defective work; then the causes of such trends can be corrected before actual work spoilage begins. The purpose of quality control is not only to keep most of the dimensions away from the danger points and thus reduce the amount of defective work, but it also improves the average quality of the finished product.

Gaging Tapering Parts and Measuring Angles

The gaging of tapering parts may or may not require actual measurements. In many cases, the taper is checked by direct comparison with a gage having the taper required; hence, the gaging is a fitting rather than a measuring operation. This applies particularly to taper plugs and holes. Other classes of work may require actual measurements either to check the taper per foot or to determine the taper or angle in degrees.

What method of dimensioning tapering parts will insure accurate fits?

The dimensions of tapering machine parts are given on drawings in various ways and frequently incorrect fits are the result of improper or insufficient dimensions. The method of dimensioning should conform to an adequate method of checking or gaging the size of the taper and its location relative to a shoulder or other important surface.

A common method of dimensioning tapers is to give one diameter, and, in addition, either the taper per foot or the taper number if the taper is some generally recognized standard, such as the Morse or the Brown & Sharpe.

Another method is to give the taper per foot (or number of a standard taper) and the diameters at the large and small ends of the taper, but not the length of the tapering section.

A third method which has proved successful is to give, in addition to the taper per foot, a diameter at some intermediate point between the large and small diameters. This method is often employed in connection with precision work. The location of this basic diameter either from one end of the taper or possibly from an important shoulder, is indicated by a dimension, which, for precision work, should

415

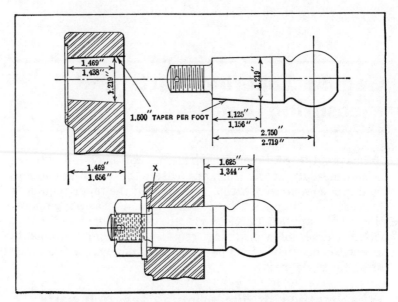

Fig. 1. Illustration Showing How a Taper Stud is Dimensioned
in Order to Insure its Location in a Taper Hole, within
Certain Maximum and Minimum Limits

have a tolerance. This general method of dimensioning
tapers is illustrated by the example, Fig. 1. When this tapering stud is assembled, as shown by the lower diagram, a
certain clearance X is required. To insure holding this clearance within certain maximum and minimum limits, the stud
must have a basic diameter of 1.219 inches at a distance from the end which may vary from 1.125 inches to
1.156 inches. The hole also has the same basic diameter of
1.219 inches, and this may vary from the small end from
1.469 inches to 1.438 inches. When the stud and hole conform to these tolerances, the maximum clearance X will
equal 1.469 — 1.125 = 0.344 inch. The minimum clearance X will equal 1.438 — 1.156 = 0.282 inch.

In applying this method of dimensioning tapers, the plug
or internal member and the hole should have the same
basic diameter without a tolerance. This basic diameter is
located by a dimension with a tolerance and from a surface
that is available during machining and one that is of chief
importance in the final assembly of the parts.

What types of limit gages are used for internal and external tapers?

Many taper gages are so arranged that the longitudinal movement of the gage, relative to the work, must be within certain limiting marks or shoulders. The taper plug and ring gage shown at *A* in Fig. 2 is used only for reference purposes; *B* shows a type of taper plug and ring gage in which the "go" and "not go" limits are indicated by two lines. Another type of taper plug and ring gage is shown at *C*. Here, instead of having the limit lines on the plug and ring, the two members are milled down as shown, the distance between the two milled cuts being the amount of tolerance on the work. Another type of limit plug and ring gage is shown at *D*. In this case, the plug consists of a handle to which two bushings are attached, which are ground to the correct taper. With this type of plug, it is a comparatively simple matter to obtain a correctly machined

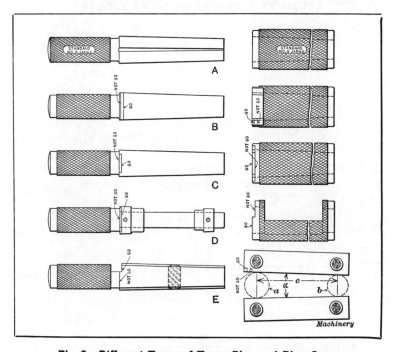

Fig. 2. Different Types of Taper Plug and Ring Gages

taper hole without the use of Prussian blue or other fitting pastes. The taper in the hole can be tested by the wabble of the plug, as it rests in the hole at two points only, instead of its entire length. A similar principle is applied to the ring, which is cut away and relieved in the center as illustrated.

In using plug gages of the type illustrated at B and C, difficulty is sometimes experienced, especially when the taper is slight, due to the plug "sticking" in the hole. One way of eliminating this is to make the plug as shown at D, but probably a more satisfactory way is to make it as shown at E. Here the plug is flattened on both sides, which allows free passage of the air; this will be found especially advantageous in gaging blind holes. The only disadvantage of this plug is the difficulty of lapping it accurately.

How are adjustable straightedges and disks used for the accurate measurement of tapers?

The gage shown at the right of E, Fig. 2, may be used for very accurate work or for originating tapers and angles. The adjustable straightedges are attached to a stand or holder and they are set to a given taper per foot or angle a, by setting disks a and b of known diameters, to a calculated center distance c.

Center Distance for Given Taper per Foot.— To determine center distance c, between the disks, divide the taper by 24 and find the angle corresponding to the quotient in a table of tangents; then find the sine corresponding to this angle and divide the difference between the disk diameters by twice the sine.

Example.—Gage is to be set to ¾ inch per foot, and disk diameters are 1.25 and 1.5 inch, respectively. Find the required center distance for the disks.

$\dfrac{0.75}{24} = 0.03125$. The angle whose tangent is 0.03125 equals

1 degree 47.4 minutes;

$$\sin 1° 47.4' = 0.03123; \quad 1.50 - 1.25 = 0.25 \text{ inch};$$

$$\text{center distance } c = \frac{0.25}{2 \times 0.03123} = 4.002 \text{ inches.}$$

Center Distance for a Given Angle.—When straight-edges must be set to a given angle find the sine of half the angle a in a table of sines; divide the difference between the disk diameters by double this sine to obtain the center distance c between the disks.

Example.—If an angle a of 20 degrees is required, and the disks are 1 and 3 inches in diameter, respectively, find the required center distance c.

$$\frac{20}{2} = 10 \text{ degrees}; \quad \sin 10° = 0.17365;$$

$$\text{center distance } c = \frac{3-1}{2 \times 0.17365} = 5.759 \text{ inches.}$$

In gaging taper holes, what type of gage usually is employed?

The taper plug form is a simple and dependable type of gage for tapering holes. In precision work, these taper plug gages must enter the hole within certain maximum and minimum limits, as previously mentioned. The left-hand diagram (X), Fig. 3, shows a "step" form of taper plug gage. When the step or surface A at the small end of the gage is flush with the face of the work, the basic diameter of 1.219 inches is at the maximum limit of 1.156 inches from the same face. When step B is flush with the face of the work, the basic diameter is at a minimum limit of 1.125 inches from the gaging face.

The diagram (Z), Fig. 4, shows another taper plug gage of the step type. In this case, the gaging steps or faces are at the large end of the plug gage and the distance between the gaging steps is 0.024 inch which represents the tolerance.

A taper plug gage of the flush-pin type is shown by diagram (Y), Fig. 5. This gage is for checking the location of the basic diameter of a hole in a gear, relative to one face of this gear. When the pin is flush with step A on the arm of the gage, the basic diameter of 1.452 inches is 0.234 inch from the face of the gear. When the pin is flush with step B, the basic diameter is at a maximum distance of 0.258 inch from the face of the gear.

Another taper plug gage of the flush-pin type is illustrated by diagram (Y), Fig. 4. This is similar to the one

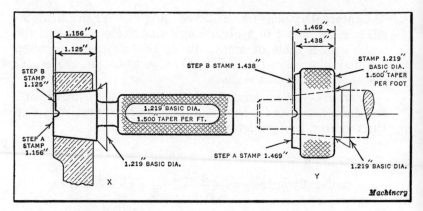

Fig. 3. Plug and Ring Taper Gages of Step Type

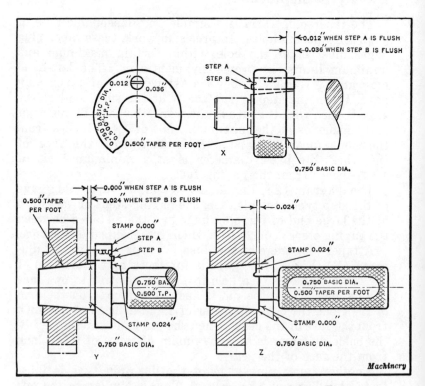

Fig. 4. Taper Gages of the Flush-pin and Step Types

just described, excepting that the gaging steps are on the end of the pin and one face of the gear hub is used for checking the location of the basic diameter.

The method of gaging illustrated in Figs. 3 to 5, inclusive, is similar in principle to an approved method of dimensioning tapers which is explained at the beginning of this section. This method is based upon the principle of establishing the same basic diameter for both plug and hole, accompanied by whatever minimum and maximum limits for the location of this basic diameter are required to obtain the proper fit or location of the assembled parts. Gaging is such an important feature in machinery manufacture and conditions vary so widely that a great many types and designs of gages are used. In this treatise, the plan is to show the more common types or those illustrating important fundamental principles.

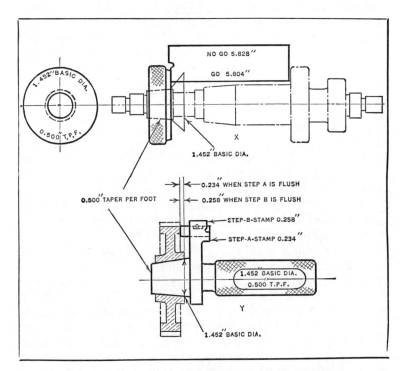

Fig. 5. Gages used in the Inspection of Taper Parts

What type of gage is commonly used for tapering plugs or shafts?

External tapering surfaces on plugs, shafts, etc., usually are checked by using a ring type of gage. This ring gage has a hole which conforms to the taper required on the plug or shaft. If the taper part is threaded, as in the case of pipe threads, the size may be checked by using a threaded ring gage. An allowable variation in the position of a taper ring gage relative to the plug or other part being tested may be indicated in different ways, as shown by the following examples.

The diagram at Y (Fig. 3) shows how a ring gage is used for testing the tapering end of a shaft. The small end of this gage has two steps or surfaces at different levels. These are designated as steps A and B. When step A is flush with the small end of the shaft, the basic diameter of 1.219 inches, in this case, is 1.469 inches from the small end. When step B is flush, the basic diameter is 1.438 inches from the small end. Hence, it will be seen that this is a limit type of taper ring gage and the tolerance for the position of the gage is represented by the height of the step which, in this case, equals $1.469 - 1.438 = 0.031$ inch.

The upper diagram X (Fig. 5) shows another application of a ring gage. This ring gage is on a tapering part of a shaft which will receive a gear when the mechanism is assembled. To insure the proper fit and location for this gear, the ring gage must be within certain minimum and maximum limits from a gear at the right which is integral with the shaft. The gage location is checked by a length gage (as shown by the diagram) which has a maximum or "not go" length of 5.828 inches and a minimum or "go" length of 5.804 inches.

Another ring gage of the limit type is shown by the upper diagram (X), Fig. 4. The two limiting positions of this gage are indicated by a "flush-pin." The basic diameter of 0.750 inch at the large end of this ring gage will be 0.012 inch from the shoulder of the shaft when step A of the pin is flush with the small-end surface of the ring gage. When step B is flush with this surface, the basic diameter will be 0.036 inch from the shoulder. By finishing the tapering part of the shaft to whatever size is required to locate the gage within these minimum and maximum limits, a correct fit is obtained between the shaft and a gear that is to be mounted on it.

In making taper plug gages, how is the taper per foot checked?

The taper per foot can be checked very accurately by using the adjustable straightedge type of gage shown at *E*, Fig. 2. If the taper per foot is to be checked by actual measurement, this can be done by taking two measurements (as at *A* and *B*, Fig. 6), over a pair of cylindrical plugs and at points preferably near the large and small ends as shown. By supporting these plugs upon precision

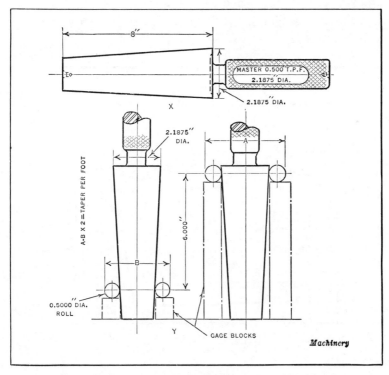

Fig. 6. Master Taper Plug and Method of Checking it for Accuracy of Taper

gage-blocks, the distance between the two points of measurement may be determined very accurately. When dimensions A and B and the distance between the points of measurement are known, the taper per foot is determined as follows:

Rule 1.—Subtract measurement B from A and multiply the difference by 12 divided by the distance between the points of measurement.

Example.—Measurement A is 3.1482 inches and measurement B is 2.8982 inches. If these measurements are made at points 4 inches apart. what is the taper per foot?

$$\text{Taper per foot} = (3.1482 - 2.8982) \times \frac{12}{4} = 0.75 \text{ inch.}$$

Rule 2.—If the gage is long enough to permit taking measurements at points 6 inches apart (as shown in Fig. 6), the rule can be simplified as follows:

Subtract measurement B from A and multiply the difference by 2 to obtain the taper per foot.

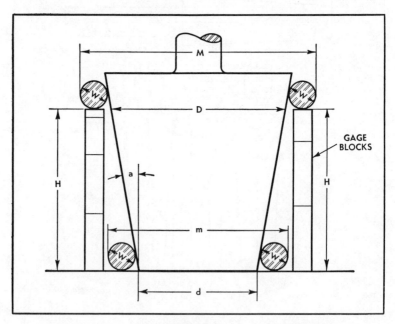

Fig. 7. Diagram Illustrating Method of Checking Diameter D
at Given Height H

Is there a simple precise method of measuring the diameters of taper plug gages?

The diameter of a taper plug gage at any given point may be checked accurately by taking a measurement as at M, Fig. 7, over accurate cylindrical plugs of known diameter. Suppose, for example. that the gage must have a certain basic diameter D at some height or distance H from the small end. The diameter D at height H may be checked by first determining what measurement M should be, when using plugs of a given known diameter W. The plugs or rods are supported at the same height on each side by using gage-blocks so that the exact height H is known. The problem is to find the correct measurement M for a given diameter D or, it may be to determine the diameter D equivalent to any measurement M.

In checking taper gages, how is measurement over cylindrical plugs determined?

To find measurement M (Fig. 7) equivalent to a given diameter D, proceed as follows:

Rule.—First find angle a or one-half the included angle of the plug gage or other tapering part; subtract angle a from 90 degrees and find the cotangent of *one-half* this angle; then add 1 to the cotangent and multiply the sum by the diameter W of the cylindrical plugs or wires used. This product is then added to the required diameter D to obtain the equivalent measurement M. This rule, expressed as a formula, is as follows:

$$\text{Measurement } M = D + W \left[1 + \cot \frac{1}{2}(90 - a) \right]$$

To find measurement m equivalent to a given diameter d at the small end, merely substitute in the rule or formula the small end diameter d.

If the taper per foot is given, first find the equivalent angle. (See table, Tapers per Foot and Corresponding Angles.) The angle equivalent to a given taper per foot may also be determined as follows:

Rule.—Divide the taper in inches per foot by 24. Find the angle corresponding to the quotient in a table of tangents and double this angle.

Tapers per Foot and Corresponding Angles

Taper per Foot	Included Angle	Angle with Center Line	Taper per Foot	Included Angle	Angle with Center Line
1/64	0° 4' 28"	0° 2' 14"	1 7/8	8° 56' 2"	4° 28' 1"
1/32	0 8 58	0 4 29	1 15/16	9 13 51	4 36 56
1/16	0 17 53	0 8 57	2	9 31 37	4 45 49
3/32	0 26 52	0 13 26	2 1/8	10 7 11	5 3 35
1/8	0 35 47	0 17 54	2 1/4	10 42 41	5 21 21
5/32	0 44 45	0 22 23	2 3/8	11 18 12	5 39 6
3/16	0 53 44	0 26 52	2 1/2	11 53 38	5 56 49
7/32	1 2 39	0 31 20	2 5/8	12 29 2	6 14 31
1/4	1 11 38	0 35 49	2 3/4	13 4 25	6 32 13
9/32	1 20 33	0 40 16	2 7/8	13 39 44	6 49 52
5/16	1 29 31	0 44 46	3	14 15 0	7 7 30
11/32	1 38 30	0 49 15	3 1/8	14 50 15	7 25 8
3/8	1 47 25	0 53 42	3 1/4	15 25 27	7 42 43
13/32	1 56 24	0 58 12	3 3/8	16 0 34	8 0 17
7/16	2 5 18	1 2 39	3 1/2	16 35 41	8 17 50
15/32	2 14 17	1 7 8	3 5/8	17 10 42	8 35 21
1/2	2 23 12	1 11 36	3 3/4	17 45 40	8 52 50
17/32	2 32 10	1 16 5	3 7/8	18 20 35	9 10 18
9/16	2 41 7	1 20 34	4	18 55 31	9 27 45
19/32	2 50 4	1 25 2	4 1/8	19 30 18	9 45 9
5/8	2 59 3	1 29 31	4 1/4	20 5 1	10 2 31
21/32	3 7 57	1 33 59	4 3/8	20 39 44	10 19 52
11/16	3 13 56	1 38 28	4 1/2	21 14 20	10 37 10
23/32	3 2 51	1 42 55	4 5/8	21 48 55	10 54 28
3/4	3 34 48	1 47 24	4 3/4	22 23 27	11 11 43
25/32	3 43 44	1 51 52	4 7/8	22 57 50	11 28 55
13/16	3 52 42	1 56 21	5	23 32 12	11 46 6
27/32	4 1 38	2 0 49	5 1/8	24 6 28	12 3 14
7/8	4 10 32	2 5 16	5 1/4	24 40 43	12 20 21
29/32	4 19 31	2 9 46	5 3/8	25 14 50	12 37 25
15/16	4 28 26	2 14 13	5 1/2	25 48 53	12 54 27
31/32	4 37 25	2 18 42	5 5/8	26 22 52	13 11 26
1	4 46 19	2 23 10	5 3/4	26 56 48	13 28 24
1 1/16	5 4 12	2 32 6	5 7/8	27 30 35	13 45 18
1 1/8	5 22 2	2 41 1	6	28 4 20	14 2 10
1 3/16	5 39 55	2 49 58	6 1/8	28 37 59	14 19 0
1 1/4	5 57 45	2 58 53	6 1/4	29 11 36	14 35 48
1 5/16	6 15 38	3 7 49	6 3/8	29 45 4	14 52 32
1 3/8	6 33 29	3 16 44	6 1/2	30 18 28	15 9 14
1 7/16	6 51 21	3 25 41	6 5/8	30 51 49	15 25 55
1 1/2	7 9 10	3 34 35	6 3/4	31 25 2	15 42 31
1 9/16	7 27 0	3 43 30	6 7/8	31 58 11	15 59 5
1 5/8	7 44 49	3 52 24	7	32 31 14	16 15 37
1 11/16	8 2 38	4 1 19	7 1/8	33 4 10	16 32 5
1 3/4	8 20 28	4 10 14	7 1/4	33 37 3	16 48 32
1 13/16	8 38 17	4 19 8	7 3/8	34 9 49	17 4 55

Example 1.—A taper plug gage, Fig. 7, is to have a taper of 3 inches per foot and a basic diameter D of 3.756 inches at a distance H of 4½ inches from the small end. Diameter W of the cylindrical plugs used in measuring is 0.500 inch. When diameter D is correct, what is measurement M over the rods?

A taper of 3 inches per foot is equivalent to an angle of 14 degrees 15 minutes; hence, angle $a = 7$ degrees 7½ minutes, and $90° - 7°\ 7½' = 82°\ 52½'$. The cotangent of one-half of this angle is 1.13278; hence,

$$M = 3.756 + 0.5 \times (1 + 1.13278) = 4.8224 \text{ inches.}$$

The gage-blocks are combined to hold the plugs on each side at a height H of 4½ inches since the diameter at this height is to be checked.

Example 2.—Find diameter d of the plug gage referred to in Example 1 and also determine measurement m equivalent to this small-end diameter.

$$\text{Diameter } d = 3.756 - \left(\frac{3}{12} \times 4.5 \right) = 2.631 \text{ inches.}$$

$$\begin{aligned}\text{Measurement } m &= 2.631 + 0.5 \times (1 + 1.13278) \\ &= 3.6974 \text{ inches.}\end{aligned}$$

If an attempt is made to check the small end diameter d by direct measurement, contact with the micrometer or other measuring instrument would have to be at some slight distance from the end, which would, of course, affect the measurement especially with the larger angles or tapers.

In checking tapers, how is the diameter found when measurement M, Fig. 7, is known?

If the preceding problem is reversed and the diameter D or d equivalent to a certain measurement M or m is required, the procedure is the same as previously described, excepting that M or m replaces D or d in the formula, and the final result is obtained by subtraction instead of addition, as shown by the following formula:

$$\text{Diameter } D = M - W \left[1 + \cot \frac{1}{2} (90 - a) \right]$$

Example.—Diameter D, Fig. 7, is to be 3.756 inches. If measurement M is 4.835 inches, how close is diameter D to the diameter required?

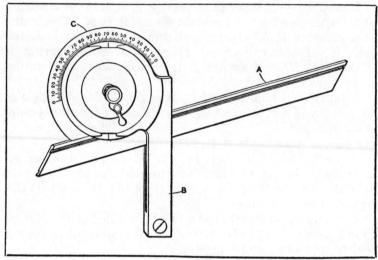

Fig. 8. Universal Bevel Protractor

$$\text{Diameter } D = 4.835 - 0.5 \times (1 + 1.13278)$$
$$= 3.7686 \text{ inches}$$

Hence, when measurement M is 4.835 inches, the diameter D is about 0.012 inch over size.

What is a protractor used for?

A protractor is an instrument used for measuring and for laying out angles. There are many different forms of protractors, but they all embody the same general principles. The type generally used by machinists and toolmakers is known as the *bevel protractor*. It has a straight edge or blade which can be set at any angle with the base or stock; the angle for any position is shown by degree graduations. One design of bevel protractor is shown in Fig. 8. The angular position between blade A and stock B can be varied as may be required, and disk C, which is graduated from 0 to 90 degrees in each direction, shows what the angle is for any position. The blade, which is clamped by an eccentric stud, can be adjusted in a lengthwise direction so that it can be used in any position.

If a protractor has a vernier, how is the angular setting determined?

The graduations on the protractors commonly used by machinists are ordinarily not finer than whole degrees, so that measurements of fractional parts of a degree cannot be made with accuracy. By the addition of a vernier scale, subdivisions of a degree are easily read. The vernier scale of a bevel protractor is shown in Fig. 9. This particular vernier makes it possible to determine the angle to which the instrument is set, within five minutes (5') or one-twelfth of a degree. It will be noted that there are practically two scales of twelve divisions each, on either side of the vernier zero mark. The left-hand scale is used when the vernier zero is moved to the left of the zero of the true scale, while the right-hand scale is used when the movement is to the right. The total length of each of these vernier scales is equal to twenty-three degrees on the true scale, and, as there are twelve divisions, each division equals 1/12 of 23 or 1 11/12 degrees. One degree equals 60 minutes (60') and 11/12 degree equals 11/12 of 60, or 55 minutes; hence, each division on the vernier expressed in minutes equals 60' + 55' = 115 minutes. Now as there are 120 minutes in 2 degrees, each space on the vernier is 5 minutes shorter than 2 degrees; therefore, when the zero marks on the true and vernier scales are exactly in line, the first graduation (either to the right or left) on the vernier is 5 minutes from the first degree graduation; the next two are 10 minutes apart; and the next two, 15 minutes, etc. It is evident then that,

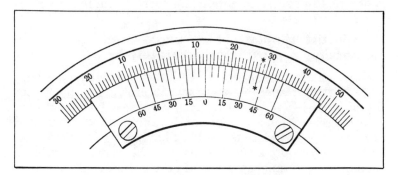

Fig. 9. Protractor Scale and Vernier

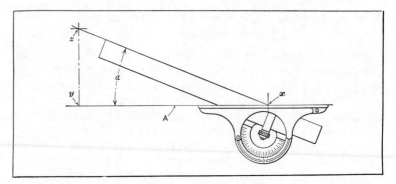

Fig. 10. Accurate Method of Setting Protractor

if the vernier is moved, say, to the right, until the third line from zero is exactly in line with one on the true scale, the movement will be equal to 15 minutes, as indicated by the number opposite this line on the vernier.

Rule.—To read the protractor, first note the number of whole degrees passed by the vernier zero, and then count in the same direction the number of spaces between the vernier zero and that line which exactly coincides with one on the regular scale; this number of spaces multiplied by 5 will give the number of minutes to be added to the whole number of degrees.

The reading of a protractor set as illustrated is 12 whole degrees plus 40 minutes. The vernier zero has passed the twelfth graduation, and the eighth line on the vernier coincides with a line on the true scale; hence, 40 minutes is added to 12 degrees to obtain the correct reading.

How is the tangent of an angle used for setting a protractor accurately?

Occasionally it is necessary to either lay out or measure angles with considerable accuracy. A protractor that is not equipped with a vernier scale can be set to a fractional part of a degree within close limits, by the method illustrated in Fig. 10. A flat plate is required having a straightedge A, and a line is laid out on this plate to the required angle by using a table of tangents to obtain the necessary dimensions. (Tables giving the tangents and other functions of angles are included in all engineering handbooks.) To illustrate the method, suppose an ordinary machinists' protractor is to be set to an angle of 21 degrees 10 minutes. This angle is laid out on the plate as follows: First two points are located any distance x–y apart. Assume that this distance is 10 inches. The tangent of the required angle is next found in a table of tangents. The tangent of 21 degrees 10 minutes equals 0.3872. Next scribe a fine line with a needle-point scriber at right angles to edge A and through point y. On this line, lay off a distance y–z equal to the distance x–y multiplied by the tangent of the required angle, or 10 $\times$ 0.3872 = 3.872 or 3⅞ inches, nearly. Then draw a fine line through points z and x; the angle between this line and the edge A will equal, in this case, 21 degrees 10 minutes, and the protractor can be set by direct comparison with this line, as the illustration indicates.

Rule.—Multiply any convenient distance x–y by the tangent of the required angle to obtain the dimension y–z.

Very accurate results can be obtained by this method, if care is taken in locating points x, y, and z, and in drawing the line from z to x so that it exactly coincides with these two points. Very fine lines should be drawn and an auxiliary scriber can be made by inserting an ordinary sewing needle into some form of holder.

What is a sine-bar and why is it so named?

A sine-bar is used either for measuring angles accurately or for locating work to a given angle in connection with such work as surface grinding operations on templets, gages and other angular work requiring great accuracy. Sine-bars are commonly used by toolmakers and gage-makers because they provide a very precise method of measuring or checking angles. A common form of sine-bar is illustrated by the diagram, Fig. 11. This particular form is notched at the ends for receiving cylindrical plugs D. These plugs must be lapped to the same diameter and the distance C between their centers usually is either 5 or 10 inches to simplify the use of the sine-bar, as shown later by an example. This center distance should be as accurate as possible and the upper and lower edges of the bar should be parallel with a plane intersecting the axes of the plugs.

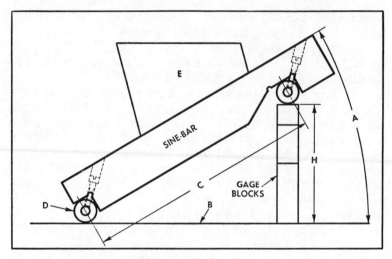

Fig. 11.   Setting Sine-bar to Given Angle A

The sine-bar is always used in conjunction with some true surface B from which measurements can be taken.

The angle A to which the sine-bar is set depends upon the height H of one plug above the surface B upon which the other plug rests. The sine-bar frequently is set to the required height H by using gage-blocks to obtain great accuracy. If the sine-bar is to be set to a given angle, height H for this angle is determined by using the sine of the angle as shown by an example to follow. Hence, the name "sine-bar."

Rule.—To set a sine-bar to a given angle, find the sine of this angle in a table containing the sines of angles; multiply this sine by the center distance C to obtain height H, Fig. 11.

Example.—A sine-bar is to be set to an angle of 30 degrees in order to hold a gage or templet E for grinding its edges so that the angle between these edges is also 30 degrees. A 10-inch sine-bar is to be used, which means that the center-to-center distance C is 10 inches. To what height H must the sine-bar be set?

The sine of 30 degrees is 0.5000; hence,

$$\text{Height } H = 0.5000 \times 10 = 5 \text{ inches}$$

How is a sine-bar used for measuring angles?

The sine-bar is not only used for locating precision work at a given angle, but it may also be utilized for checking or measuring either the angle of a surface or the included angle between two surfaces. The diagram, Fig. 12, illustrates the use of a sine-bar for determining the angle A between two surfaces and the angle a between the top surface and surface B.

Rule.—Find the difference between heights H and h when the sine-bar is in contact with the upper surface. Then place the sine-bar in contact with the lower surface (as indicated by the dotted lines) and find the difference between heights H_1 and h_1. Divide the difference between dimensions H and h by the length of the sine-bar to get the sine of the angle a between the upper edge and surface B from which the measurements are made. Then divide the difference between measurements H_1 and h_1 by the length of the sine-bar to obtain the angle b between the lower edge and surface B.

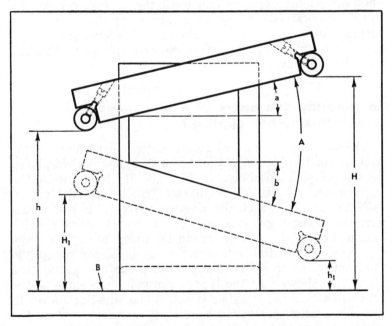

Fig 12. Checking Angle A by Means of Sine-bar

The sum of the two angles thus obtained equals the total angle A.

Example.—Height $H = 8.75$ inches, height $h = 6.5$ inches, height $H_1 = 5$ inches, and $h_1 = 2.15$ inches. Find angle A.

$8.75 - 6.5 = 2.25$. Dividing this difference by 10, we obtain the sine 0.225, which, by referring to a table of sines, is found to be equivalent to 13 degrees 1 minute. This is angle a.

$5 - 2.15 = 2.85$, and this difference divided by 10 equals 0.285 which is the sine of 16 degrees 34 minutes. This is angle b. The sum of these angles or $13° 1' + 16° 34' = 29$ degrees 35 minutes $=$ angle A.

The design of sine-bar shown in Fig. 11 differs from the one in Fig. 12 in regard to the arrangement of the faces or shoulders against which the cylindrical plugs are held. In making the form of sine-bar shown in Fig. 11, if too much material is ground from one locating surface or shoulder, it is simply necessary to regrind the surface or shoulder at the opposite end until the correct center distance is obtained. Many sine-bars have disks or plugs attached to the sides, but this change in the form or arrangement does not, of course, affect the principle governing the use of a sine-bar.

In checking the angle of a plug gage, how is a sine-bar applied?

The sine-bar is set to whatever angle is equivalent to the included or total angle of the taper. The gage is then placed on the sine-bar as shown in Fig. 13. If the angle of the gage is correct, its upper surface will be parallel to the surface plate on which the sine-bar rests. This test to determine if the upper surface of the gage is parallel with the surface plate may be made by using a surface gage equipped with a dial indicator. If the indicator reading is the same with all points along the top surface of the plug gage, this shows that the taper or angle is the same as the angle to which the sine-bar is set. (The sine-bar shown in this illustration has seven holes in it merely to reduce the weight.)

What type of sine-bar fixture is adapted to work having compound angles?

Various forms of work-holding devices for precision angular work have been arranged to permit setting them to the required angle by applying the principle of the sine-bar. Figs. 14 and 15 illustrate applications of a magnetic chuck which can be set accurately to the required angle by applying the sine-bar principle. This chuck is a commercial design that is made in two styles: One is for angular adjustments in one plane; the other can be tilted to compound angles or angles in two directions. Precision gage-blocks placed between flat surfaces and cylindrical bars insure accurate settings of the chuck table. The chuck designed for compound angles (see Fig. 14) consists essentially of a base which is placed on the table of the machine. Hinged to one end of the base is a plate that can be tilted to any angle by merely employing precision gage-blocks between the top of

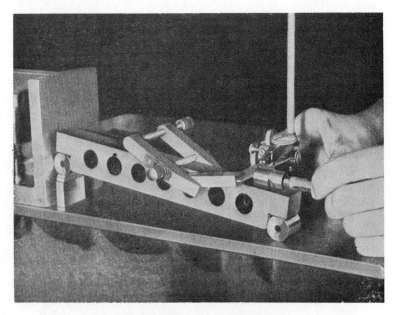

Fig. 13. Using Gage-blocks in Combination with a Sine-bar to Check the Taper of a Plug Gage

Fig. 14. Sine-bar Type of Chuck for Compound Angles

Fig. 15. Sine-bar Type of Chuck, Set for Grinding Dovetail

the base and the cylindrical bar which extends the full length of the hinged plate on the under side. The chuck table is hinged in a similar manner to the plate, except that the hinge is at right angles to the plate hinge. Gageblocks are used between the top surface of the hinged plate and the cylindrical bar that extends across the under side of the chuck table to insure accurate settings. With this construction, it is possible to set the chuck table to any desired compound angle. In Fig. 14, for example, the operation consists of grinding a block to a combination of two angles—5 degrees 10 minutes 32 seconds in one direction, and 10 degrees 31 minutes in the other direction.

Another example of work is the grinding of dovetails, both internal and external. An internal dovetail is shown being ground in Fig. 15. After one side of the dovetail is finished, it is an easy matter to grind the opposite side by merely turning the work end for end. The chuck is tilted 30 degrees for this operation.

How are very accurate functions and angles found by interpolation?

In engineering handbooks, the values of trigonometric functions are usually given to degrees and minutes; hence, if the given angle is to degrees, minutes and *seconds*, the value of the function is determined from the nearest given values, by interpolation.

Interpolation to Find Function of an Angle.—Assume that the sine of 14° 22′ 26″ is to be determined. It is evident that this value lies between the sine of 14° 22′ and the sine of 14° 23′. Sine 14° 23′ = 0.24841 and sine 14° 22′ = 0.24813. The difference = 0.24841 — 0.24813 = 0.00028. Consider this difference as a whole number (28) and multiply it by a fraction having as its numerator the number of seconds (26) in the given angle, and as its denominator 60 (number of seconds in one minute). Thus $\frac{26}{60} \times 28 = 12$ nearly; hence, by adding 0.00012 to sine of 14° 22′, we find that sine 14° 22′ 26″ = 0.24813 + 0.00012 = 0.24825. The correction value (represented in this example by 0.00012) is *added* to the function of the *smaller* angle nearest the given angle in dealing with *sines* or *tangents* but this correction value is *subtracted* in dealing with cosines or cotangents.

Interpolation to Find Angle.—Find the angle whose cosine is 0.27052. The table of trigonometric functions shows that the desired angle is between 74° 18′ and 74° 19′ because the cosines of these angles are, respectively, 0.27060 and 0.27032. The difference = 0.27060 — 0.27032 = 0.00028. From the cosine of the *smaller* angle or 0.27060, subtract the given cosine; thus 0.27060 — 0.27052 = 0.00008; hence, $\dfrac{8}{28} \times 60 = 17''$ or the number of seconds to add to the smaller angle to obtain the required angle. Thus the angle whose cosine is 0.27052 = 74° 18′ 17″. Angles corresponding to given sines, tangents, or cotangents may be determined by the same method.

Precision Gage-Blocks and their Application

In manufacturing machines or other mechanical devices in accordance with the interchangeable plan, the *tolerances* or *allowable errors* on machine parts often are very small because great accuracy is required. For example, the tolerances frequently vary from 0.001 or 0.002 inch up to 0.004 or 0.005 inch. Then there are tolerances that are less than 0.001 inch and many that are greater than 0.005 inch. In any case, if the *product* must be accurate, the *gage* used in checking it requires even greater accuracy; consequently, in making these gages and in connection with certain other classes of precision work, some extremely accurate and reliable method of measurement is necessary.

What are precision gage-blocks and why are they so important?

Suppose you had to make a limit gage to a size of 2 inches, with an allowable error of only 0.0001 inch (which is not unusual for precision gage work). It is evident that this would require some extremely precise method of measuring exactly 2 inches and possibly 1.9999 inches. The method of checking these very precise dimensions should be a simple and practical one. How can such measurements be made and will they conform exactly to the established standard governing length measurements? There is one practical shop method and that involves the use of what are called "precision gage-blocks."

Gage-blocks are small blocks of steel. Each block in a set has a given thickness or length, and the size of each block is marked on it. The dimension marked on any block represents the distance between two parallel surfaces on opposite sides. If the block, for example, is a 1-inch size, this means precisely 1 inch, within, at most, a few millionths of an inch variation. In other words, precision gage-blocks are practically errorless. Many gage-blocks do not vary from the given size more than two millionths of an inch. The measuring surfaces are not only exact as to the distance between them, but these surfaces must also be flat and parallel with practically no error. Gage-blocks are sold in sets. By combining two or more precision gage-blocks (as explained later) a large range of extremely accurate dimensions can be obtained. The blocks are combined in this way when there is no single block in the set of exactly the size wanted. Gage-blocks or combinations of them are very generally used in machine building plants as ultimate standards of reference for checking inspection or working gages and other precise measuring and gaging equipment.

What range of dimensions can be obtained by using different combinations of gage-blocks?

The total number of gage-blocks in commercial sets vary. One very complete set contains 85 blocks. By placing together different combinations, about 120,000 different gaging lengths are obtainable. Frequently, a given dimension can be obtained by two or more combinations of blocks either for checking one combination against another or for use on different jobs.

The block sizes in a given set vary with the number of blocks. In a well-known commercial set containing 81 blocks, the smallest is 0.050 inch thick. The next is 0.100 inch thick. This is followed by a series of 9 blocks beginning at 0.1001 and increasing by 0.0001 up to 0.1009 inclusive. Then there is a series of 50 blocks beginning with 0.1010 and increasing by 0.001 up to 0.150 inclusive. A third series of 16 blocks begins at 0.200 and increases by 0.050 up to 0.950 inclusive. The fourth and last series contains 4 blocks measuring 1, 2, 3, and 4 inches, respectively.

With this set of gage-blocks, any dimension from 0.100 inch to over 10 inches can be obtained in increments or steps of 0.001 inch, and any dimension from 0.200 inch to over 10 inches can be obtained in steps of 0.0001 inch. By the addition of four sizes (1/16, 5/64, 3/32, and 7/64 inch), all combinations in 64ths from one-sixteenth of an inch up may be obtained in addition to the decimal sizes previously referred to. With a set of 34 blocks, any dimension from 0.200 to over 8 inches can be obtained in steps of 0.001 inch, and any dimension from 0.300 inch to over 8 inches can be obtained in steps of 0.0001 inch. While this 34-block set gives a very large range of sizes, in the majority of cases there is only one combination of blocks for a given dimension. In this respect, it differs from the 81-block set. Another set containing 28 very thin blocks may be used for many combinations in the smaller sizes or under 0.200 inch. The thinnest block in this series is 0.010 inch. These very thin ones are not necessarily flat as individual blocks, but this condition is corrected when the thin blocks are used in combination with other blocks. Another set of 8 blocks is for checking very large dimensions. These block lengths range from 5 to 20 inches.

How are gage-blocks assembled to form the equivalent of a single block?

Two or more blocks are assembled or combined to form the equivalent of a single block and a given dimension for gaging, by "wringing" the blocks together. All rust-proofing, grease, dust, or other foreign matter should first be removed. Then place one block upon the other and twist or oscillate them to obtain good contact (see upper view at left in Fig. 1 which shows Hoke gage-blocks). Next, slide one block partially out of engagement with the other (upper view at right) and then bring them back into full engagement, while pressing the blocks together firmly (see lower views). This assembling of the blocks is known as wringing them together. As the surfaces of gage-blocks are practically perfect planes, they adhere to each other when properly wrung together and considerable force is required to separate them; in fact, the force required to separate two blocks is much greater than that resulting from the atmospheric pressure, as explained later.

In building up gage-blocks to a given dimension, how is the correct combination determined?

Since many dimensions can be obtained by using two or more combinations of blocks, it is preferable, as a general rule, to use the simplest combination or the one requiring the smallest number of blocks. For example, suppose the dimension is 1.9504 inches. Since there is no one block having this dimension, it is necessary to use a combination. Begin by selecting a block for the right-hand figure. Since this is 4, it is necessary to begin by using the 0.1004-inch size. Following the decimal point in the given dimension, we have 0.950; hence, the entire decimal part of the dimension can be obtained by adding the 0.850-inch size (0.1004 + 0.850 = 0.9504). Then, by adding the 1-inch size, the dimension is completed, as shown below at the left. Another method of obtaining this same gaging length is to use a combination of four blocks as shown at the right.

First block 0.1004		First block 0.1001
Second block 0.850		Second block 0.1003
Third block 1.000		Third block 0.950
		Fourth block 0.800
Total dimension ... 1.9504		Total dimension ... 1.9504

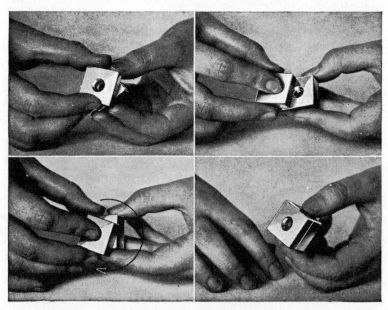

Fig. 1. How Precision Gage-blocks are Assembled by "Wringing" Them Together

How are gage-blocks used in measuring or checking various classes of precision work?

Gage-blocks may be applied in many different ways. A few applications from actual practice are shown in Figs. 2 to 7.

A machine set up for grinding "go" and "not go" snap gages is shown in Fig. 2. Three combinations of gage-blocks are lying on the machine carriage. All three combinations are used to check either the "go" or "not go" snap gages. As material is ground off and the opening between the jaws becomes larger, a larger gage-block combination is needed for checking. Instead of replacing one block in a combination with another 0.0001 inch or so larger in thickness, the toolmaker merely applies a larger combination already made up. Then as the opening between the jaws is ground still larger, the third combination is used until the snap gage is ground as specified. The snap gage after grinding is lapped to the required size.

The method of applying these gage-block combinations to a snap gage is illustrated in Fig. 3. Three gage-blocks are wrung together to obtain a width corresponding to the required dimension between the "not go" surfaces of the gage.

Fig. 4 illustrates an amplifying gage being used to check a master thread gage by the three-wire method. The distance between the upper contact point of the amplifying gage and the block on which two of the wires are supported, was previously established by applying the four gage-blocks that are seen lying on the table. The amplifying gage indicates the amount that the thread gage varies from the specified pitch diameter.

Gage-blocks are commonly used in setting up various adjustable inspection devices. Fig. 6, for example, shows three gage-blocks being employed to locate the contact point of an optical inspection instrument. This instrument is used to check whatever gage or machine part must conform to the gage-block dimension. In other words, it is not used for direct measuring but for comparing the size of the work with the known dimension of the gage-blocks. Instruments of this general type are often referred to as *comparators*.

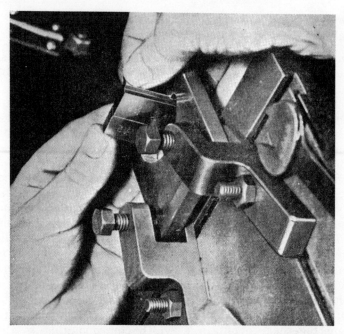

Fig. 3. Precision Gage-blocks are being used to Check a Snap Gage while it is Set up in a Grinding Machine

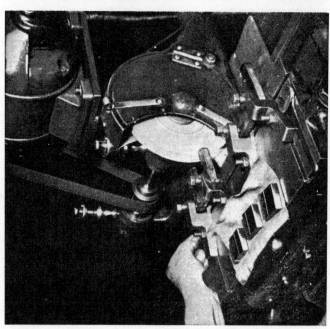

Fig. 2. Use of Gage-blocks for Checking Snap-gages which are being Ground

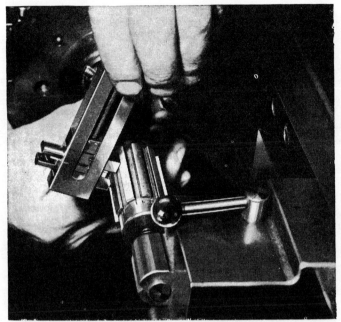

Fig. 5. Gage-blocks and Precision Jaws in an Adjustable Holder Provide a Temporary Snap Gage

Fig. 4. Gage-blocks Provide a Convenient Method of Adjusting Amplifying Gages for Precision Inspection

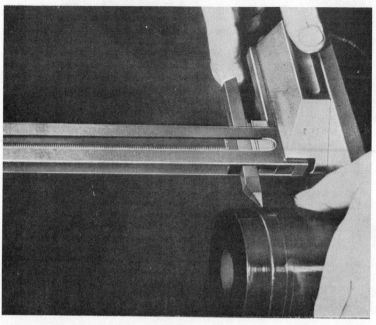

Fig. 7. Using Gage-blocks for Locating a Scriber in a Holder to Insure Marking a Line at a Specified Height

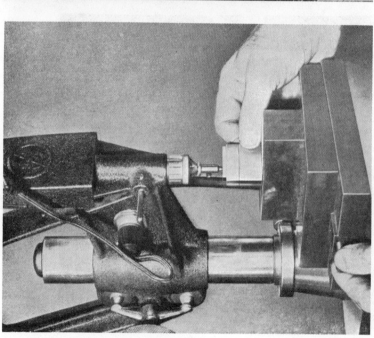

Fig. 6. Accurate Settings of Optical Inspection Devices are Facilitated by the Use of Precision Gage-blocks, as Shown

How are adjustable holders and other accessories used to increase the applications of gage-blocks?

Various accessories can be obtained for use with the gage-blocks that greatly increase their applications. Adjustable holders are available in which the gage-blocks can be built up to required heights for use in different ways.

In Fig. 7 is illustrated a height gage made up by mounting an adjustable holder in a foot-block. Positioned in the holder at a height determined by using three gage-blocks is a scriber. The illustration shows this scriber being used to mark a line around a cylindrical part that has been coated with an acid-resisting substance so that only the line will be etched in the surface when the acid is applied.

The use of gage-blocks and their accessories for the accurate checking of splines is shown in Fig. 5. In this illustration, a temporary snap gage has been made up by inserting two jaws with flat measuring surfaces in an adjustable holder. Two gage-blocks placed between the jaws insure that these jaws are separated the specified distance.

Are precision gage-blocks held together by atmospheric pressure alone?

When precision gage-blocks are wrung together, they will resist separation in a direction at right angles to the faces in contact, with a force considerably greater than the atmospheric pressure on the area of contact. This phenomenon has caused some to believe that actual molecular adhesion takes place when surfaces that are nearly perfect planes are brought into intimate contact. The error of this theory has been revealed by investigations showing that the adhesion results from the presence of a very thin liquid film. Some blocks of hardened steel were prepared, each weighing $1\frac{1}{2}$ ounces and having surfaces of 0.7 square inch and flat to within a millionth of an inch of accuracy, and these were used to test the adhesive properties of many liquids. The contact faces were carefully freed from moisture and grease with alcohol before being coated with a very thin film of the liquid under test. When wrung together while perfectly clean, they fell apart, under their own weight; in order to separate blocks which were held together by films, a force ranging from 17 pounds for Rangoon oil to 22 for lubricating oil, 29 for turpentine, and 35 for condensed water vapor was necessary. After washing the hands with soap, blocks rubbed on them showed adhesion as high as 90 pounds. There was no adhesion from volatile liquids, such as alcohol and benzine; and very little from viscous liquids, such as glycerine and glucose. The microscope showed that the films, drawn out in thin lines, covered only a tenth or less of the metal faces. From varied experiments it appeared that in the case of paraffin film, for instance, the 27 pounds required to part the plates included about one pound due to atmospheric pressure, one to surface tension and 25 pounds to the actual tensile strength of the liquid. The tensile strength of water, under these conditions, seemed to be as high as 443 pounds per square inch.

What is the legal standard of length in the United States?

The international meter is the *fundamental unit of length* in the United States. The primary standard is deposited at the International Bureau of Weights and Measures near Paris. This platinum-iridium bar has three fine lines at each end; the distance between the middle lines of each end, when the bar is at a temperature of 0 degree C., is one meter, by definition. The legal equivalent of the meter for commercial purposes is 39.37 inches.

There is a difference in the relation between the standards of measurements as defined in the United States and Great Britain, but the difference is so small that it is of no importance in ordinary mechanical work, as it amounts to only 1/363,000 inch in one inch. The difference, however, becomes of importance in the more precise length measurements of science and industry, where accuracy of 1/1,000,000 of an inch, or even greater, may be required. In the United States, the official relation is:

$$\frac{1 \text{ yard}}{1 \text{ meter}} = \frac{3600}{3937}$$

In Great Britain the official relation is:

$$\frac{1 \text{ yard}}{1 \text{ meter}} = \frac{3600}{3937.0113}$$

From these relations may be derived the following approximate relations: 1 United States inch = 25.40005 millimeters; 1 British inch = 25.39998 millimeters. The use in industry of 25.4 millimeters as a simplified practical equivalent of one inch has been approved by the American Standards Association. This equivalent has also been adopted by industry in Great Britain (where the legal equivalent of one inch is 25.39998 millimeters) and in Germany, Italy, Russia, Switzerland, Sweden, and other countries.

If all standards of measurement were destroyed, could they be duplicated?

If every standard bar representing the yard or meter should be destroyed, it would be possible to duplicate them without error by the light-wave method of measurement. Light is a form of wave motion. Different colors of light have different wave lengths ranging from 0.0000169 inch (the average length of violet waves) to 0.0000268 inch for red waves. Daylight contains all the colors and has an average wave length of approximately 0.00002 inch. The relation between the meter and the wave length of cadmium light, as determined by Benoit, Fabry, and Perot, is as follows: 1 meter equals 1,553,164.13 wave lengths of red cadmium light. This wave length is based on standard conditions of temperature, pressure and humidity, and the number of waves per meter as given is probably correct to one part in 10,000,000, which means that the meter may be defined in terms of light waves with an accuracy of one part in 10,000,000.

We not only know the equivalent of the standard meter or standard yard in terms of light waves, but apparatus has been developed for determining the number of waves in a given space. The instrument used for this purpose is known as an *interferometer*. An important practical application of the interferometer is in measuring precision gages by this fundamental method of measurement. The use of this optical apparatus is a scientific undertaking. For this reason all commercial methods of checking accuracy must be comparative, and the taking of fundamental measurements is necessarily confined to the basic or primary standards, such as are used to a very limited extent for checking working masters, where the greatest possible degree of accuracy is required. The interferometer is used in determining the number of light waves of known wave length which at a given instant are between two planes coinciding with the opposite faces of a gage-block or whatever part is to be measured. When this number is known, the thickness can be computed because the lengths of the light waves used have been determined with almost absolute precision. The light, therefore, becomes a scale with divisions—approximately 0.00002 inch apart.

Generating Plane Surfaces and Angles by Precision Methods

Very accurate plane surfaces, straightedges and angular surfaces can, of course, be produced mechanically or by the use of modern machine tools, but the fundamental methods of *originating* or generating such surfaces should be understood. These generating methods are based upon important mechanical principles which may prove very useful in connection with certain classes of precision toolmaking and gage-making. The fundamental methods to be described make it possible to arrive at a precise result solely by the aid of the principles employed.

How are straightedges originated by the triple method?

This method is based upon the principle that three straightedges cannot fit together, interchangeably, unless the edges are straight or plane surfaces; therefore, when employing this method, it is necessary to make three straightedges in order to secure accurate results. The general method of procedure is as follows: Three blanks are first machined as accurately as possible and these should be numbered 1, 2, and 3. That one of the three blanks which is believed to be the most accurate is then selected as a trial straightedge and the other two are fitted to it; for instance, if No. 1 is to be the first trial straightedge, Nos. 2 and 3 are fitted to it. This fitting should be done so accurately that no light can be seen between the straightedges when No. 1 is in contact either with No. 2 or 3. The accuracy of Nos. 2 and 3 will now depend upon the accuracy of No. 1. If it is assumed that No. 1 is slightly concave, as shown exaggerated at A, Fig. 1, then Nos. 2 and 3 will be convex; hence, the next step in this operation is to place Nos. 2 and 3

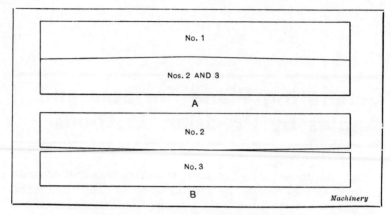

Fig. 1. (A) Straightedges Nos. 2 and 3 Fitted to No. 1. (B) The Inaccuracy Copied from No. 1 is Revealed when Nos. 2 and 3 are Placed Together

together to determine if such an error exists. As the diagram *B* indicates, the inaccuracy will then appear double. One of these blanks, say, No. 2, is next corrected and made as nearly straight as possible. When making this correction, one should be guided by the error shown by test *B*. No. 2 is then used as the trial straightedge and Nos. 1 and 3 are fitted to it. The entire operation is then repeated; that is, blanks 3 and 1, after being fitted to No. 2, are placed together to observe whatever error may exist, and then No. 3 is changed as indicated by the test. No. 3 is then used as the trial straightedge and Nos. 1 and 2 are fitted to it. The latter are then placed together; No. 1 is corrected and again used as a trial straightedge, to which Nos. 2 and 3 are fitted. By repeating this operation, the original error will be gradually eliminated and a straight surface originated. If an accurate surface plate or other plain surface is available, the method just described will be unnecessary, as the straightedge could be fitted directly to the surface plate.

The method of finishing the edges depends not only upon the form of the straightedge, but, to some extent, upon the material of which it is made and, in the case of steel, whether or not the edges are hardened. Large straightedges are often made of cast iron to secure greater rigidity. These can be finished after planing by carefully scraping the edges.

Soft steel straightedges having plane surfaces or edges can be finished by scraping and lapping, whereas, if the edges are hardened, the "high spots" or areas can be reduced by stoning or lapping. The edge should preferably be ground on a surface grinder; then, any slight errors which may exist can be lapped down by using a cast-iron lap similar to the one shown in Fig. 2. As will be seen, this lap is simply an L-shaped piece of cast iron which is charged along the under surface *A*. This charged surface is at right angles to the side of the lap, which latter is held against the side of the straightedge when lapping, to prevent the lap from being canted.

Is it possible to generate precision straightedges when only two are fitted together?

The usual method of generating straightedges involves fitting three edges together interchangeably. This method is based upon the fact that any three edges that will fit interchangeably are necessarily straight. There is a newer method, however, which simplifies the work by reducing the number of straightedges to two. It is based upon the principle that any two edges that will fit each other side by side and face to face are inevitably straight. The application of the method can be demonstrated in a simple manner by starting with a thin surface, such as a sheet of paper, folded and lying flat. Cut through the pieces of paper, thus forming two pieces lying side by side, and with edges that match. Now turn the two pieces edge to edge, reversing one of them. The variation from a straight line is immediately apparent, because the error is doubled. This calls for a process of trimming and continued matching of the edges in reversed positions by which edges are obtained, finally, which show no deviation In this way two straightedges have been generated in the simplest manner possible.

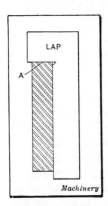

Fig. 2. Lap for Straightedges

This same principle can be applied to the making of straightedges in the shop. As a starting point, take two straight-

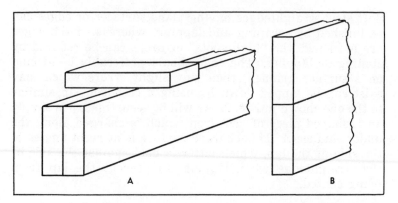

Fig. 3. Simplified Method of Making Precision Straightedges

edges that have been roughly matched, as with a file. Place them side by side, as at *A*, Fig. 3, and apply Prussian blue or other coloring material, so that when a small block or straightedge is rubbed along the edges, the coloring will be scraped off at the high spots, indicating where reduction is needed. When the high spots have been removed, by scraping, place the edges together as at *B*. This doubtless will show that they are still wavy, and the coloring material will produce bearing marks as a guide to further scraping operations. Now scrape both edges in accordance with the bearing marks. This completes the first cycle of operations in generating straightedges by the use of only two shapes. The greater part of the error is already removed. Ordinary shop methods of measurement would probably reveal no error at all. It is necessary, however, to assume that error still exists, which is true of all efforts to obtain precision; in fact, it is not possible to obtain precision in any other way. Next turn the edges back to the original position, side by side, and repeat the operation as before; follow by again placing them edge to edge, and then by reversing one of them with its edge against the other, continuing this until they fit in every position. The inevitable result is that edges are produced that are practically straight. This result is based on the fact that any two edges that will fit each other side by side and edge to edge are straight. By this method, however, but two edges are required to produce this result.

What is the meaning of the term "symmetrical distribution of errors"?

This expression may be applied to any method in precision work which results in dividing or "splitting" errors until they finally disappear. The basic principle of dividing the errors is one of the oldest in mechanics, as well as one used in daily practice. One of the commonest applications of it is that long used by carpenters in locating the center of a board. Instead of measuring the entire width of the board with a pocket rule, and dividing this total by two, the center is located by "splitting the difference." With a pocket rule, or even a stick, the carpenter measures from one side to a point somewhere near the center. At this point he makes a pencil mark. From the other side he measures the same distance toward the center, and makes a second mark. He then knows that the center lies half way between the two marks thus established, regardless of whether the measurements have overlapped or fallen short of one another. By the application of this same principle, we can achieve high precision in mechanical operations, the chief difference being that of degree. The carpenter finds one division close enough for his purposes. If you want to go further, and obtain higher accuracy, simply continue the process of splitting the error until it reaches the vanishing point. This principle of dividing errors is applied in generating a triangle as described in the following paragraph.

In generating a 60-degree triangle, what is the procedure?

In originating or generating an accurate 60-degree triangle, place two triangular pieces of hardened steel side by side in a fixed position and lap the three sides upon a surface lap. After this step, one of the pieces is turned 120 degrees, fitted against the other piece as before, and the two are again lapped. The turning and lapping operations are continued until the forms match each other in all three positions. When this has been brought about, the pieces are precise 60-degree triangles, because any two triangles which match each other in every position must be accurate.

To demonstrate the principle, cut two pieces of strawboard into a form approximating a 60-degree triangle. Hold

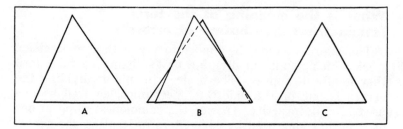

Fig. 4. Diagrams Illustrating Natural Method of
Generating Precision Triangles

the two pieces firmly side by side (as represented by diagram *A*, Fig. 4), and rub, successively, all three sides of this double formation on a flat sheet of sandpaper. Then turn one of the pieces 120 degrees (see diagram *B*) and continue to rub and turn until finally they fit each other interchangeably as at *C*. The result is the production of two equilateral triangles of quite high precision. This method is based upon the fundamental law that things which are equal to something else are equal to each other. The sum of the angles of any triangle is 180 degrees; one third of this sum is 60 degrees. It is clear, therefore, that if the three angles of each piece are equal to each other, and their sum is 180 degrees, each angle must be one-third of 180 degrees or 60 degrees. This simple experiment illustrates the ease and accuracy with which precise forms can be generated by natural methods. The same principle can be applied to the production of polygons with any number of sides.

How are parallel planes and 90-degree angles generated?

In the generation of two parallel plane surfaces, begin with the creation of parallel lines. To demonstrate, take two sheets of strawboard which are wedge-shaped. The purpose is to change the sides of each wedge into lines which are parallel. Hold the pieces firmly side by side and match up the edges on two opposite sides by rubbing them on a sheet of sandpaper laid flat (see diagram *A*, Fig. 5). Then turn one of the pieces end for end and place it side by side with its mate, as at *B*. The fact that the edges are not parallel is immediately apparent in exaggerated form, as the error is doubled. To remove the error, the edges are again rubbed on the flat sandpaper, with the pieces held firmly side by side, thus obtaining the result indicated at *C*. The interchanging and rubbing are continued until the two edges match each other when the pieces are placed side by side and also when one piece is turned end for end.

The strawboard and sandpaper are used merely to illustrate the principle. With accurate surface laps and hardened steel forms, the surfaces generated will be accurate, parallel planes. The same method may be applied to the two other edges for the purpose of making them parallel to each other. This will produce a parallelogram, as at *D*, which, however, is not square, owing to the fact that the transpositions have been 180 degrees, or half way round the circle. To demonstrate by converting the strawboard pieces into perfect squares, these pieces are held side by side and the four edges rubbed on the flat sandpaper. One of the sheets is then turned 90 degrees, as at *E*, and the four edges again lapped on the sandpaper. The 90-degree turning and lap-

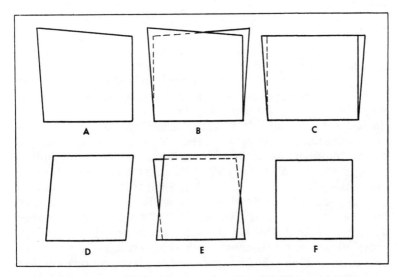

Fig. 5. Natural Method of Producing Parallel Planes and Edges that are Square with Each Other

ping operations are continued until all the edges match each other in every position, as at *F*, resulting in two pieces each of which has four equal sides and four equal angles, the latter being necessarily 90 degrees. This carries out the theorem of Euclid that the sum of the four angles in any quadrilateral figure is 360 degrees, and that if all the angles are equal each of them must be one-fourth of 360 or 90 degrees. This principle may be used in providing knife-edge squares with angles of 60 degrees, 90 degrees, or of such width as will produce a polygon of any given number of sides, all identical.

How are precision angle-blocks and squares generated?

We all know the trick of folding a sheet of paper to make a desk ruler. The principle is susceptible of wide extension. With the folded sheet of paper, for example, we know that in order to make a right angle, the sheet is folded once more so that the edges match; this generates an angle of 90 degrees. By applying this principle, it is possible to generate such forms as precision squares, precision cubes, and plane parallel opposite faces.

In making hardened steel angle-blocks, either with flat edges or knife-edges, an accurate plane surface lap must be used for abrasion. The same methods as were explained for the strawboard and sandpaper, when carried out accurately with steel forms and a surface plate, will produce high-precision angle-blocks. In the production of knife-edge angle-blocks (see diagram *A*, Fig. 6), the operation is conducted in the manner already described for the simpler demonstrations with cardboard. The blocks are simply placed together, as at *B*, while generating the right angles.

Suppose the job is to make two perfect squares of hardened steel, 2 inches square and $\frac{1}{4}$ inch thick. It is required that the edges be perfectly square with the sides, the angles truly 90 degrees, and the four faces equal to each other. This means that the blocks must be perfectly squared in every dimension. To accomplish this result requires either two plane surface laps or one surface plate and one surface lap. We will assume the use of the latter. The first step is to make the sides of the two pieces plane and parallel.

This is achieved by laying both pieces flat on the surface plate, with two of their edges touching, as at *C*, Fig. 6. The two surfaces are then lapped with the surface lap for a period of time, after which one of the pieces is transposed from the right to the left side, this transposition bringing together the edges 4 and 6 that were previously on the outside. The surface lap is then used again to reduce the two surfaces to the same plane. The same operation should be repeated after transposition of the two other edges of each piece; that is to say, the right-hand block is now rotated 90 degrees while still in contact with the face of the surface plate. The left-hand block is also rotated 90 degrees, or one fourth revolution. This rotation brings together edges 1 and 5 that have not previously been in contact. The same lapping and transposition are continued until the lap rests evenly on the entire surface of both blocks, regardless of which edges may be placed together. This proves that the surfaces have become plane parallel opposite faces.

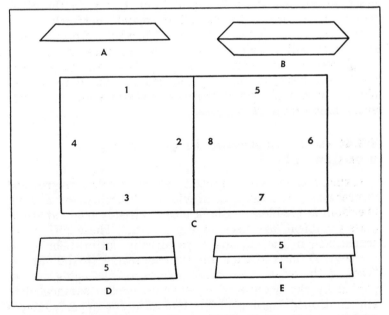

Fig. 6. Method of Generating Square Blocks Having 90-degree Angles and Equal Edges which are Square with the Sides

The next operation is to lap the edges of both blocks. The two blocks are placed with their flat sides together (as at *D*) and held firmly while the four pairs of edges are lapped on the surface lap. One of the blocks is now rotated 90 degrees, the edges are matched up evenly, and the four pairs of edges again lapped, as previously described. This process of turning and lapping should be continued until the edges match in every position. When this result has been reached, we have generated what is theoretically the frustrum of a pyramid with 90-degree corners.

In order to assure that the edges are truly square with the sides, as well as with each other, it is now necessary to introduce another transposition. This transposition brings into contact with each other the sides of the blocks that have been outside. This can be done by removing the block from underneath and placing it on top without otherwise turning either block, as shown at *E*. When the edges are lapped in this relation, it will become apparent that the edges were not square. The same method of turning one block 90 degrees while it is still in contact with the other one is continued until the edges match perfectly when turned in every position and with either side of either block in contact with its mate. This means that these blocks may be placed in any position and the edges will match perfectly. We have, therefore, produced two 90-degree angle-blocks, both with plane parallel opposite sides and with every angle truly 90 degrees.

What is the procedure in generating precision cubes?

If the problem is to produce two perfect cubes, the method is practically the same as previously described for making precision angle-blocks. Blank pieces, already made approximately cubical, are used to begin with. These pieces are transposed in the various ways already outlined, bringing the several faces of each one into contact with the various faces of the other, the transpositions always being accompanied by the process of leveling up on the surface plate and continued lapping of the two adjacent upper surfaces with the surface lap. This must be repeated until the surfaces, placed against each other in any position, are found

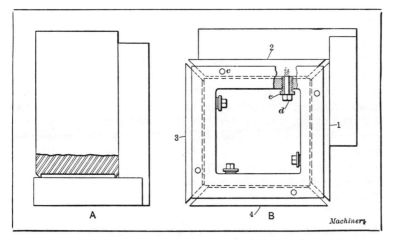

Fig. 7. Two Methods of Testing a Square

to be in the same plane when the blocks are lying on the surface plate. The prime essential in producing cubes is to see that the sides that are in contact with each other are held in full contact during the lapping operations.

By these operations two practically perfect cubes may be produced. Each cube contains six faces, eight corners, twelve edges, and twenty-four right angles formed by the corners. All of these have been created by the application of a simple principle. The method carries within itself the principle of accuracy which, if followed out, must inevitably result in the production of two precision cubes. Each face is a true plane of equal area with each other face. These planes intersect each other at angles of 90 degrees. All edges form straight lines of equal length, each of which is parallel to each of its mates. All angles are right angles.

How is a cylindrical plug used for testing the accuracy of a square?

In order to make a reliable test, a 90-degree angle should be originated, unless a master square of known accuracy is available. A comparatively simple way of doing this accurately is to make a cylindrical plug similar to the one shown at *A*, Fig. 7. The lower end of this plug is recessed to form a narrow edge which is beveled on the outside so that there will be no bearing in the corner where the blade joins the stock. This plug is ground on dead centers and lapped to form as perfect a cylinder as possible. The narrow edge at the end is then ground true so that it will be exactly at right angles to the cylindrical surface. By holding the square against the side and end of the plug, as the illustration indicates, and subjecting it to the light test, a very minute inaccuracy in the position of the square blade can be detected. The outside edge of the blade can be tested by placing the plug and square on an accurate surface plate, and bringing the blade edge into contact with the side of the plug.

What type of testing device for squares is based upon the cumulative-error principle?

The adjustable test block shown at *B*, Fig. 7, depends upon the principle of cumulative errors. The test block is formed of a square cast-iron frame which is grooved around the outside and contains four close-fitting adjustable strips which, in the illustration, are numbered from 1 to 4. The reliability of this test block depends largely upon the outer edges of these strips which must be accurately finished plane surfaces. The strips are held in place by close-fitting pins *c* near the ends, and by bolts *d*. The latter pass through clearance holes in set-screws *e* which are screwed through the frame and bear against the inner edges of the strips. By clamping one of these strips against the set-screws, it is locked in position after being properly adjusted.

The method of using this test block for determining the accuracy of a try-square is as follows, assuming that the edges have not previously been adjusted: The square is first placed against two of the strips or straightedges of the test block. These strips are then adjusted until they exactly fit the square being tested. If the square were first applied to strips Nos. 1 and 2 (as shown in the illustration), strips 2 and 3 would next be adjusted to fit the square, and then strips 3 and 4. After making these adjustments, if the square is applied to the strips Nos. 4 and 1, any error which might exist would be multiplied four times; whereas, if the square fitted these last sides perfectly, this would indicate that the angle between the square blade and stock was 90 degrees, within very close limits.

To illustrate how the error accumulates in going around the test block, suppose the angle between the blade of a square and its stock were 90 degrees 15 minutes. Evidently, then, sides 1 and 2 of the test block would also be set to this angle. Therefore, taking side No. 1 as a base, side No. 2 would be out 15 minutes. As side 2 is used in setting side 3, the error of the latter with reference to side 1 would be 30 minutes; similarly, side 4 would have an error of 45 minutes, and when the square was applied to sides 4 and 1 for the final test, the error would be four times the original amount, or 1 degree.

In order to originate a 90-degree angle, or, in other words, to set the test block to this angle, a sheet steel templet may be used. This simply forms a temporary try-square and is cut away so that there are two small projections along each test edge, in order that changes can be made by simply altering these small projections. This templet is first made as accurately as possible and it is then used in setting the test block. After adjusting the block, if comparison with the fourth and first sides shows an error, the templet is corrected and the test block again adjusted. This operation is repeated until the 90-degree angle is originated. The accuracy of a square can then be tested by comparison with any two sides of the test block and without making any adjustments.

Engineering Standards Applied in Machine Building

In the construction of machines or other mechanical devices, there are parts or elements which are utilized so generally that the adoption of standard forms, sizes, etc., greatly simplifies the design, manufacture and maintenance.

The machinist and machine shop executive should be familiar with the commonly used standards. Some of the main features of standards which are particularly important in machine building will be referred to. Information concerning such standards is especially useful in connection with shop work and also in the reading of blueprints or mechanical drawings, as indicated in the following chapter which deals with this subject.

Most of the standards used in machine building practice consist of established dimensions. Some of these standard dimensions, which are of particular importance in the shop, will be found in various parts of this treatise. It is impracticable to include them all because this would require more space than is available; furthermore, such standards (usually in the form of tables) are found in all engineering handbooks intended for the machine building industry. The object is to present in this chapter the main facts only, rather than details and tabulated dimensions. Some of these standards apply to commonly used machine parts such as bolts, screws, screw threads, shafts, gears, etc. Others apply to the more important and commonly used small tools such as drills, taps, jig bushings, milling cutters, etc.

SCREW THREADS.—In the United States most of the small and medium size threads on bolts, machine screws, set-screws, studs, and other threaded parts now conform to the American Standard for Unified Screw Threads which represents the development of the former American National thread form. The former American National thread form is practically the same as the new American Standard Unified thread form, but the Unified system is more complete and interchangeable. The Acme form of thread is generally employed for lead screws and other comparatively large screw threads.

464

The general subject of screw threads is so important that it has been covered in another chapter beginning on page 167 of this volume. The standardization of screw threads is of great practical value not only to the manufacturers and users of bolts, screws and other threaded parts but also to manufacturers of taps, dies and thread forming equipment of all kinds. The tolerances and allowances forming part of the American Standard Unified system represent practical degrees of accuracy and make it possible to obtain readily the different classes of fits referred to on page 383.

BOLTS AND NUTS.—The 1941 American Standard covered head dimensions only. In 1952 and 1955 the American Standard was revised to cover the entire product. Some bolt and nut classifications were simplified by elimination or consolidation in agreements reached with the British and Canadians. These are recognized in the present American Standard as "unified."

Except for Heavy series bolts, head dimensions of all hexagon bolt and cap screws are uniform and have basically the former across-flats dimensions of automotive hexagon head bolts and cap screws for sizes up to and including 9/16 inches, and former across-flats dimensions of the Regular series hexagon bolts for bolts ⅝ inches and larger, and a head height based on a ratio of ⅝ of the diameter.

Light and Regular series nuts were consolidated and have the proportions of the Light series for sizes up to and including the ⅝-inch size and proportions of the Regular series nuts for sizes above ⅝ inch. The 7/16-inch nut is a modification of both the Light and Regular series.

The term, "finished" hexagon bolt designates the consolidated automotive hexagon head bolt and the close body-toleranced regular semi-finished bolt. The term "cap screw" is retained in the ¼ to 1½-inch size range for products that are the same as "finished" bolts. The term, "finished" is also used to designate the consolidation of Light and Regular series of washer-faced double chamfered nuts. The term does not indicate that surfaces are necessarily machined.

UNITED STATES STANDARD BOLT HEADS AND NUTS.—The United States Standard has largely been superseded by the American Standard Heavy Bolt Heads and Nuts which have the same widths across the flats as corresponding sizes in the United States Standard.

S.A.E. HIGH NUTS.—These S.A.E. Standard nuts are for bolt sizes ranging from ¼ to 1 inch. The nut is much higher than the ordinary form to allow for castle-nut slots and also, in some cases, for a counterbore at the bottom.

S.A.E. CAP OR ACORN NUTS.—The tapped hole in a cap nut is "blind" or does not pass through the nut which has a closed rounded top to conceal the end of a screw, bolt, or threaded rod.

MACHINE SCREWS.—The American Standard for machine screws covers a range of sizes which are commonly designated by numbers, with the exception of the ¼-inch and larger sizes, as shown by the table on page 4, Volume 2. This table gives the decimal equivalents or actual sizes, number of threads per inch. the tap drill size, and the clearance hole drill size for either a close fit or a free fit. The American Standard gives the proportions of nine shapes of machine screw heads known as flat head, 100-degree flat head. round head, oval head, fillister head, pan head, binding head, truss head and hexagon head. Each size of machine screw is made in a number of different lengths. These lengths are not standardized.

CAP-SCREWS.—The American Standard includes a hexagonal form for an ordinary wrench; a slotted form (for screw driver) such as the flat head, round head, and fillister head cap-screws; and, in addition, both the hexagon-socket and fluted-socket types. The heads of these socket types may be inserted in counterbored holes so that they are flush with, or do not project above, the adjacent surface. The hexagonal cap-screws range in diameter from ¼ to 1½ inches; the fluted-socket types range from No. 0 to 1½ inches; the round head cap-screws range from ¼ to ¾ inch; the fillister head cap-screws range from ¼ to 1 inch; and the flat head cap-screws range from ¼ to 1½ inches. Most cap-screws are threaded according to the Coarse Series of pitches in the American Standard, but the Fine Series is preferred for some applications.

SET-SCREWS.—American Standard set-screw heads include the square form, the hexagon-socket type, and the fluted-socket type. The American Standard square head form ranges from No. 10 to 1½ inches diameter, whereas the hexagon-socket and fluted-socket types range from No. 0 (same as machine screw size) up to 2 inches diameter.

T-BOLTS AND T-NUTS.—These American Standard T-bolts and T-nuts are for use in conjunction with machine tools having T-slots in the table for holding, aligning, or clamping jigs, fixtures, or the work itself. The thread diameters of the T-nuts range from ¼ to 1¼ inches, whereas the bolt diameters vary from ¼ to 1½ inches. This standard has been approved not only by the American Standards Association, but by the National Machine Tool Builders' Association, the A.S.M.E., the S.A.E., and the Metal Cutting Tool Institute.

AMERICAN STANDARD RIVETS.—The American Standard Large Rivets includes diameters ranging from ½ to 1¾ inches. The proportions of six standard heads are given. These are the button head, high button or acorn head, cone head, flat-top countersunk head, round-top countersunk head, and pan head. The American Standard Small Rivets range in diameter from 3/32 to 7/16 inch, inclusive.

STANDARD TAPS.—The American Standard applies to both cut-thread and ground-thread taps. The standard includes the exact dimensions of various types of taps with tolerance data for cut threads and ground thread taps as well as giving recommendations for tapping Unified threads. Such data are, of course, particularly useful to tap manufacturers. The American Standard applies to hand taps, machine screw taps, nut taps, tapper taps, boiler taps, and pipe taps in the different ranges of sizes to which these various taps are ordinarily manufactured.

TWIST DRILLS.—The American Standard for Twist Drills covers: (1) straight shank drills of short and long lengths in wire gage sizes, fractional sizes, and letter sizes ranging from 0.0135 to 2.000 inches, inclusive, in diameter; (2) taper shank drills of regular shank and of shanks smaller and larger than regular and ranging from ⅛ to 3½ inches, inclusive, in diameter; and (3) automotive series straight shank drills of short and long lengths ranging from 0.2500 to 0.6875 inch, inclusive, in diameter, including millimeter, fractional, and letter sizes.

Tables giving the wire gage and letter sizes will be found on page 294 of this volume. In addition to these sizes, the straight shank twist drills are available in diameters ranging from 1/64 to 1¼ inches in increments of 1/64 inch; from 1-9/32 to 1½ inches in increments of 1/32 inch; and from 1-9/16 to 2 inches in increments of 1/16 inch.

STANDARD TAPERS.—Many small tools such as drills, reamers, end-mills, cutter-holding arbors, etc., have taper shanks which fit either into a hole of corresponding taper in a machine spindle or into an intervening collet, sleeve, or adapter. These taper-shank tools are so prevalent that tapers conforming to certain established standards are essential. Taper shank twist drills, for example, all conform to one of a series of eight Morse tapers. The different standard tapers in common use are listed on pages 90 to 92 of this volume. Tapers such as Morse, Brown & Sharpe, and Jarno are designated by numbers. Handbook tables give the dimensions equivalent to different standard tapers.

MILLING CUTTERS.—There is an American Standard for certain commonly used forms of milling cutters. The standard includes the range of sizes and the main proportions. It applies to such cutters as the plain cylindrical type; end-mills; angular cutters; Woodruff keyslot cutters; T-slot cutters; slitting saws; concave, convex and corner-rounding cutters. Such a standard is chiefly for cutter manufacturers, but the shop man should be familiar with all standardization as it applies to important classes of metal-working tools.

FORMING TOOLS.—The general application of forming tools is explained on pages 263 and 264 of this volume. Such tools are widely used on turret lathes and automatic screw machines or other classes of semi-automatic and automatic turning machines. Because of this general application, both circular and straight or dovetail forming tool *blanks* have been standardized. (The term "blank" means that the tool must be formed to suit the job by the user, since the shape of the cutting edge obviously cannot be included in a general standard.) This standard was established to obtain interchangeability of such tools on various makes of machines of comparable stock capacity. Group numbers are used to identify the tool sizes, with the machines for which these sizes are adapted. For example, a No. 00 B & S screw machine is in Group No. 1, whereas No. 0 is in Group No. 2. There are six of these group numbers and each includes a range of tool blank sizes suitable for the machines included in that same group. To illustrate, there are five sizes of *circular* tool blanks and two sizes of *straight* blanks for machines in the No. 1 group. Handbook tables give the standard tool blank sizes and also the makes of machines included in each group.

GRINDING WHEELS.—The current Simplified Practice Recommendation R45 was proposed by the Grinding Wheel Institute and incorporates various standard wheel shapes and a range of sizes for each shape. (These shapes are illustrated on pages 338 and 339 of the Machine Shop Training Course—Volume 2.) The different types or shapes are designated by numbers. No. 1 wheels, for example, are the "straight" or disk type; No. 2 wheels are the "cylinder" type, etc.

WIRE AND SHEET METAL GAGES.—The term "wire gage" may indicate a wire gaging device or it may relate to a standard series of dimensions. In referring, for example, to the American or Brown & Sharpe wire gage, the term indicates ordinarily a standard series of gage sizes. Some wire gages are applied both to wires and to sheet metals. For example, the American or Brown & Sharpe wire gage was used for various non-ferrous wires such as brass, copper, etc., and also for sheets of brass, copper, aluminum, etc. Gage sizes are designated either by a number or by giving the actual dimension which the number represents. When the number only is given, the equivalent dimension for any gage may be found in handbook tables.

Gage for Sheet Steel: Wire and sheet metal gage numbers ordinarily represent a standard dimension such as diameter or thickness. The United States Standard Gage for all uncoated sheet steel and iron is a *weight gage* rather than a thickness gage. Since workmen ordinarily want the equivalent thickness, this is given in handbook tables. The thicknesses in tables, as now published, are based upon a weight for steel of 41.82 pounds per square foot per inch thick, although the basic weight of steel used in the manufacture of steel products is 40.8 pounds per square foot per inch of thickness. The modified figure allows for variations in the thickness from the edges to the center of sheets due to the rolling process.

SHAFTING.—The smaller sizes of shafting are cold-finished by drawing through a die which produces a bright smooth surface and diameters usually within 0.002 to 0.005 inch of the nominal size. The former Standard for finished "transmission shafting" varies from 15/16 inch to 8 inches diameter. For "machinery shafting," the diameters range from ½ inch to 8 inches. The tolerances within this range are minus and vary from 0.002 to 0.005 inch. These tolerances represent the maximum allowable variation below the exact nominal size.

SQUARE AND FLAT KEYS.—A square key is square in cross section, whereas the so-called "flat key" is rectangular, the width exceeding the thickness or height. Dimensions of plain or headless type and gib-head keys are given in handbooks. Tapering keys have a taper of ⅛ inch per foot, and the height or thickness is measured at a distance from the large end equal to the key width.

WOODRUFF KEYS.—This type of key is in the form of a circular segment. The circular side fits into a keyseat formed by sinking a cutter of suitable radius and width into the shaft. Key sizes may be designated by giving actual dimensions or by some number. A ¼-1⅛ Woodruff key has a nominal width of ¼ inch, and it is a segment-shaped section of a bar having a diameter of 1⅛ inches. The Whitney Mfg. Co.'s size numbers are supplemented by a few letter sizes such as A, B, etc. The American Standard size numbers indicate nominal dimensions. The last two digits give the key bar diameter in eighths of an inch; the digits preceding the last two give the key width in thirty seconds. For example, No. 204 indicates a key 2/32 by 4/8 or 1/16 by ½ inch. Designating the nominal size directly (1/16-½ in this case) appears to be simpler, more direct, and has the additional merit of being self-explanatory.

KEYS FOR CUTTERS AND ARBORS.—In order to promote interchangeability, there is an American Standard for keyseat, keyway and key dimensions for milling cutters and arbors. This standard covers arbor diameters from ½ inch to 5 inches, with corresponding key sizes in each case, and maximum and minimum dimensions for keys, keyseats and keyways.

SPLINED SHAFTS.—Splined shafts have a number of equally spaced keys formed on the shaft itself. There are two types of splines;

one type has straight or parallel sides, and the other is of involute form like the tooth of a gear. These two forms are covered by S.A.E. and American Standards. When straight splines are formed by hobbing (method employed for quantity production), the hob teeth must have special curvature in order to generate straight-sided splines. This special curvature must be carefully laid out either graphically or mathematically. On the other hand, involute splines are generated by using hobs with straight-sided teeth inclined at an angle of 30 degrees on each side according to the American Standard. Hence, the hobs for involute splines are easier to make, and the splined shaft size may also be checked readily, by measurement over pins, the method being similar to that employed for many gears of the smaller sizes.

GEAR TEETH.—Gear teeth, like screw threads and other machine elements in common use, conform to generally accepted standards. In standardizing gears, the rack tooth is the basis. How an entire system of gear teeth can be standardized, merely by giving the angle and other proportions of a rack tooth, is explained in Volume 2. (See chapter beginning on page 278, and the special reference beginning on page 285.)

GAGES.—Some form of gage is used in connection with practically every machining or fitting operation, especially in the interchangeable manufacture of duplicate parts. The American Standard for gages is to promote the use of approved gage forms and proportions. (See pages 407 to 412 of this volume.)

TOLERANCES AND ALLOWANCES FOR FITS.—Tolerances and allowances must be governed by an almost endless variety of conditions existing in different lines of manufacture; hence, they can only be standardized in a general way, as applied to average conditions. The main idea is to adopt as standard those tolerances and allowances which represent good practice as determined by wide experience. (For general information on American and British Standards see pages 381 to 383.)

STANDARD STEELS.—Standards have been adopted for different classes of steels, cast irons, and also non-ferrous alloys such as brasses, bronzes, aluminum alloys, magnesium alloys, etc. The S.A.E. (Society of Automotive Engineers, Inc.) standard compositions for steels and non-ferrous alloys are especially important in machine-building, because these steels frequently are specified on drawings both in and out of the automotive industries. In the case of steels, the S.A.E. number indicates, in a general way, the composition. These numbers consist of four figures. The first figure indicates the general class of steel. For example, 1 means carbon steel; 2, nickel steel; 3, nickel-chromium steel; 4, molybdenum steel; 5, chromium steel; 6, chromium-vanadium steel; 7, tungsten steel; 9, silico-manganese steel. The second figure generally indicates the approximate percentage of the chief alloying element. The last two or three figures usually indicate the average carbon content in "points" or hundredths of 1 per cent. To illustrate, S.A.E. steel No. 2340 is a nickel steel (Group 2) containing about 3 per cent nickel and 0.40 per cent carbon.

JIG BUSHINGS.—Since drill jigs are used in all types of machine shops, the dimensions of the important classes of bushings have been standardized. For information on the forms of bushings and types included in the American Standard see pages 302 and 303.

PIPE SIZES AND WEIGHTS.—The nominal sizes of wrought iron and steel pipe up to 12 inches, inclusive, conform quite closely to the inside diameter, with the exception of sizes below 1 inch, which are larger inside than the nominal sizes indicate. The nominal sizes for pipes larger than 12 inches are the same as the outside diameters, and these larger sizes commonly are designated as O.D. pipe. According to the American Standard, the wall thicknesses available for a given nominal pipe size are designated by wall thickness "Schedule Numbers." These thickness schedule numbers are intended eventually to supersede the general terms such as "standard weight," "extra strong," and "double extra strong."

STANDARD HARDNESS NUMBERS.—Some notes, abbreviations and symbols which appear on drawings and on operation lists do not pertain ordinarily to the work of the machine shop, but, nevertheless, they should be understood. Numbers or symbols indicating the hardness of steel or other materials are examples.

Brinell Hardness Number: The Brinell hardness test consists in forcing a ball-shaped point 10 millimeters in diameter into the surface of the material. A standard load of 3000 kilograms is employed for hard metals and 500 kilograms for softer metals. In some cases, the load is reduced to 100 kilograms for extremely soft metals. The Brinell hardness number represents the ratio of the load on the indenting tool, in kilograms, to the surface area of the indentation in square millimeters. A high-carbon steel, after quenching in brine, might have a hardness of 725 to 750 Brinell; and this same steel drawn to, say, 750 degrees, might have a hardness of 475 to 490 Brinell. The tensile strength of steel, in pounds per square inch, ranges from about 490 to 515 times the Brinell hardness number.

Rockwell Test: The Rockwell hardness test is based upon the principle of determining the depth of penetration when standard loads are applied to a standard penetrator. These tests differ in regard to the size and form of the penetrator and the loads applied. The hardness number is followed by a letter indicating the general type of test, there being several adapted to different classes of materials. Hardness No. 50 C, for example, means 50 on the C scale and indicates that a diamond cone penetrator was used in conjunction with a major load of 150 kilograms. The C scale is usually applied in testing hardened steel. There are several other Rockwell scales adapted either for softer materials, relatively thin materials, etc. To illustrate the difference between the B and C scales, 50 B is equivalent to 93 Brinell, whereas 50 C is equivalent to 484 Brinell and indicates a much harder material.

Scleroscope: This hardness testing instrument is equipped with a diamond-tipped hammer which is allowed to drop from a known height onto the metal, thus indicating the hardness by the rebound of the hammer or in terms of elasticity. The harder the metal, the greater the rebound. Handbook tables show equivalent hardness numbers as obtained by different commonly used tests.

STANDARDS FOR DRAWINGS.—The American Standard for drawings and drafting-room practice is primarily for engineers or draftsmen, but many features of this standard are of importance to shop men because they *use* drawings. This point is illustrated repeatedly in the following section on the reading of drawings. There are also American Standard abbreviations for scientific and engineering terms. Handbook tables give these various terms and their abbreviations.

How to Read Blueprints
or Mechanical Drawings

Everyone engaged in mechanical work, especially in a machine shop or pattern shop, should know how to read blueprints or drawings. The expression "reading a drawing" simply means *understanding* the drawing. The designer of a machine, by means of mechanical drawings, shows the man in the shop the form and proportions of the different parts and some drawings also show the relation of these parts when they are assembled in the completed machine or mechanism. Drawings also provide records so that a given part or mechanism can be reproduced readily at any future time.

The shop man who cannot read drawings is handicapped almost as much as though he could not read or write. Now, in order to read mechanical drawings, it is necessary to understand certain basic or foundation principles underlying the making or arrangement of such drawings. In other words, if you know what the different views of a drawing represent and understand the methods of dimensioning drawings, as well as the meaning of certain commonly used terms, abbreviations or symbols, then you are capable of obtaining from a drawing the information required in the shop. It does not follow that you could actually make a mechanical drawing yourself. This requires practice and dexterity in the use of instruments, as well as a knowledge of machine or tool design in case the drawn part represents the development of some original form or type of mechanical device. It is evident that ability to *read a book* does not mean, necessarily, that the reader could *write* one, but he must know the language. Similarly, reading a drawing requires a knowledge of the special line and symbol language employed in the mechanical industries. The purpose of this section is to explain as briefly as possible the points that are essential in reading or interpreting drawings.

What is the meaning of the term "mechanical drawing"?

The drawings of mechanical devices, or individual parts of such devices, are known as mechanical drawings. Such drawings are made ordinarily by the use of instruments to obtain straight lines, true circles or arcs, and at least fairly accurate proportions; but a more important fact about *mechanical* drawings is that they represent the true shape of an object as seen from different sides. This usually requires two or more separate views. As these views represent different sides of the object, they do not resemble

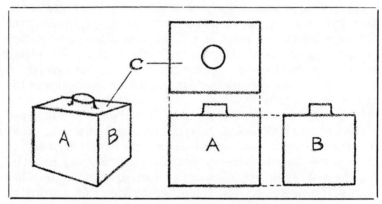

Fig. 1. Pencil Sketches showing (at Left) a Perspective View and (at Right) a Mechanical Drawing of the Same Object

perspective drawings or photographs. The underlying principle of mechanical drawing is very simple; and when the general procedure is understood, such drawings reveal a great deal more than a perspective view or photograph, with the possible exception of parts or objects which are much simpler in form than most machine parts. In other words, mechanical drawings have practical advantages in the machine shop and also in making patterns for cast parts. Just what these advantages are will be understood when certain fundamental principles have been explained.

The best way to understand just what distinguishes *mechanical* drawings from *perspective* drawings or photographs is by a direct comparison of these methods: The perspective drawing at the left in Fig. 1 represents a block having, on the top side, a boss or small extension. This drawing represents a block as it would appear to the eye or in a photograph. A mechanical drawing of the same block is shown at the right. In this particular mechanical drawing, three views are used: One shows side *A* just as it would appear if viewed squarely from the front; another shows side *B* just as it would appear if viewed squarely from the side; the upper view shows the top *C* as it would appear if viewed squarely from above. This is known as the projection method of drawing, or sometimes as *orthographic projection* which, incidentally, is not as complicated as it sounds. All mechanical drawings are based upon this fundamental principle of projection. The projection method shows clearly the shape and proportions of each surface or part drawn, including interior or hidden cavities in many cases, as explained later. The number of projected sides or views varies.

How many views are required to represent a given part?

The number of views depends upon the shape of the part. Sometimes a single view is sufficient; but, as a general rule, two or three views are necessary to show clearly the complete shape of a machine part. In addition to such general views, separate views of important details may be necessary. Such detail views may, in some cases, be drawn to a larger scale than the main drawing in order to show clearly some small but important feature. In determining the number of views in any case, the designer is governed largely by judgment and experience. Drawings to follow will show simple examples of parts requiring only two views in some cases and three views in other cases.

What are the advantages of the projection method of drawing?

An important advantage of the projection method is indicated by again referring to the simple object shown in Fig. 1. Suppose that we had only the perspective drawing at the left. Could you tell at a glance whether or not this block is in the form of a cube with sides of equal length? Furthermore, would you know definitely whether the boss on the top side is round or slightly oval? While roundness is to be expected, there would be no definite assurance. The mechanical drawing at the right shows at once that the block is somewhat rectangular in form and that the boss is round. While the machinist does not rely upon the proportions of the drawing itself but rather upon the dimensions given on the drawing, it is, nevertheless, important to have views of the different sides which are not only dimensioned correctly but also proportioned with a fair degree of accuracy. This not only assists the designer in his development of the design, but also is useful in the shop partly because a reasonably true drawing is easier to read or understand. A working drawing must convey to the eye of the workman a clear idea of what the designer wants made. It should be so complete that, when it passes into the shop, no further questions or explanations will be necessary; hence, a complete working drawing contains all the necessary information as to materials, treatment, dimensions, finish, etc., that the shop man requires.

Blueprint Reading Charts.— The series of charts which follow are designed to explain the ABC's of reading blueprints or drawings by a direct method which deals with each step in a logical order, thus greatly simplifying the procedure in acquiring a practical working knowledge of this important subject. The illustrations used on these charts have been selected to show clearly and quickly whatever feature or principle is represented. These chart drawings are of simple objects and machine parts, but they illustrate the procedure in reading or interpreting even the most complicated mechanical drawings. While dimensions are always given on regular mechanical drawings, they have been omitted on the preliminary Chart illustrations to simplify them and thus reveal more clearly the drawing itself and the methods employed in representing the forms of different parts. The drawing may be thought of as a picture of the object arranged to suit shop requirements, whereas the dimensions supplement the drawing and are in the nature of instructions.

Chart No. 1 — READING BLUEPRINTS OR MECHANICAL DRAWINGS

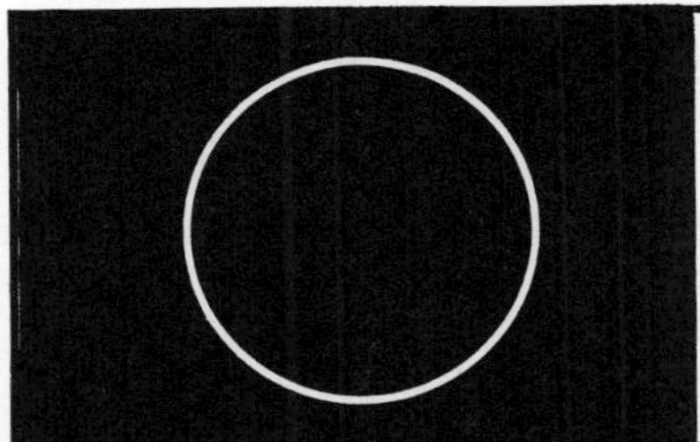

Here is an outline drawing of some circular object. Is it a spherical or hemi-spherical shape, or the side view of a flat disk with parallel sides? This one view only shows that the part has a circular edge or surface. As a working drawing, it is incomplete.

Here is another outline drawing of some object. Is it round, square, or triangular in form? This one view does not show; it *does* show that the part is uniform in width, or in diameter if the shape is cylindrical. Again, we have an incomplete drawing.

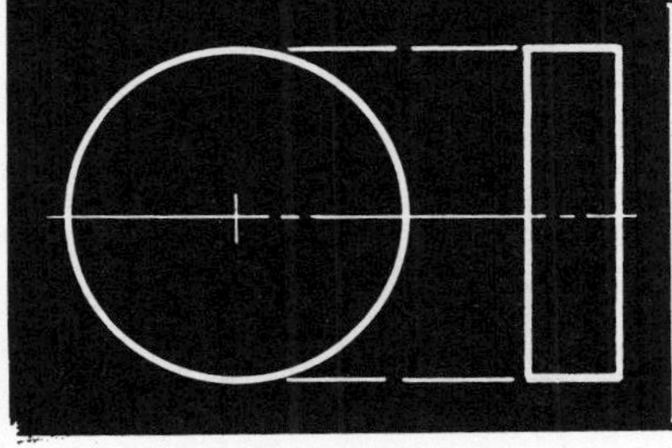

The two views referred to above are of the same object; here they have been combined on one drawing to show that the object is a disk with parallel sides. If you held this disk square to your line of vision and turned it first sidewise and then edgewise, the two outlines would be as here shown. This principle is applied in all mechanical drawings.

Chart No. 2 — READING BLUEPRINTS OR MECHANICAL DRAWINGS

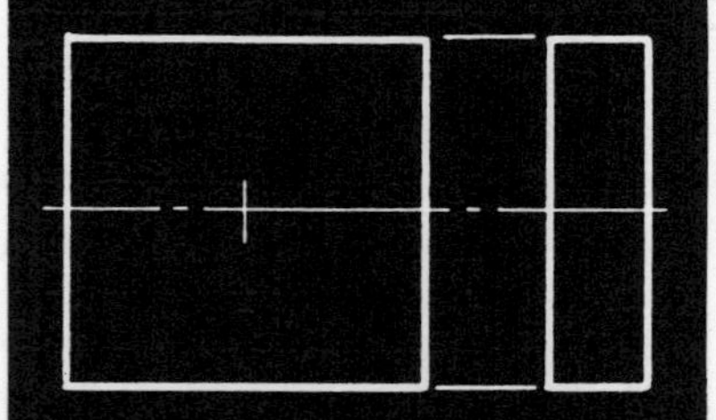

The edgewise or end view at the right is exactly like the one of the disk on Chart No. 1, but the view at the left shows that the object has square sides. This simple example illustrates the importance of having at least two views on most mechanical drawings. Some require three or more and extra views of important details.

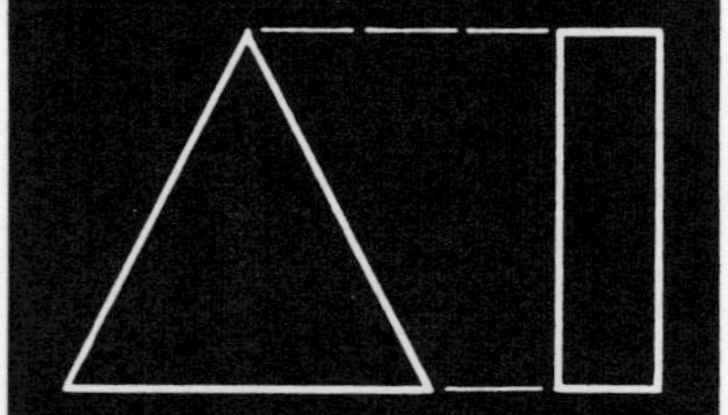

Again, the edgewise or end view merely shows one outline of the object, but the side view shows a triangular form. In reading or interpreting mechanical drawings, the views of different sides are combined mentally to obtain a complete picture. Each side is represented in its true proportions, which is a great advantage.

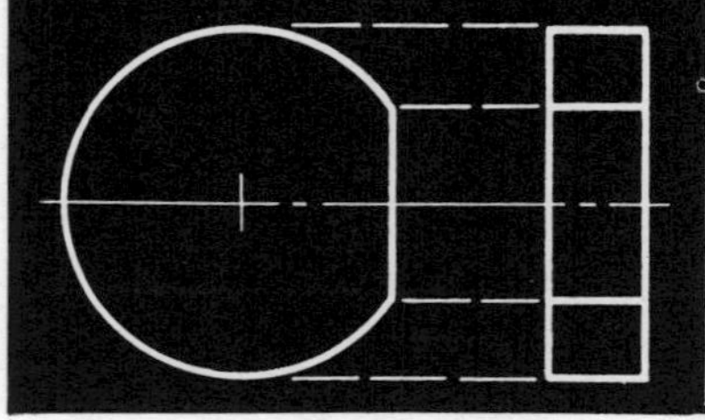

This edgewise or end view has the same rectangular outline as the two preceding end views, but two additional lines have been drawn across it. The side view at the left shows why these lines are required. The disk-shaped part has a flat side and the cross-lines on the end view represent the upper and lower edges of this flat surface.

Chart No. 3 — READING BLUEPRINTS OR MECHANICAL DRAWINGS

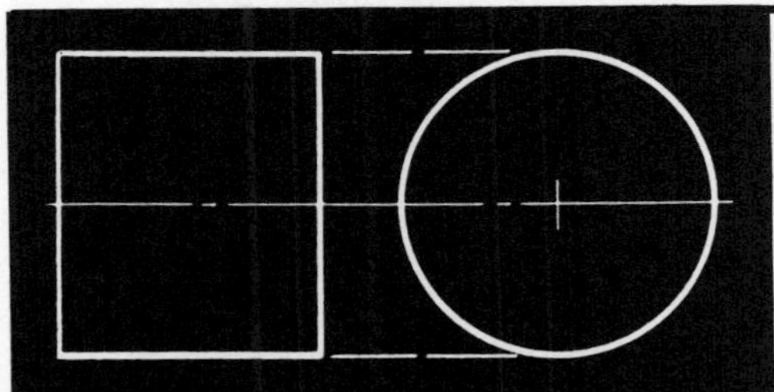

The mechanical drawing of a short cylindrical part is shown here. The side view at the left, if seen separately, might represent some rectangular object, but the end view shows that it is round; hence it must be cylindrical. This end view might have been placed on the left-hand side because each end is alike; its position in this case is immaterial.

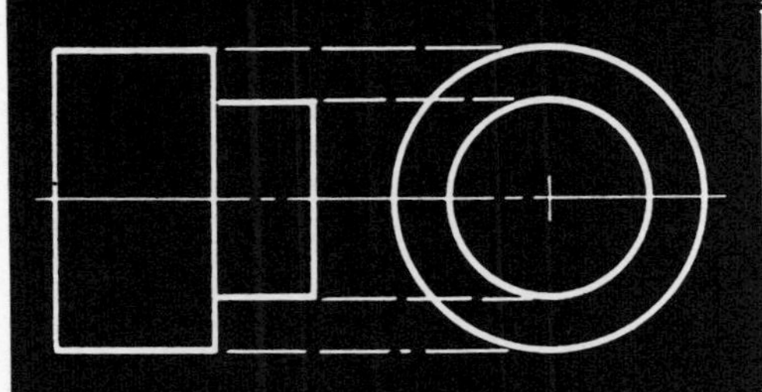

This cylindrical part has two diameters. When only one end view is required, it represents whichever end has the most to be shown. This end view is placed on the right-hand side in this case to show clearly the reduced end. The broken projection lines are used as shown on this and certain other drawings, to connect the views and indicate more clearly the relation of one view to another.

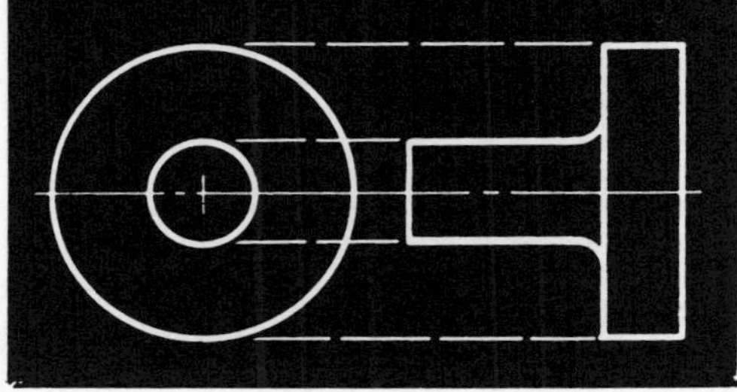

The end view in this case represents the object as seen from the left because the left-hand end has a reduced section which would not be visible when looking squarely at the right-hand end. This reduced part might be indicated on a right-hand end view by using dotted lines to represent a concealed surface (as explained later); but the arrangement here shown is preferable as a general rule.

Chart No. 4 — READING BLUEPRINTS OR MECHANICAL DRAWINGS

When these two views are combined mentally to obtain the complete form of the object, we see that it consists of three round sections each differing in diameter and width or length. The end view, as in previous examples, is directly opposite the side it represents. This is the general practice in the United States.

The end view here is exactly like the one above. It shows that the object is circular and has three circular edges or surfaces. The side view shows that the body of this part is conical, and there is a small extension or end of cylindrical form. The projection lines show that the large circle represents the cone base; the intermediate circle, the top; and the small circle the cylindrical end.

The *side* view here is just like the preceding one, but the end view at the right shows that the body of the tapering object is square at each end and the extension at the small end is round. Again, the projection lines show clearly the relationship between the different views. With a little practice, the different views can be combined mentally without such lines.

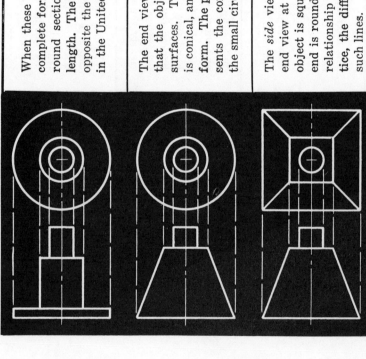

Chart No. 5 — READING BLUEPRINTS OR MECHANICAL DRAWINGS

The two views here show a part having a U-shaped opening. Note that the open side is represented in the end or edgewise view by full lines. Thus, as in previous examples, this view shows the part as it would appear if turned edgewise to the line of vision. Full or unbroken lines are used to represent surfaces which would actually be visible in any view. Invisible surfaces follow.

Here is the drawing of a collar which has a hole through the center. The edgewise view is like the one shown above, excepting the dotted lines which represent the hole. Since this hole would not be visible in the edgewise view, the lines are dotted. This is a method of showing invisible surfaces on mechanical drawings. Most mechanical drawings have some dotted lines.

Here is another drawing of a part which has a hole through the center. In this case, however, the hole is counterbored or enlarged at one end. This is revealed by noting the two inner circles in conjunction with the dotted lines of the edgewise view. Interior openings are not always represented by dotted lines, as shown on some of the charts to follow.

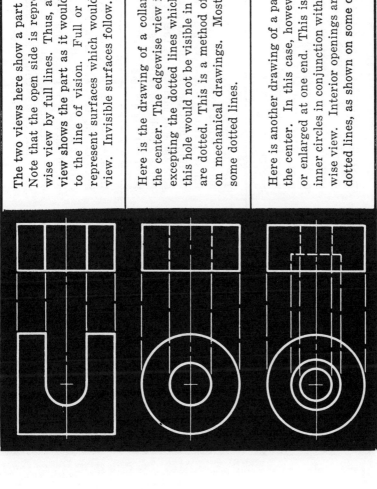

Chart No. 6 — READING BLUEPRINTS OR MECHANICAL DRAWINGS

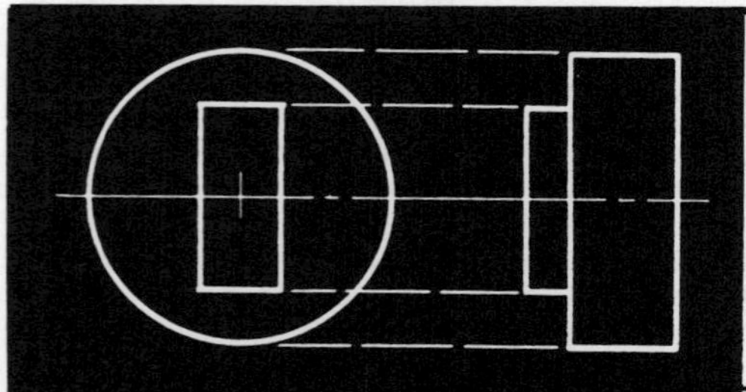

Does the rectangle on the left-hand view represent a slot or rectangular opening? The right-hand view gives the answer. It shows that the rectangle at the left is the outline of a projecting piece on one side of the disk-shaped part. Note that all views on mechanical drawings are arranged to show each important part or shape in its true proportions.

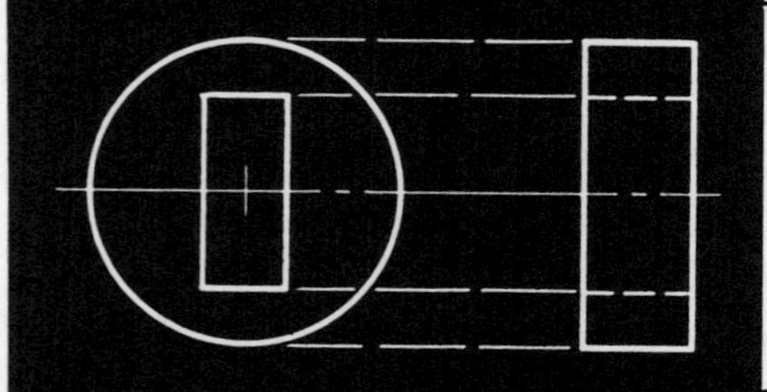

The left-hand view on this drawing is just like the one above. What does the rectangle now represent? The dotted lines of the edgewise view show that it is an opening extending through the circular part. These dotted lines represent the end surfaces of the rectangular slot. Drawings of these simple objects illustrate the general procedure in reading all drawings.

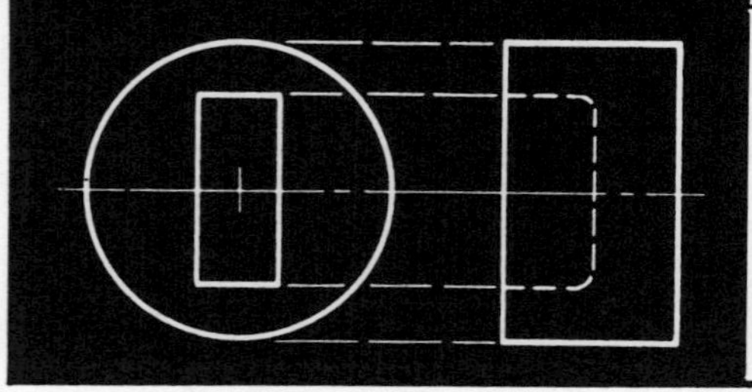

In this case, what does the rectangle represent? The dotted lines of the edgewise view show that it is a pocket that extends about halfway through the part. Perspective views would show at a glance the forms of many of the simple objects illustrated on these charts, but they would not be as practical for designing and dimensioning purposes. Such drawings could not be used at all for complicated forms.

Chart No. 7 — READING BLUEPRINTS OR MECHANICAL DRAWINGS

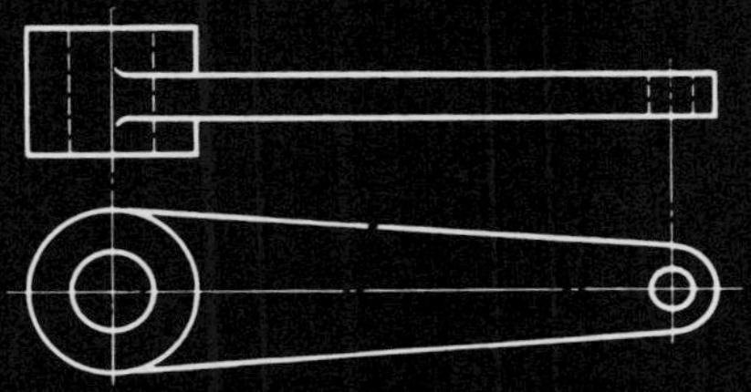

Here is the drawing of a lever. One view is placed above the other because views from these two directions show the shape and proportions to the best advantage. The positions of these views might have been reversed without affecting the drawing because a top view of this lever is the same as a bottom view.

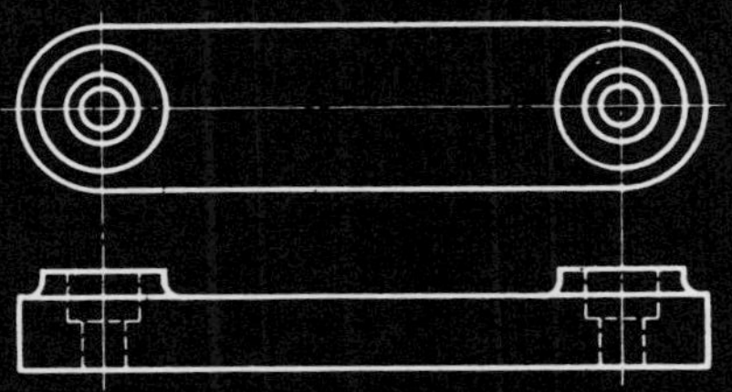

This drawing shows a link having counterbored holes at each end surrounded by bosses or raised surfaces. These two views could not be reversed according to American practice. The upper view represents the upper side which has the important details. The dotted lines show that the holes are counterbored.

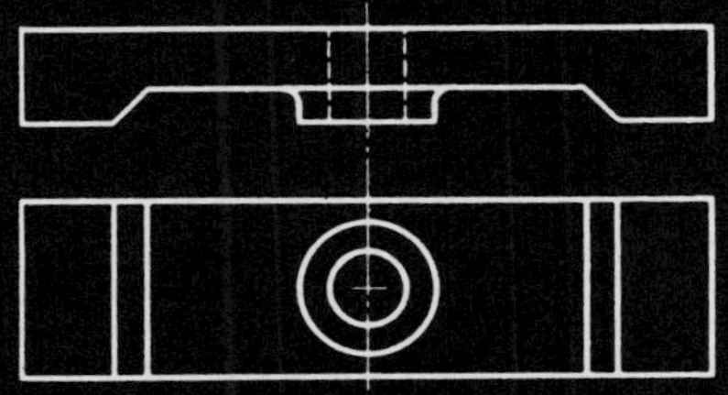

The main view of a part, or the most characteristic one is known as the *front view*. Other views may be placed relative to the front view so as to show the top, bottom, and sides or ends, as may be required. If the upper view here is considered the main one, it is accompanied by a bottom view because the lower side is the most important.

Chart No. 8 — READING BLUEPRINTS OR MECHANICAL DRAWINGS

Three views are required to show clearly every important feature of the part shown by this drawing. Without the upper or top view, it would be impossible to determine the shape of the elongated slot. The side or end view at the right is also necessary to show the dovetail on the bottom. This end view might have been drawn opposite the top view (as shown at A) instead of opposite the main view. This is done sometimes merely because position A happens to be more convenient as, for example, in regard to available space.

The bracket shown by this drawing has projecting lugs at each end. The dotted lines of the front view show openings through these lugs and also a central opening through the base. The end view shows the circular form of the lugs and the holes through them; also a projecting part extending to the right of the base is seen in this end view. The top view shows the circular form of this projection and indicates definitely that a counterbored hole extends through the center of the base. A working drawing would include necessary dimensions.

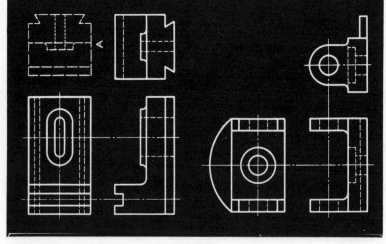

Chart No. 9 — READING BLUEPRINTS OR MECHANICAL DRAWINGS

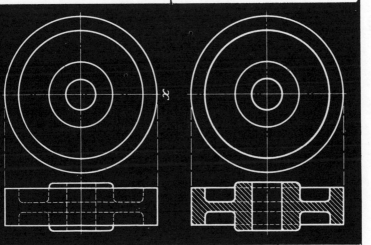

Here is a small wheel or pulley. The dotted lines representing the concealed surfaces in the view at the left, show that the wheel has a rim, a central hub with a hole through it, and a section connecting rim and hub. The right-hand view shows that this disk-like section or web is solid because no spokes or openings are indicated. The length of the hub is somewhat greater than the width of the rim. This is shown by the left-hand view. Another way to draw this wheel is illustrated below.

Assume that the wheel above is cut apart along center line x–x; then the cut surface, when perpendicular to the line of vision, would appear as shown here by the left-hand view. This is called a sectional view or cross-section. Diagonal lines are used to make the shape of the cut surface stand out clearly. These section lines by their spacing or arrangement may also represent the general class of material used. The different methods of arranging section lines to represent different materials is shown on Chart No. 29.

Chart No. 10 — READING BLUEPRINTS OR MECHANICAL DRAWINGS

Here is another sectional view of a wheel or pulley. The right-hand view represents only half of the pulley because it is evident that the remaining half is the same. This practice is common in drawing symmetrical parts such as pulleys, gears, etc. The sectional and end views show that both rim and hub have a reinforcing ridge in the center. Noting such details is important in reading blueprints or mechanical drawings. Theoretically, the spokes should be shown in section because the cutting plane passes through them. This point will be dealt with later.

The pulley shown by this drawing is for a V-belt drive. The sectional part of the view only extends down to the center line partly because the other half would merely be a duplicate as in the preceding examples. By showing the remaining part as it would actually appear, the drawing often is simplified and may indicate more clearly the exact form of the object. While the half end view is not a true representation of a pulley having one-quarter section removed, nevertheless, it meets all practical requirements. The preceding sectional views might have been terminated at the center line as in this case.

Chart No. 11 — READING BLUEPRINTS OR MECHANICAL DRAWINGS

This drawing illustrates a partial or broken-out section. Such incomplete sections are often used instead of a full section when the latter is unnecessary, and especially when a partial section makes the drawing easier to understand. In this case, the sectioned part shows the holes clearly and the unsectioned part illustrates the hexagonal end. An end view has been omitted, although, ordinarily, one would be included. This sectioned part is in the plane of the center line but this is not always the case, as explained later. The section lines indicate brass or bronze.

Some shafts, bolts and other parts are so long that it would be inconvenient or impossible to show the entire length on a drawing; moreover, a complete drawing of such parts frequently is unnecessary. The drawing here shows a flanged shaft. If the length x is too large to permit drawing the entire shaft, it is common practice to show the ends only. The sectioned ends indicate that most of the cylindrical part has been omitted on the drawing. This broken-out part is a plain cylindrical form and does not vary in size.

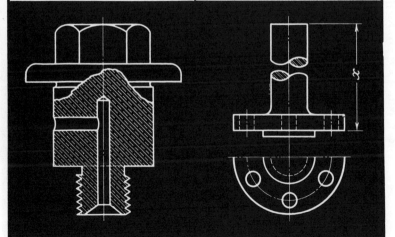

Chart No. 12 — READING BLUEPRINTS OR MECHANICAL DRAWINGS

Here is a section and a top or plan view of a casting. The section or cutting plane is along line x–x or right through the central stiffening rib, but section lines on the rib are omitted. This is the usual method of drawing such sections. The object is to simplify the drawing and make it less confusing. While the drawing is not theoretically correct, it is more practical in this, and many similar cases, than one which conforms strictly to the principle governing the drawing of sectional views.

The sectional view here shows another method of representing a rib when it lies in the cutting plane. According to this method, the rib has double-spaced section lines, alternate section lines having been omitted. This method is convenient on some drawings, but, as a general rule, section lines on ribs are omitted and this practice conforms to the American Standard. Other exceptions common in mechanical drawing practice will be shown on charts to follow.

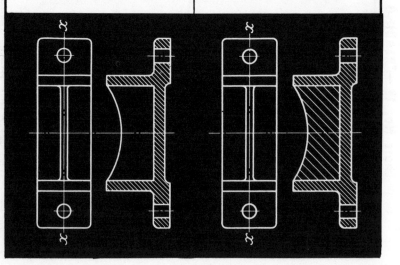

Chart No. 13 — READING BLUEPRINTS OR MECHANICAL DRAWINGS

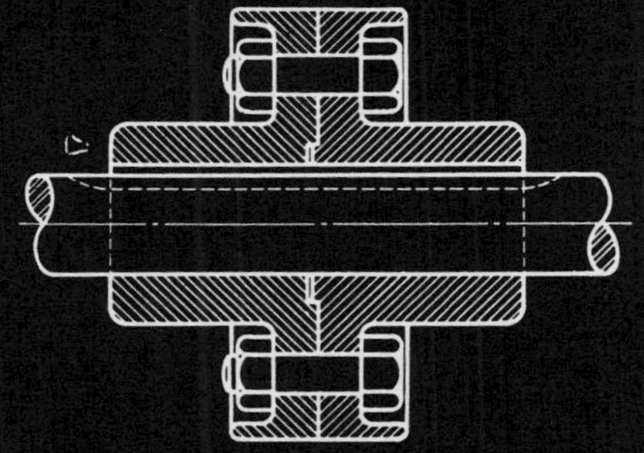

The shaft coupling shown here consists of two parts which are held together by bolts. The section lines on adjoining parts incline in opposite directions, as shown, so that each individual part can be seen readily. Note that the bolts are not sectioned, although they lie in the cutting plane. The shaft is also shown unsectioned. When the section lines are omitted from such details, the drawing is both simpler and clearer. The general practice is to leave unsectioned all parts such as bolts, keys, pins, rivets, ribs and shafts which lie in the cutting plane. This improves the readability of the drawing.

This drawing illustrates two exceptions to a theoretically correct section. One pertains to the stiffening ribs which, as explained on Chart No. 12, are usually drawn without section lines. The second exception is in the location of the holes in the sectional view. These holes are located in this sectional view at the true distance from the center line instead of in true projection or in alignment with the holes of the end view. The dotted lines show hole location on sectional view, for true projection. In mechanical drawings, clear representation of construction is always more important than adhering to drawing theories.

Chart No. 14 — READING BLUEPRINTS OR MECHANICAL DRAWINGS

When the arms or spokes of pulleys, gears, handwheels, etc., lie in the cutting plane, section lines are always omitted, as shown by this drawing of a handwheel and by the upper pulley on Chart No. 10. The drawing is thus simplified and the form of rim and hub is more apparent. Note how the cross-sectional shape of the handwheel arms is indicated by the small section drawn directly on one arm in the right-hand view. These auxiliary sections often appear on drawings, especially when needed to show the shapes of arms, levers or similar parts.

This handwheel has five arms but in the sectional view, two arms are shown as though they were directly opposite; hence, the lower arm is not drawn strictly according to the principle of projection. This exception, like the others mentioned, is to simplify the sectional view and make it clearer. The other view shows how the arms are located. Whenever parts have an odd number of arms, ribs, etc., it is the general practice to ignore the true projection in sectional views, thus making the drawing simpler in appearance and easier to understand. Clearness is the first consideration.

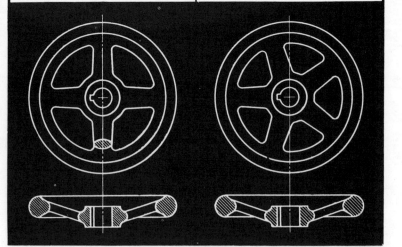

Chart No. 15 — READING BLUEPRINTS OR MECHANICAL DRAWINGS

Sectional views usually represent parts as they would appear if cut straight through on one continuous plane which may or may not intersect the center line. Frequently, however, the direction of the cutting plane is changed, as here shown by the line *A–A*, in order to make the sectional view include two or more important features. The arrows at the ends of the cutting-plane line show the direction in which the section is viewed. When more than one sectional view is required, the letters *A–A*, *B–B*, *C–C*, etc., are used to mark different cutting-plane lines and their corresponding views, thus definitely locating each section.

The cutting-plane line in this case extends vertically down to the center, then changes its direction so as to intersect a small boss, then swings back to the vertical center line, and, finally, passes through the lower lug; hence, the sectional view includes the boss and shows the tapped hole in it. The reference letter (*A* in this case) should, as a rule, be repeated wherever the direction of the cutting plane is changed. Sectional views, especially of details, are often located at any convenient place on the drawing; but by marking both cutting-plane lines and sections with corresponding reference letters, the location of each section is clearly indicated.

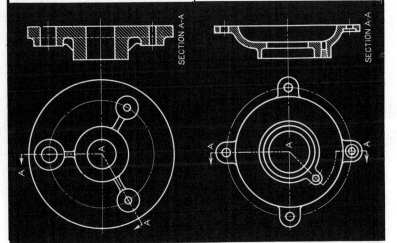

SECTION A-A

SECTION A-A

Chart No. 16 — READING BLUEPRINTS OR MECHANICAL DRAWINGS

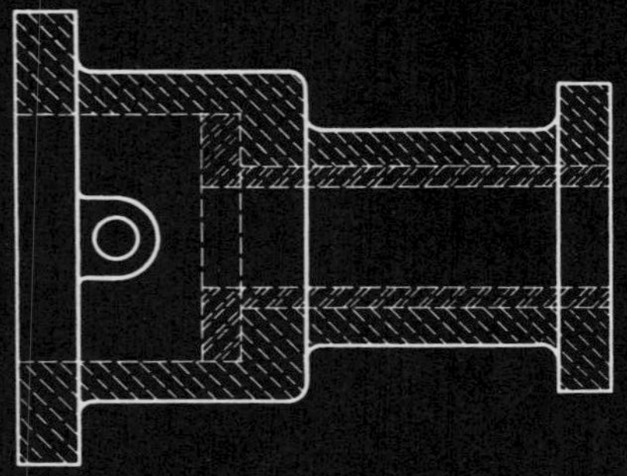

On some drawings, exterior views and interior sections are combined. This is done to make a single view on a drawing reveal both the outer and inner construction of a part. The casting here illustrated contains a removable inner lining. This is shown by what is known as a *phantom* or dotted section. The inner shape of the main casting is also shown by the dotted section lines. This method of sectioning may reduce the number of views required. The drawing here reproduced is incomplete and is only intended to illustrate the phantom or dotted-line method of sectioning.

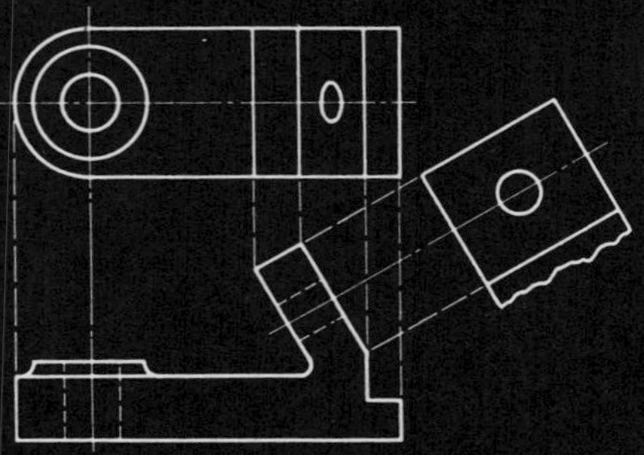

This drawing consists of a front view, a plan or top view, and a detail view of the inclined surface which is drawn or projected perpendicular to this surface or on a plane parallel to it, and is known as an *auxiliary view*. This auxiliary view shows the angular surface in its true proportions or as it would appear if placed square to the line of vision; hence, it is more practical than an end view drawn in the usual manner. Most auxiliary views are incomplete and show only the inclined surface. In this case, a complete end view in the angular position is not required.

What abbreviations, notes and symbols are commonly used on mechanical drawings?

In order to read or interpret a drawing, it is necessary to understand the meaning of various abbreviations, symbols or condensed notes which have been generally accepted in the machine building industry. To illustrate, the diameter of a hole or shaft is often followed by the abbreviation D unless it is apparent from the drawing that the dimension is a diameter. When the radius of some surface is given, it usually is followed by the abbreviation R. The expression "No. 6-32" at the end of a leader or arrow pointing to a machine screw would mean a screw of No. 6 size and 32 threads per inch. If the size of a screw thread were given as "3/4-10 NC," this would mean a 3/4-inch thread with 10 threads per inch which is the standard number in the National Coarse (NC) Series of the American Standard. On an older drawing, this same screw thread might be marked "3/4-10 USS," meaning United States Standard. The accompanying Charts (Nos. 17 to 26) include symbols, abbreviations and notes which are found on working drawings. Only standard or generally recognized abbreviations should be used on drawings. Whenever there is doubt, a note always is preferable because clearness is much more important than brevity.

Some of the common mistakes made in using drawings could be avoided by a more liberal use of explanatory notes wherever mistakes were likely to occur. A drawing should tell its own story without the aid of an interpreter. If it needs an interpreter, it is seriously lacking. These explanatory notes may relate to different kinds of small tools that are to be used, such as drills, reamers, and counterbores; thus the number or size of the drill and the size of the reamer, if used, are given. If punched bolt holes are considered good enough in connection with parts made of sheet metal, and close-fitting bolts are not necessary, the holes may be so marked. Explanatory notes may also be used to designate the kind of material, as, for example, machine steel, tool steel, cold-rolled steel, etc. When several pieces of one kind are needed, the number of duplicate ones required is noted on the drawing. The charts which follow illustrate the use of notes, abbreviations and symbols.

Chart No. 17—SYMBOLS AND ABBREVIATIONS ON DRAWINGS

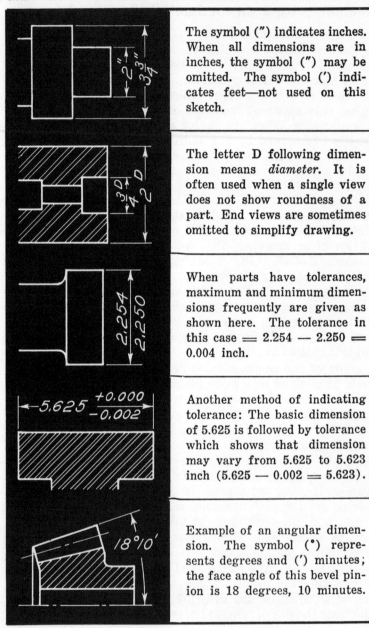

The symbol (") indicates inches. When all dimensions are in inches, the symbol (") may be omitted. The symbol (') indicates feet—not used on this sketch.

The letter D following dimension means *diameter*. It is often used when a single view does not show roundness of a part. End views are sometimes omitted to simplify drawing.

When parts have tolerances, maximum and minimum dimensions frequently are given as shown here. The tolerance in this case = 2.254 — 2.250 = 0.004 inch.

Another method of indicating tolerance: The basic dimension of 5.625 is followed by tolerance which shows that dimension may vary from 5.625 to 5.623 inch (5.625 — 0.002 = 5.623).

Example of an angular dimension. The symbol (°) represents degrees and (') minutes; the face angle of this bevel pinion is 18 degrees, 10 minutes.

Chart No. 18—SYMBOLS AND ABBREVIATIONS ON DRAWINGS

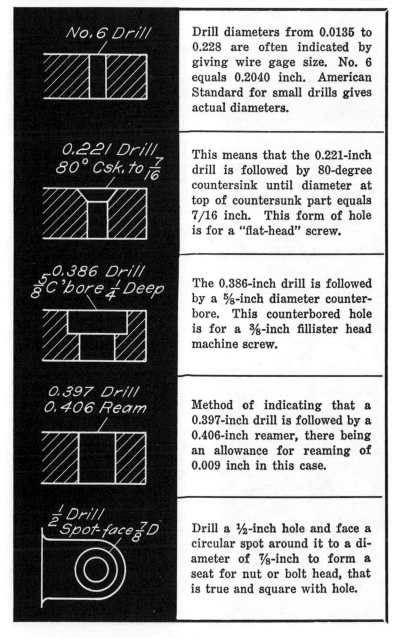

No. 6 Drill	Drill diameters from 0.0135 to 0.228 are often indicated by giving wire gage size. No. 6 equals 0.2040 inch. American Standard for small drills gives actual diameters.
0.221 Drill 80° Csk. to 7/16	This means that the 0.221-inch drill is followed by 80-degree countersink until diameter at top of countersunk part equals 7/16 inch. This form of hole is for a "flat-head" screw.
0.386 Drill 5/8 C'bore 1/4 Deep	The 0.386-inch drill is followed by a 5/8-inch diameter counterbore. This counterbored hole is for a 3/8-inch fillister head machine screw.
0.397 Drill 0.406 Ream	Method of indicating that a 0.397-inch drill is followed by a 0.406-inch reamer, there being an allowance for reaming of 0.009 inch in this case.
1/2 Drill Spot-face 7/8 D	Drill a 1/2-inch hole and face a circular spot around it to a diameter of 7/8-inch to form a seat for nut or bolt head, that is true and square with hole.

Chart No. 19—SYMBOLS AND ABBREVIATIONS ON DRAWINGS

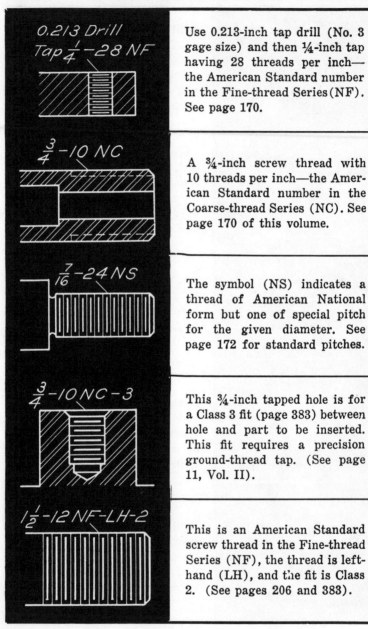

Use 0.213-inch tap drill (No. 3 gage size) and then ¼-inch tap having 28 threads per inch—the American Standard number in the Fine-thread Series (NF). See page 170.

A ¾-inch screw thread with 10 threads per inch—the American Standard number in the Coarse-thread Series (NC). See page 170 of this volume.

The symbol (NS) indicates a thread of American National form but one of special pitch for the given diameter. See page 172 for standard pitches.

This ¾-inch tapped hole is for a Class 3 fit (page 383) between hole and part to be inserted. This fit requires a precision ground-thread tap. (See page 11, Vol. II).

This is an American Standard screw thread in the Fine-thread Series (NF), the thread is left-hand (LH), and the fit is Class 2. (See pages 206 and 383).

Chart No. 20—SYMBOLS AND ABBREVIATIONS ON DRAWINGS

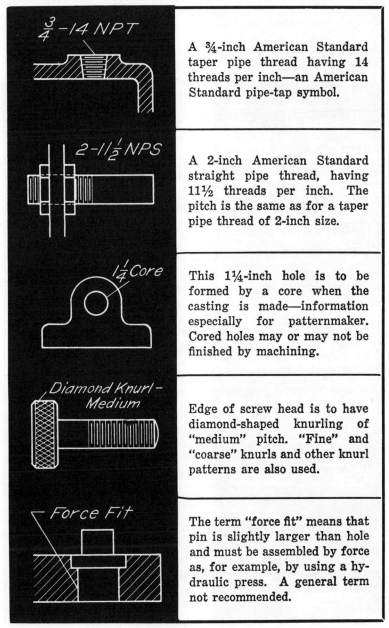

A ¾-inch American Standard taper pipe thread having 14 threads per inch—an American Standard pipe-tap symbol.

A 2-inch American Standard straight pipe thread, having 11½ threads per inch. The pitch is the same as for a taper pipe thread of 2-inch size.

This 1¼-inch hole is to be formed by a core when the casting is made—information especially for patternmaker. Cored holes may or may not be finished by machining.

Edge of screw head is to have diamond-shaped knurling of "medium" pitch. "Fine" and "coarse" knurls and other knurl patterns are also used.

The term "force fit" means that pin is slightly larger than hole and must be assembled by force as, for example, by using a hydraulic press. A general term not recommended.

Chart No. 21—SYMBOLS AND ABBREVIATIONS ON DRAWINGS

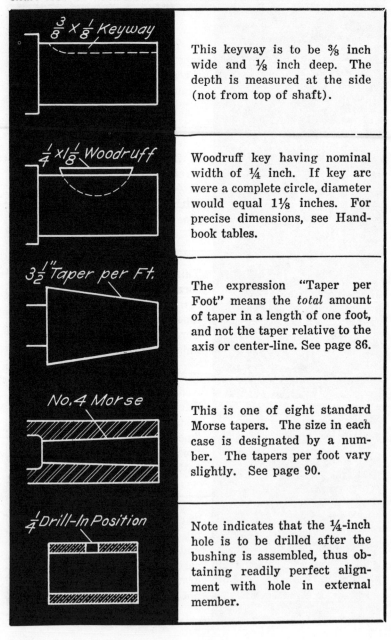

$\frac{3}{8} \times \frac{1}{8}$ Keyway

This keyway is to be ⅜ inch wide and ⅛ inch deep. The depth is measured at the side (not from top of shaft).

$\frac{1}{4} \times 1\frac{1}{8}$ Woodruff

Woodruff key having nominal width of ¼ inch. If key arc were a complete circle, diameter would equal 1⅛ inches. For precise dimensions, see Handbook tables.

$3\frac{1}{2}''$ Taper per Ft.

The expression "Taper per Foot" means the *total* amount of taper in a length of one foot, and not the taper relative to the axis or center-line. See page 86.

No. 4 Morse

This is one of eight standard Morse tapers. The size in each case is designated by a number. The tapers per foot vary slightly. See page 90.

$\frac{1}{4}$ Drill-In Position

Note indicates that the ¼-inch hole is to be drilled after the bushing is assembled, thus obtaining readily perfect alignment with hole in external member.

Chart No. 22—SYMBOLS AND ABBREVIATIONS ON DRAWINGS

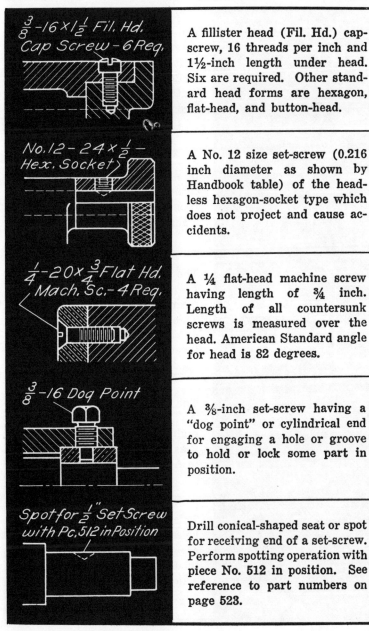

$\frac{3}{8}$-16×1$\frac{1}{2}$ Fil. Hd. Cap Screw - 6 Req.	A fillister head (Fil. Hd.) cap-screw, 16 threads per inch and 1½-inch length under head. Six are required. Other standard head forms are hexagon, flat-head, and button-head.
No. 12 - 24 × $\frac{1}{2}$ - Hex. Socket	A No. 12 size set-screw (0.216 inch diameter as shown by Handbook table) of the headless hexagon-socket type which does not project and cause accidents.
$\frac{1}{4}$-20×$\frac{3}{4}$ Flat Hd. Mach. Sc. - 4 Req.	A ¼ flat-head machine screw having length of ¾ inch. Length of all countersunk screws is measured over the head. American Standard angle for head is 82 degrees.
$\frac{3}{8}$-16 Dog Point	A ⅜-inch set-screw having a "dog point" or cylindrical end for engaging a hole or groove to hold or lock some part in position.
Spot for $\frac{1}{2}$" Set Screw with Pc. 512 in Position	Drill conical-shaped seat or spot for receiving end of a set-screw. Perform spotting operation with piece No. 512 in position. See reference to part numbers on page 523.

Chart No. 23—SYMBOLS AND ABBREVIATIONS ON DRAWINGS

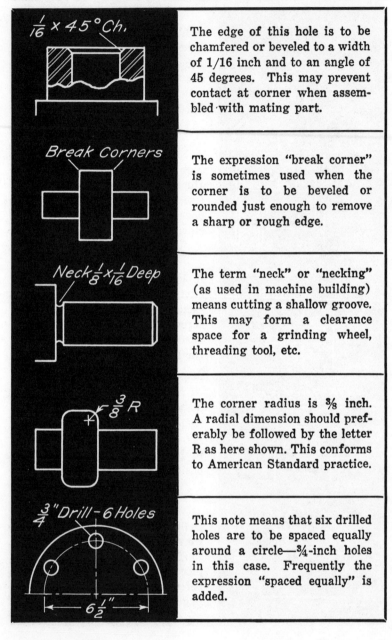

$\frac{1}{16} \times 45° Ch.$

The edge of this hole is to be chamfered or beveled to a width of 1/16 inch and to an angle of 45 degrees. This may prevent contact at corner when assembled with mating part.

Break Corners

The expression "break corner" is sometimes used when the corner is to be beveled or rounded just enough to remove a sharp or rough edge.

Neck $\frac{1}{8} \times \frac{1}{16}$ Deep

The term "neck" or "necking" (as used in machine building) means cutting a shallow groove. This may form a clearance space for a grinding wheel, threading tool, etc.

$\frac{3}{8} R$

The corner radius is ⅜ inch. A radial dimension should preferably be followed by the letter R as here shown. This conforms to American Standard practice.

$\frac{3}{4}"$ *Drill – 6 Holes*

$6\frac{1}{2}"$

This note means that six drilled holes are to be spaced equally around a circle—¾-inch holes in this case. Frequently the expression "spaced equally" is added.

Chart No. 24—SYMBOLS AND ABBREVIATIONS ON DRAWINGS

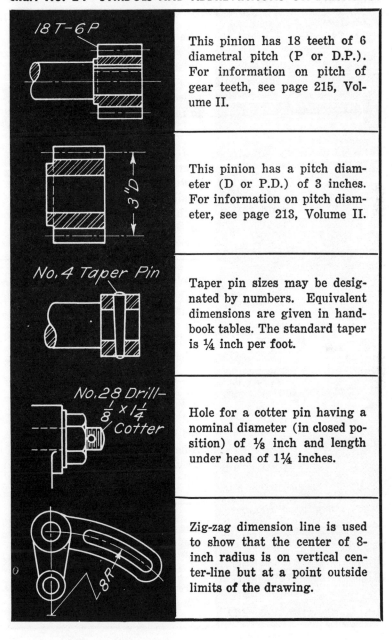

This pinion has 18 teeth of 6 diametral pitch (P or D.P.). For information on pitch of gear teeth, see page 215, Volume II.

This pinion has a pitch diameter (D or P.D.) of 3 inches. For information on pitch diameter, see page 213, Volume II.

Taper pin sizes may be designated by numbers. Equivalent dimensions are given in handbook tables. The standard taper is ¼ inch per foot.

Hole for a cotter pin having a nominal diameter (in closed position) of ⅛ inch and length under head of 1¼ inches.

Zig-zag dimension line is used to show that the center of 8-inch radius is on vertical center-line but at a point outside limits of the drawing.

Chart No. 25—SYMBOLS AND ABBREVIATIONS ON DRAWINGS

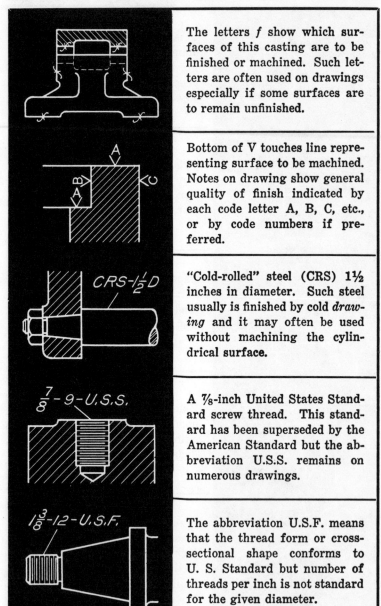

The letters *f* show which surfaces of this casting are to be finished or machined. Such letters are often used on drawings especially if some surfaces are to remain unfinished.

Bottom of V touches line representing surface to be machined. Notes on drawing show general quality of finish indicated by each code letter A, B, C, etc., or by code numbers if preferred.

"Cold-rolled" steel (CRS) 1½ inches in diameter. Such steel usually is finished by cold *drawing* and it may often be used without machining the cylindrical surface.

A ⅞-inch United States Standard screw thread. This standard has been superseded by the American Standard but the abbreviation U.S.S. remains on numerous drawings.

The abbreviation U.S.F. means that the thread form or cross-sectional shape conforms to U. S. Standard but number of threads per inch is not standard for the given diameter.

Chart No. 26 — SYMBOLS AND ABBREVIATIONS ON DRAWINGS

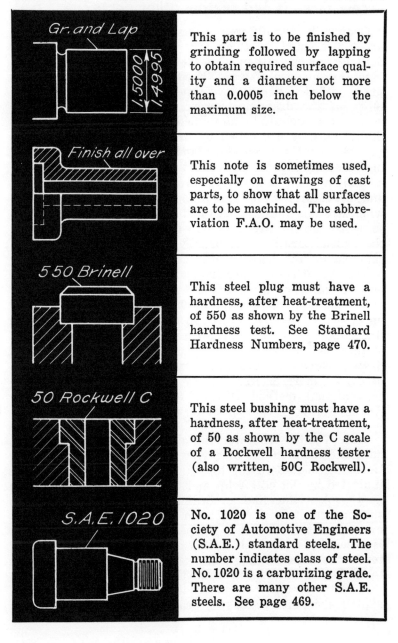

Gr. and Lap 1.5000 1.4995	This part is to be finished by grinding followed by lapping to obtain required surface quality and a diameter not more than 0.0005 inch below the maximum size.
Finish all over	This note is sometimes used, especially on drawings of cast parts, to show that all surfaces are to be machined. The abbreviation F.A.O. may be used.
550 Brinell	This steel plug must have a hardness, after heat-treatment, of 550 as shown by the Brinell hardness test. See Standard Hardness Numbers, page 470.
50 Rockwell C	This steel bushing must have a hardness, after heat-treatment, of 50 as shown by the C scale of a Rockwell hardness tester (also written, 50C Rockwell).
S.A.E. 1020	No. 1020 is one of the Society of Automotive Engineers (S.A.E.) standard steels. The number indicates class of steel. No. 1020 is a carburizing grade. There are many other S.A.E. steels. See page 469.

Why are simplified line symbols used for screw threads and certain other parts?

Ordinarily, the different parts on a mechanical drawing are represented in their true shape or as they would actually appear either in a front view, side view, or top view, as the case may be. Frequently, however, drawings are modified either to save time or to increase the readability of the drawing. Screw threads, for example, are usually represented by simplified line symbols, or "conventions," as they are called by draftsmen. Charts Nos. 27 and 28 show the American Standard methods of representing screw threads. If a screw thread is drawn as it would actually appear, this involves drawing the true thread form and curvature, which requires considerable time. Even when straight lines are used instead of lines having the true screw-thread curvature, as shown at the bottom of Chart 28, the expenditure of time usually is not justified. While a complete or true drawing of a screw thread may be pleasing to the eye, it serves no practical purpose in the shop. In order to cut a screw thread, it is necessary to know the kind of thread, its diameter, and pitch. A true picture of it is of no practical use. The object in using these conventions or line symbols is merely to show where a bolt, shaft, hole, etc., is threaded; hence, the use of simple lines which can be drawn easily and quickly. Very large screw threads may be drawn more or less as they actually appear, but some conventional method is used almost invariably for the smaller screw threads on bolts, machine screws, etc.

Gear Teeth.—The working drawings of gears usually have the teeth in the side view represented by a conventional method. Both the tops and bottoms of the teeth are indicated by dotted circles and the pitch circle of the gear is a broken line like an ordinary center line. Drawings showing carefully formed teeth are of no assistance whatever in cutting the gear. In performing this operation, it is necessary to know the pitch of the teeth, the number of teeth, the pressure angle for selecting the cutter, and the tooth depth. The curvature of the teeth either conforms to that of the cutter or is the result of a generating action as explained in the sections on gear cutting, Volume 2, pages

Chart No. 27—AMERICAN STANDARD SCREW-THREAD SYMBOLS

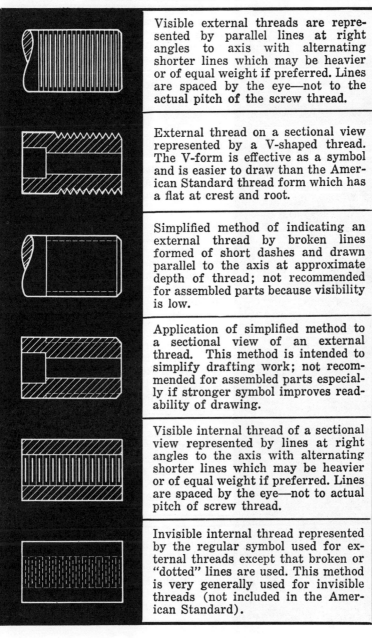

Visible external threads are represented by parallel lines at right angles to axis with alternating shorter lines which may be heavier or of equal weight if preferred. Lines are spaced by the eye—not to the actual pitch of the screw thread.

External thread on a sectional view represented by a V-shaped thread. The V-form is effective as a symbol and is easier to draw than the American Standard thread form which has a flat at crest and root.

Simplified method of indicating an external thread by broken lines formed of short dashes and drawn parallel to the axis at approximate depth of thread; not recommended for assembled parts because visibility is low.

Application of simplified method to a sectional view of an external thread. This method is intended to simplify drafting work; not recommended for assembled parts especially if stronger symbol improves readability of drawing.

Visible internal thread of a sectional view represented by lines at right angles to the axis with alternating shorter lines which may be heavier or of equal weight if preferred. Lines are spaced by the eye—not to actual pitch of screw thread.

Invisible internal thread represented by the regular symbol used for external threads except that broken or "dotted" lines are used. This method is very generally used for invisible threads (not included in the American Standard).

Chart No. 28—AMERICAN STANDARD SCREW-THREAD SYMBOLS

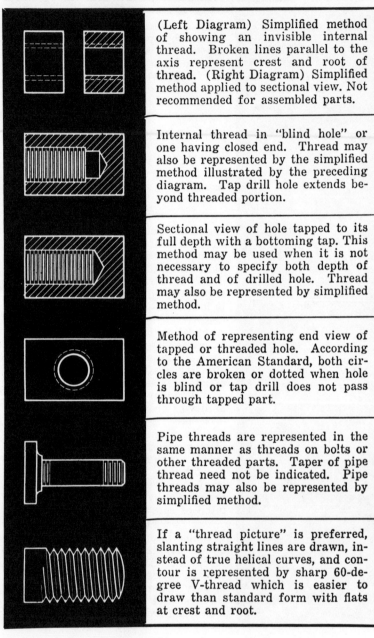

(Left Diagram) Simplified method of showing an invisible internal thread. Broken lines parallel to the axis represent crest and root of thread. (Right Diagram) Simplified method applied to sectional view. Not recommended for assembled parts.

Internal thread in "blind hole" or one having closed end. Thread may also be represented by the simplified method illustrated by the preceding diagram. Tap drill hole extends beyond threaded portion.

Sectional view of hole tapped to its full depth with a bottoming tap. This method may be used when it is not necessary to specify both depth of thread and of drilled hole. Thread may also be represented by simplified method.

Method of representing end view of tapped or threaded hole. According to the American Standard, both circles are broken or dotted when hole is blind or tap drill does not pass through tapped part.

Pipe threads are represented in the same manner as threads on bolts or other threaded parts. Taper of pipe thread need not be indicated. Pipe threads may also be represented by simplified method.

If a "thread picture" is preferred, slanting straight lines are drawn, instead of true helical curves, and contour is represented by sharp 60-degree V-thread which is easier to draw than standard form with flats at crest and root.

212 to 309. Drawings showing each tooth require considerable time, and such fancy details are useless in the shop.

Broken Sections.—Long parts such as shafts, etc., may
have the central section omitted on the drawing, thus saving space in permitting the ends to be drawn to a larger
scale. Chart No. 11 shows a shaft having a flanged end.
As the shaft is turned to one diameter throughout, it is
unnecessary to draw the complete shaft. In fact, this would
make it necessary to reduce the scale of the drawing. Similar broken out sections are found on many mechanical drawings. Such drawings are true to scale excepting, of course,
the length of whatever part is broken.

Why are cross-section lines used on mechanical drawings?

By referring to Charts Nos. 10 to 15, inclusive, which
show examples of sectional drawings, you will see that
rather closely spaced diagonal lines are drawn across all
cut surfaces in a sectional view. These section lines may be
thought of as the marks that would be left by saw teeth if
the part were cut literally. Such lines serve two general
purposes: They make the section or the imaginary cut
surfaces stand out from the rest of the drawing, thus showing more clearly the interior shape; hence, the drawing is
less confusing, especially when it is complicated in form.
Another purpose of using section lines is to show, in a general way, the kind of material used. Their use, however,
for this purpose is very limited, as will be explained.

What kinds of section lines are used to show different materials?

The diagonal section lines representing the cut or sectioned surfaces are drawn or arranged differently to indicate the kind of material represented by the sectional view,
or the different materials, when, as is frequently the case,
more than one is used in the construction of a part; however, since many different kinds and grades of materials
are now used for machine parts, it is evident that the sec-

Chart No. 29—AMERICAN STANDARD CROSS-SECTION LINES

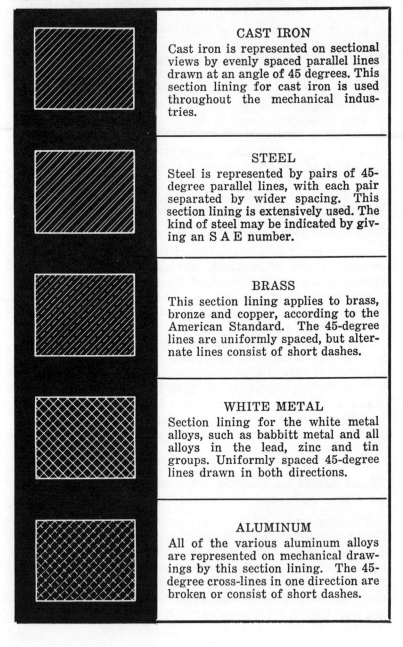

CAST IRON

Cast iron is represented on sectional views by evenly spaced parallel lines drawn at an angle of 45 degrees. This section lining for cast iron is used throughout the mechanical industries.

STEEL

Steel is represented by pairs of 45-degree parallel lines, with each pair separated by wider spacing. This section lining is extensively used. The kind of steel may be indicated by giving an S A E number.

BRASS

This section lining applies to brass, bronze and copper, according to the American Standard. The 45-degree lines are uniformly spaced, but alternate lines consist of short dashes.

WHITE METAL

Section lining for the white metal alloys, such as babbitt metal and all alloys in the lead, zinc and tin groups. Uniformly spaced 45-degree lines drawn in both directions.

ALUMINUM

All of the various aluminum alloys are represented on mechanical drawings by this section lining. The 45-degree cross-lines in one direction are broken or consist of short dashes.

tion lines only show to what *general class* a given material belongs. For example, if the part is made of cast iron, the section lining will show this but it does not, of course, indicate whether the part is made of ordinary gray cast iron or of some other grade, such, for example, as high-strength alloy cast iron. Chart No. 29, American Standard Cross-section Lines, shows the different kinds of section lines that are used to represent five classes of materials commonly used in machine construction. Another section lining chart covering a wider range of materials is shown on page 528 of Volume 2. While these additional materials are not used much on mechanical drawings in connection with machine-building operations, they are often required in other branches of work such as electrical engineering, drawings for building construction and for civil engineering projects. The particular section lines illustrated on Chart No. 29 are the ones most commonly used in the machine-building industry to represent the different materials mentioned, but there is some variation in different plants, especially for materials other than cast iron and steel.

Why are general classes of materials indicated on drawings by different kinds of section lines?

The chief reason for representing different classes of materials by means of section lines is to assist in making mechanical drawings clearer or more readable. Even though all section lines were alike and no attempt was made to identify the material by them, still the use of section lines would be desirable because they mark clearly the sectioned surface so that it can be distinguished readily from the rest of the drawing. When the kind of section lining also shows what general class of material is to be used, it assists further in understanding a drawing. For example, if a cylinder casting has a steel lining, a sectional view would show this at a glance because the section lining for steel differs from the section lining for cast iron. Furthermore, the different kinds of section lines provide additional contrast in the sectional views. The exact material, however, must be covered by separate specifications. Take steel as an example. The section lining merely shows that *some* kind of steel is to be used. When we consider that the specifications of the Society of Automotive Engineers include over 200 different kinds of structural steels, it becomes evident that section lining is impractical as a means of indicating the exact composition required. Incidentally, the S.A.E. steels are identified by numbers. These numbers or symbols provide a simple way of showing on a drawing or in specifications exactly which steel is required. Cast iron and also the various non-ferrous alloys such as brass, bronze, aluminum, etc., are also made in many different grades and compositions so that no attempt is made to identify by section lines more than the general type of material in any case.

Are the different views of a mechanical drawing always arranged in the same way?

The views of a mechanical drawing, as a general rule, are arranged according to a definite plan, even though the number of views may vary. The general practice in the United States is illustrated by the mechanical drawings shown on the charts previously referred to. Usually there is what might be called the main or *front view*. If a view of the right-hand side is required this *side view* is drawn opposite the end represented. If a side view of the left-hand end or side had also been required, because of a difference in shape at this end, it would be placed at the left of the front view. The *top view* is placed above the top. If a drawing also requires a bottom view, this would be placed below the front view. In other words, the practice in the United States is to place the views in their natural positions and this method, incidentally, is known as *third-angle projection*.

In England and certain other countries, the arrangement of views is the reverse of our own practice. To illustrate, a top view would be shown below the front view and a view, say, of the right-hand end, would be drawn to the left of the front view. This is known as *first-angle projection*. This second method is referred to because drawings from some foreign source may, at times, be used. It might be well to explain at this point that a front view is sometimes called a

front elevation; an end view may be known either as an
end elevation or, as a *side elevation.* The top view frequently
is referred to as the *plan view.*

How are angular surfaces or parts represented on mechanical drawings?

As explained previously, each projected view on a drawing shows its side or surface just as it would appear if
placed square to the line of vision. This principle is applied
not only to vertical end surfaces and horizontal top surfaces, but also to angular surfaces whenever it is important
to show them in their true proportions. An example is
shown on Chart No. 16—lower diagram. This *auxiliary
view,* as it is called, shows the inclined part just as though
it had been projected upon a plane parallel to this inclined
surface. In other words, the auxiliary drawing might be
thought of as a plan or top view of the inclined part. Such
auxiliary views ordinarily are confined to the angular part
of the surface and do not include the remainder of the part

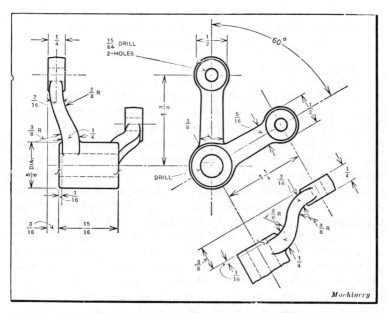

Fig. 2. Working Drawing of a Bellcrank

or object, since a complete projection in the angular plane would serve no practical purpose. Another example of an auxiliary view is shown in Fig. 2 which is the drawing of a bellcrank. The arm or lever, which is located at an angle of 60 degrees, has an auxiliary view in the lower right-hand corner. If both arms of the bellcrank were alike, the auxiliary view would not be needed. It would simply be necessary to give the dimensions for one arm, as shown in the left-hand view, and then place a note on the drawing indicating that the other arm is a duplicate. In this case, however, a special detail drawing is needed. As will be seen, it shows the inclined arm just as if it were viewed squarely from the side; consequently, the length of the arm and the curves are represented in their true length and form. Such a view meets the practical requirements of the patternmaker or machinist who wants to see the angular part *in its true proportions*. This auxiliary view is incomplete because it shows only the inclined surface. Complete views in such cases would ordinarily complicate the drawing without serving any useful purpose.

In reading drawings, are the different views examined according to a certain fixed order?

When there are two or more views on a mechanical drawing it is evident that one may reveal more than the others. While such a view might be examined first, the general procedure is to glance at the different views in whatever order or rotation seems preferable in obtaining a clear mental picture of the object. For example, the front view, side view and top view might be examined either in the order named, or possibly in some other way; there is no fixed rule. Examination of the different views is repeated as long as may be required to obtain a complete picture. Some views reveal at the first glance the general shape of, say, a casting; but usually careful comparison of all the views is necessary to see clearly every detail. The drawing of a part is comparatively easy to read when the part is at hand, because the general shape of the piece itself conforms to the different views on the drawing. In attempting to read drawings, it is good practice to compare actual machine parts with their drawings. Practice of this kind will soon enable the student to see, in his mind's eye, the complete form of a machine part merely by referring to the drawing itself.

Before starting to machine a casting, forging, or other part, be sure that you understand the drawing thoroughly. First, get a clear picture of the part; then examine the dimensions related to machining operations, and also any supplementary notes. Such notes may give information concerning the proper sequence of operations when more than one is required and important details such as drill and tap sizes, kind or quality of finish and other items as indicated by the charts, Symbols and Abbreviations on Drawings.

Why are sectional drawings used frequently?

Many parts of machines or other mechanical devices have internal passages or cavities which are partly or entirely concealed. This is especially true of castings for certain classes of work. For example, the casting for a globe valve (see Fig. 3) has interior cavities formed by cores in the foundry, the cylinder of a steam engine has cored steam ports, and a great many other parts which might be mentioned have inner openings and surfaces which, in some cases, require more or less machining.

Now, suppose that a casting containing such internal openings is cut right through the center, thus forming two half-sections. If this were actually done, it is apparent that a view of one of these cut or half-sections would show the internal openings clearly, especially if the casting was divided along whichever line or plane would reveal the interior to the best advantage. You doubtless have seen at commercial exhibitions some models of airplane motors, automobile motors, etc., that are actually cut apart at certain points in order to demonstrate clearly the interior form and the action of hidden parts. For the same reason, mechanical drawings frequently are made to represent sectional views. In other words, a sectional drawing is made which shows the object practically as it would appear if cut apart. These sectional views may be, and usually are, accompanied by ordinary exterior views. The designer, in making a sectional drawing, reveals clearly the shapes and dimensions of inner openings or parts by including, on the drawing, one or more views representing the part just as though it literally had been divided with a saw.

Do sectional views always represent parts as though they were cut through the center?

Fig. 3 illustrates, at the left side, an outline drawing of an ordinary globe valve; at the right, this same valve is illustrated by a sectional view. This view shows the valve as half of it would appear if the valve had been divided in a vertical direction. There is one exception to this statement—the valve stem to which the handle is attached is not shown in section. This part is shown unsectioned to make the drawing a little clearer. Other modifications for improving sectional drawings are explained on Charts Nos. 10 to 16, inclusive.

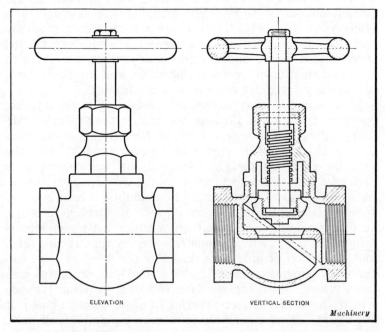

ELEVATION   VERTICAL SECTION

Machinery

Fig. 3. Outline Drawing and Sectional View of a Globe Valve

Whenever a sectional drawing is required, in order to show clearly interior cavities or passages, the *cutting plane* or section usually represents a part as though it had been severed right through the main center line or axis; but this is not always the case, as explained on Chart No. 15. The idea is to show whatever section or sections will reveal the inner form or details most clearly. For example, the section or cutting plane may be parallel with the center line but not intersect it; or an offset view might be used in conjunction with a section through the center line to provide additional information. In other cases, the section might be crosswise or perpendicular to the main center line or axis. Frequently both lengthwise and cross-sections are required.

The judgment and experience of the draftsman or designer play an important part in determining just what sectional views are required. The shop man's job is to determine, readily, the location of the section relative to whatever part or object is represented by the drawing. When a section is through the long axis or in a lengthwise direction, it is known as a *longitudinal section*. This term might also be applied to a lengthwise section that is parallel to but offset relative to the center line. When the sectional view is crosswise, it is known as a *cross-section*. When the cutting plane is at an angle relative to the center line, it is known as an *oblique section*. Such angular or oblique sections sometimes are required because they are needed to show the form of some interior part which is at an angle. In some cases, the drawing represents the part as though it had been cut along two different planes at right angles to each other and extending into the center. One of these half sections is shown on Chart No. 10.

The section shown at the right in Fig. 3 may be referred to as a vertical section simply because it is in a vertical direction through the valve body. Suppose, in this case, that the section had been taken along a vertical center line but perpendicular to the one shown or across the main body of the valve. In this case, the upper part of the sectional view would be the same as that shown, but the general shape of the valve body and the threaded ends would not be included. The section, then, is taken in whatever direction shows the largest number of important features.

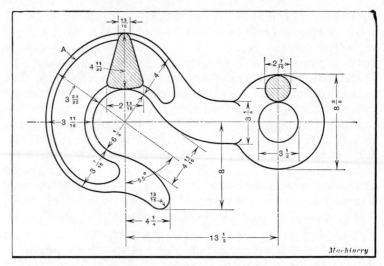

Fig. 4. Simple Method of showing Cross-sectional Shapes by placing Sectional Views directly on Drawing

The drawing of a crane hook is shown in Fig. 4. This drawing illustrates a simple method of showing cross-sectional shapes without using separate sectional views. In this case, the right-hand sectional view shows that the eye of the hook is of circular cross-section and the other sectioned part shows that the hook is somewhat V-shaped. The flat surface A of the hook is given this V-shaped form. This method of placing cross-sections right on another view and at the point where the section is taken, is often resorted to, especially on drawings of simple parts, and it is not only convenient, but frequently shows the shape of the object more clearly than would separate views.

What is a cutting plane line and why is it used?

When a drawing contains a sectional view, the location of that section may be apparent, but this is not always the case. It is evident that the sectional view, Fig. 3, represents the globe valve as it would appear if cut through the middle. Chart No. 15 shows other sectional views. In these cases, to avoid any misunderstanding, the location of the section is clearly indicated. The sectional view is marked "Section *A-A*." Now, by referring to the view at the left, we see a heavy line marked *A-A* and terminating with arrows. This is known as a *cutting plane line*, and, according to the American Standard, it is broken at intervals by a series of double dashes. This line shows that the cross-sectional view represents the part as though it had been cut through along the plane indicated. The arrows at each end of the cutting plane line point to the left, thus showing that the cross section represents a view in the direction of these arrows.

When a sectional view represents a part as though it had been cut along two or more different planes, the cutting plane lines are indispensable. The cutting plane line on Chart No. 15, extends in to the center and then the direction changes because this will make the sectional view show a great deal more than it would if the cutting plane passed straight through the part. In such cases, the sectional view represents the object in each different cutting plane as though the line of vision were perpendicular to each of these planes.

Drawings frequently require two or more sectional views and then cutting plane lines are particularly important because they show clearly on the main drawing just where each cutting plane lies. When there is a single sectional view, the general practice is to place it directly opposite the sectioned part, the same as any other view and according to the principle of projection; however, when a cutting plane line is used, the sectional view, or views, might be at any convenient place on the drawing because its relation to the main drawing or view is clearly indicated. This use of any available space on the drawing for sectional views is particularly desirable when a number of sectional views are required; in fact it may be necessary to utilize available space in order to place all essential views on one sheet.

Why do the lines forming a drawing vary in character?

While the practice in making mechanical drawings varies somewhat in different plants, as a general rule such draw-

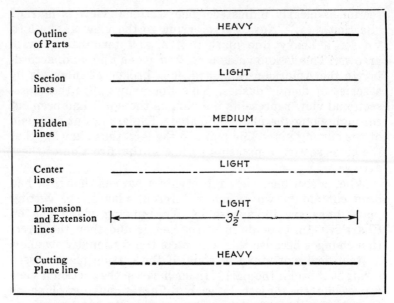

Fig. 5. American Standard Lines for Engineering Drawings

ings consist of several different kinds of lines. The illustration, Fig. 5, shows certain lines that are commonly used. Fairly heavy lines are used to represent the general outline of the part. The center lines are broken at fairly regular intervals by short dashes. The dimension lines are light and unbroken, excepting an open space usually near the center and large enough for the dimension. This is done so that the dimension lines will not pass through the dimension figure. If maximum and minimum limits are given, one figure may be above and the other below an unbroken dimension line. Lines representing hidden parts or surfaces are of medium weight and consist of a series of dashes. Cutting plane lines are drawn as heavy as the outlines but are broken at fairly regular intervals by a series of double dashes. A note or dimension on a drawing is often placed at the end of a *leader* which is a *fine* unbroken line leading to whatever part the note or dimension applies. Leaders are commonly used in giving the sizes of holes and small screw threads. See Symbols and Abbreviations on Drawings—Charts Nos. 17 to 26.

What are extension lines and when are they used?

Dimension lines terminating with arrows are used in most cases in conjunction with extension lines which show to what part or surface the dimension applies (see Fig. 4 as an example). Dimension lines are sometimes placed within the outline of the drawing itself, so that the arrows indicate directly the dimensioned part. This is often done when there is plenty of room, but most dimension lines are adjacent to the drawing and connected with it by the extension lines. This is done to make the dimensions stand out more clearly from the rest of the drawing. When a lot of dimensions are placed directly on the drawing, they are less conspicuous and frequently there is insufficient room to make clear legible figures. The drawing may also be obscured partially by its own dimensions.

The American Standard dimension and extension lines are light full lines. A center line should never be used as a dimension line in cases where it *might* serve such a purpose. It is also bad practice to use any outline of the drawing itself as a dimension line.

Why are drawings made on sheets of different sizes?

Drawings or blueprints in machine-building plants conform, as a rule, to several different standard sizes; in fact, there is an American Standard for mechanical drawing sizes. The smallest is 8 1/2 by 11 inches, which is the size of commercial letters in general use in the United States. The larger sizes are: 11 by 17 inches; 17 by 22 inches; 22 by 34 inches; and 34 by 44 inches. By using these multiples of the basic sheet size of 8 1/2 by 11 inches, small tracings and folded blueprints may be stored in commercial standard letter files.

Working drawings for use in the shop should not be unnecessarily large because they are inconvenient to handle. The important point is to make the drawing large enough to show clearly all details. Many parts can be drawn to their full size without using large cumbersome sheets but, in many other cases, the drawings must be made to some reduced scale to avoid these large sheets and to permit using the standard sheet sizes.

What is the scale of a drawing?

The term "scale" as applied to mechanical drawings indicates the relation between the actual dimensions of a drawn part and the corresponding proportions on the drawing itself. A full or life size drawing usually would be too large; hence, it is drawn to some reduced *scale*. To illustrate: If the piston-head of an engine is to be drawn one-half its actual size, then any part of the piston-head actually measuring 1 inch, for example, would only measure 1/2 inch on the drawing; consequently, 6 inches along any line on the drawing would actually equal 1 foot on the piston-head; hence, the scale of the drawing in this case is said to be 6 inches equals 1 foot, or 1/2 inch equals 1 inch. If still greater reduction in the drawing size was required, it might be made one-fourth actual size, in which case 3 inches would equal 1 foot. Other common scales are 1 1/2 inches = 1 foot (one-eighth size); 1 inch = 1 foot (one-twelfth size); 3/4 inch = 1 foot (one-sixteenth size). Various scales are shown in the accompanying table.

To facilitate the making of drawings to reduced scales, draftsmen have special rules or measuring *scales*, as they are also called, with different sets of graduations which give direct readings to these reduced scales. For example, in making a drawing to one-fourth size, a scale of 3 inches = 1 foot would be used. On such scales, graduations 3 inches apart are marked to represent feet, and each foot

Scales Used for Engineering Drawings

REDUCTION IN SIZE	EQUIVALENT REDUCTION RELATIVE TO 1 FOOT	EQUIVALENT REDUCTION RELATIVE TO 1 INCH
1/2 size	6 inches = 1 foot	1/2 inch = 1 inch
1/4 size	3 inches = 1 foot	1/4 inch = 1 inch
1/8 size	1 1/2 inches = 1 foot	1/8 inch = 1 inch
1/12 size	1 inch = 1 foot	1/12 inch = 1 inch
1/16 size	3/4 inch = 1 foot	1/16 inch = 1 inch
1/32 size	3/8 inch = 1 foot	1/32 inch = 1 inch
1/48 size	1/4 inch = 1 foot	1/48 inch = 1 inch

is subdivided into 12 inches, with finer subdivisions of 1/2, 1/4, and 1/8 inch. The advantage in using such scales is that they permit measurements to be made and checked directly, the same as though a full-size scale were being used.

Does the scale of a drawing affect the method of reading it?

The reading or understanding of a drawing is not affected by the scale to which it is drawn, assuming that the size is large enough to show clearly the essential details. A mechanical drawing, like the photograph of an object, does not need to be "life size" in order to represent that object. Mechanical drawings are made to reduced scales merely as a practical method of reducing the overall size of a drawing, while, at the same time, retaining proportions that are true because every dimension has been reduced proportionately and according to whatever scale has been adopted. In producing the drawn part, a mechanic relies upon the actual dimensions given on the drawing; the proportions of the drawing itself assist only in showing the general shape of a piece, or, possibly, the arrangement of assembled parts. Suppose, for example, that the scale of a drawing is 3 inches = 1 foot, or one-fourth size. If the diameter of a shaft on such a drawing is given as 4 inches, it is, of course, actually made to this diameter (within whatever limits of accuracy may be allowable), but the actual size as measured on the drawing would be 1 inch only, since all parts have been reduced to one-fourth their natural size as a matter of convenience.

Why are both common fractions and decimal fractions used in dimensioning drawings?

In interchangeable manufacture, it is necessary to give limiting dimensions or tolerances on working drawings to safeguard against excessive errors; but even where precision manufacturing is done, many parts or surfaces do not require great accuracy and some might be quite inaccurate without causing trouble. Some surfaces, for example, are machined chiefly to improve the appearance; in other cases, surfaces do not require machining at all. This is particularly true of many parts of castings. For example, the bed of a lathe is machined only where true surfaces are required. The drawings, however, must give the dimensions of all parts. In some cases, dimensions may not be needed in the machine shop but are required in the pattern shop.

Generally speaking, when a dimension is given on a drawing by using a common fraction, instead of a decimal fraction, this means that great accuracy is not required. Some manufacturers believe that the allowable inaccuracy should be specified even when it is comparatively large. In many other plants the accuracy of dimensions unaccompanied by tolerances is left to the judgment of the workmen. Still another method is to establish the rule that dimensions without tolerances must be accurate within a certain fixed amount. One rule is to allow a maximum error of 0.010 inch in such cases. The rule covering this point in the American Standard is as follows: Dimensions of parts that can be measured or that can be produced with sufficient accuracy by using an ordinary scale should be written in units and common fractions. Parts requiring greater accuracy should be dimensioned in decimal fractions.

According to the American Standard, mechanical drawings should preferably have all dimensions expressed in inches, unless greater than 72 inches, in which case the dimension is given in feet and inches. In structural drawing, dimensions of 12 inches and over ordinarily are expressed in feet and inches. A dimension given in inches and decimal fractions is a general indication of accuracy.

The symbol (″) is used to indicate inches. When all dimensions are given in inches, the symbol is preferably omitted. A note may be placed on the drawing stating that all dimensions are given in inches.

The symbol (′) is used to indicate feet. Dimensions in feet and inches should be hyphenated, thus 4′-3″; 4′-0 1/2″; 4′-0″.

How are tolerances or allowable errors indicated on a drawing?

In interchangeable manufacture, all dimensions of parts or surfaces requiring accuracy must indicate directly or indirectly the maximum and minimum limits or the allowable error as explained previously on page 365. One common method is to give the actual maximum and minimum dimension. For example, the diameter of a shaft might be given as $\frac{5.225}{5.223}$. According to the American Standard, the maximum limit is placed above the line for *external* dimensions; for *internal* dimensions, the minimum limit is placed above the line. For example, the diameter of a hole might be given as $\frac{2.354}{2.356}$. The maximum and minimum limits, according to the American Standard, should be used for smaller parts and where gages are extensively employed. A second method, applied to larger parts and where few gages are employed, is to give a basic dimension followed by whatever plus or minus tolerances may be allowable. Example:

$$8.625 \begin{array}{l} +.000 \\ -.002 \end{array}$$

The plus tolerance is placed above the minus. In this example, however, there is no plus tolerance, thus indicating that the dimension may be 8.625 or any smaller size down to 8.623. If both limiting dimensions were given they would be written as follows:

$$\frac{8.625}{8.623}$$

Additional information on tolerances and methods of indicating them will be found in the section beginning on page 359.

What is the general practice in dimensioning circles or holes?

When a circular opening is large, the dimension line may be placed within the circle on the drawing representing this opening. The sizes of ordinary drilled holes usually are placed somewhere outside of the drawing outline. When there are several holes, it is common practice to give the dimension of one only and then mark the total number required. The dimensions of small holes which should be drilled and tapped, etc., usually are marked in a clear space near the hole with a leader or arrow indicating which hole is intended—for example, .204 inch drill—2 holes. This means that the hole indicated and another, obviously the same size, are to be drilled. Here is another typical exam-ample: 0.397 drill—0.406 ream 6 equally spaced holes. This note, which indicates that the .397-inch drill is followed by a .406-inch reamer, might be connected by a leader with one of six equally spaced holes located on a circular center line.

Are all dimensions on a drawing intended for use in the machine shop?

The answer to this question may depend upon what the drawing represents. When a casting is required it may be advisable to make a special drawing for the patternmaker, although, in most cases, he uses the same drawing as the machinist. The patternmaker requires certain dimensions that are not used in the machine shop because they apply to parts which do not require machining. If a drawing is rather complicated, the patternmaker may be obliged to locate, in a maze of lines and dimensions, the particular ones which apply to his work. This explains why it is advisable in some cases to make special drawings for patterns.

The patternmaker usually decides the amount of stock necessary for finish and, if the drawing is rather complex, he often loses time in distinguishing pattern dimensions from those necessary for machining operations. Drawings intended for use in both pattern shop and machine shop may also confuse the machinists who work repeatedly on this piece, and who are compelled to use a drawing bearing a lot of pattern dimensions. Very often, too, these drawings are made at a reduced scale, which may be inconvenient for the patternmaker, especially when a full-size drawing shows the form or proportions more clearly.

How does a drawing show which surfaces are to be machined?

Many drawings have so-called "finish marks" to show what surfaces require machining or finishing. If a casting, for example, is to have some finished or machined surfaces, finish marks are useful in showing just where machining is required. (See Chart No. 25.) If all the surfaces on a part are to be machined, the finish marks may be omitted and a note substituted. The expression "finish all over" is often used or its abbreviation "F.A.O."

According to another method, a surface to be machined or finished is marked with a 60-degree V, as shown by the second diagram, Chart No. 25.

The American Standard provides a set of symbols for use on drawings in specifying allowable roughness values. A V-shaped or check mark is used to designate the surface as shown in Fig. 6. The roughness height (as an arithmetical average deviation from the mean surface) in micro-inches is placed above the vee. There is a horizontal extension line

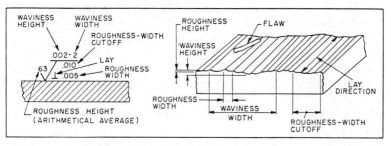

Fig. 6. (Left) Example Showing Use of Surface Finish Symbols.
(Right) Meaning of Each Part of Surface Finish Symbols.

=	Parallel to boundary line of surface indicated by symbol.
⊥	Perpendicular to boundary line of surface indicated by symbol.
X	Angular in both directions to boundary line of surface indicated by symbol.
M	Multi-directional or random.
C	Approximately circular relative to center of surface indicated by symbol.
R	Approximately radial relative to center of surface indicated by symbol.

Fig. 7. American Standard Symbols for Lay or General Direction
of Surface Pattern.

at the top and the waviness height and width are placed above the line. The particular example shown calls for a maximum roughness height of 63 (micro-inches), a waviness height of 0.002 inch, a waviness width of 2 inches, a roughness-width cutoff of 0.010 inch and a lay that is perpendicular to the boundary line as indicated by the symbol at the right of the vee. Methods of indicating and testing the quality of surface finish are explained in Volume 2, beginning on page 419.

How are the different parts of a mechanism identified on drawings by numbers or symbols?

It is common practice to identify the different parts of a machine or other mechanism by means of numbers (or symbols consisting of letters and numbers as explained later) instead of attempting to name each part. The use of numbers is simpler and moreover, names, as applied to many parts, would be too indefinite. In fact, many odd or special parts do not have names which are generally accepted and understood; but when a number is assigned to any part, it provides a convenient definite method of identifying not only the part itself, but its pattern if the part is cast, any special tools which may be required for that part, and everything related to it.

Drawings of assembled parts give these part numbers. The drawing may show a complete mechanism or some individual unit consisting of assembled parts. In either case, the part numbers identify each part. Even though the part is only a standard machine screw or bolt, an identifying number may prove useful. These part numbers or symbols are placed on the drawing in the marginal spaces outside of the actual drawing but usually adjacent to the parts to be identified. Such numbers frequently are enclosed within a circle (to make them stand out from the rest of the drawing) or they may be underlined. A light line or "leader" connects each part number with the particular part it represents. These leader lines usually are drawn from each group of part numbers in such a way as to segregate them as far as possible from the drawing itself. One method is to draw all leader lines parallel and at an angle from the vertical or horizontal, so that they will differ from the rest of the drawing. When there are many different parts, these leader lines—especially if not drawn carefully and systematically—may be confused with those on the drawing proper, thus making the reading of the drawing more difficult. The part numbers usually are placed in consecutive order or in a straight line so that the workman may locate readily any detail.

Is there a standard method of designating machine parts by means of numbers or symbols?

The method of designating parts varies more or less in different plants and may be based upon the general class of work done. For example, when numbers and letters are combined to designate parts, the letter may indicate the general type of machine if several types are produced, or it may indicate a certain class of unit mechanism on a given type of machine. In some cases, a letter may indicate a type of machine and the number following may show its size and still another number may indicate the particular part. To illustrate, D might represent drilling machines, L, lathes, etc., and by combining a letter and number, as, for example, L-36, the symbol for a 36-inch lathe would be obtained. Serial numbers are also assigned to different parts of the machine; if 25 were the serial number of the lead-screw of a 36-inch lathe, the complete symbol would be L-36-25. This symbol (L-36) could also be used to identify the patterns. The relation between numbers may indicate the relation between parts; thus, if 30 is the serial number of a shaft, 31 may designate a bushing which is assembled on the shaft. When the numbers are arranged in this way, they enable the assembler to understand more readily the detailed drawings, since they show which parts go together.

Another method is to indicate by the size of the number whether the part is a shaft, a collar, a casting, a drop-forging, a punched part, a machine screw, etc. Thus, the numbers from 0 to 9 may represent shafts; from 10 to 29, studs, pins, screws, and so on. In addition to these numbers, letters may be used to show to what general group or part of the mechanism any detail belongs. For instance, A may represent some part such, for example, as an accumulator mechanism; B, the base frame; C, the carriage, etc. According to this system, if the symbol A-6 were used, this would show that the part represented was a shaft of the accumulator mechanism. When more than one operation is required, a number may be added to the symbol to show the number of the operation; thus, if numbers between 50 and 74 represent punched parts, then the symbol A-52-2 on the drawing of a die shows that this die is used for the second operation on a punched part for the accumulator mechanism.

What is reference-line or base-line dimensioning?

The method of dimensioning a drawing should assist the man in the shop as far as possible. Drawings in all cases should be so dimensioned that no calculations in the shop are required when machining a part. The dimensions should also be related as far as possible to proper or necessary methods of machining. Suppose, for example, that a number of holes are to be drilled and bored in a jig plate by using a precision jig-boring machine. Machines of this type (see pages 354 to 358) are so designed that precision adjustments and measurements can be made in two directions at right angles to each other. If the dimensions on a drawing are given on the drawing so that they can be used directly in adjusting the machine either in a lengthwise or crosswise direction, this will be a safeguard against error, insure a high degree of accuracy, and also save time. Base-line dimensioning is so called because all dimensions are direct from reference lines or finished edges which serve as a base. This method, for example, is applicable when the work has finished edges at right angles to each other (Plates of irregular shape may be mounted on an auxiliary plate having such edges.) The dimension lines are at right angles to each other from each base-line, so that any hole can be located by right-angle adjustments. In this case, dimensions are not given to show the center distance between the holes in a straight line. This right-angle method, as it might be called, is practicable for many classes of work, because the adjustments made by the machinist or toolmaker in locating the work for drilling and boring are frequently in two directions at right angles to each other, the machines or other work-holding equipment being arranged in this way. The direct center-to-center distance, however, is often required, which indicates that the method of arranging the dimensions on a drawing may be very closely related to shop and tool-room practice.

The designer or draftsman determines, of course, what dimensions are to be given and how they are to be placed on the drawing. These points are referred to here so that anyone studying the reading of drawings will understand why different methods are employed. Incidentally, many drawings are not dimensioned as they should be to obtain the best results in the shop, which shows why a designer should have at least a general knowledge of manufacturing operations.

In building a machine, what general types of drawings are required?

The number of drawings required in constructing any machine, or mechanism, depends upon the number of parts in the mechanism and also, to some extent, upon the simplicity or complexity of the different parts. A common method of procedure is to make small *working drawings* to show individual parts, or related groups of parts, and then a larger *assembly drawing* (or possibly more than one) of the completed machine or mechanism which shows how all parts are arranged when assembled. The principles which are applied in reading the drawings of individual parts also govern the reading of complicated drawings of assembled machines, but a little more experience and imagination usually is required. The drawings of parts are often referred to as working drawings because they are used in the shop in actual production. Assembly drawings frequently show general outlines only (or outlines accompanied by the most important or main dimensions) because any attempt to include all details would merely complicate the drawing without serving any useful purpose.

To secure additional practice in "blueprint reading," working drawings should be stu'ied whenever there is an opportunity. If actual working drawings are not available, many of the line illustrations in engineering magazines, and also in books on mechanical drawing and machine design, will serve as examples for practice.

Miscellaneous Rules and Formulas

The Machine Shop Training Course contains, in both volumes, many rules or formulas relating to various classes of machine shop problems. These are included right in the chapters on different branches of shop work and apply to whatever subjects are covered by these chapters. The miscellaneous rules and formulas which follow are also applied frequently in connection with mechanical work. These rules and formulas are accompanied by examples, especially in cases where examples and methods of solution are needed to insure a clearer understanding of the application to practical problems.

Area of Square and Distance across Corners

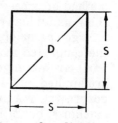

Area: If length of side S is in inches, area in square inches $= S \times S$, in inches, or S^2. If length of side S is in feet, area in square feet $= S \times S$, in feet, or S^2. Area also equals one-half the square of the diagonal dimension D or the distance across corners.

Distance Across Corners: The diagonal dimension D or distance across corners $= 1.4142 \times$ dimension S.

Length of Side for Given Diagonal: Length of side S $= 0.7071 \times D$.

Length of Side for Given Area: If the area is known, the length of the side equals the square root of the area.

Example: A square bar, in order to resist a certain torsional load, requires an area of $3\frac{1}{2}$ square inches. Find dimension S.

$$S = \sqrt{3.5} = 1\frac{7}{8} \text{ inches}$$

Area of Rectangle and Distance across Corners

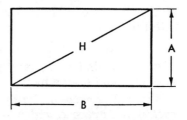

Area: Area in square inches equals length of side *A* in inches multiplied by side *B* in inches. If lengths *A* and *B* are in feet, the area will be in square feet.

Distance Across Corners: The diagonal dimension *H* is the hypotenuse of a right-angle triangle. See Right-Angle Triangle.

Area and One Side Known: Divide the area by the length of known side, to find the length of the other side.

Area and Dimensions of Parallelogram

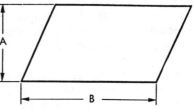

Area: Multiply length *B* by height *A* measured perpendicular to base or side *B*.

Height A: Height *A* equals area divided by length of base *B*.

Area and Length B Known: Divide area by length *B* to find height *A*.

Area and Height A Known: Divide area by height *A* to find length *B*.

Dimensions and Area of Right-Angle Triangle

To find H: Add the square of dimension *A* to the square of dimension *B* and extract the square root of the sum to obtain length of hypotenuse *H*.

To find A: Subtract from the square of hypotenuse *H* the square of side *B* and extract the square root of the difference.

To find Side B: Subtract from the square of hypotenuse

H the square of side A and extract the square root of the difference.

$$H = \sqrt{A^2 + B^2}; \quad A = \sqrt{H^2 - B^2}; \quad B = \sqrt{H^2 - A^2}$$

Area: To find area, multiply length of side A by length of side B and divide by 2.

Note: The area of a triangle equals one-half the area of a rectangle having a width A and a length B.

Depth of Cut when Tool-Slide Angle is 30 Degrees

Note: The rule which follows is based upon the fact that the side A of a right-angle triangle, opposite the 30-degree angle, is ½ the length of the hypotenuse H.

    Rule: When tool-slide is set to an angle of 30 degrees, tool movement in direction A = ½ tool-slide movement in direction H; hence move tool-slide double the depth of cut required.

    Example: In facing a flange, it is found that the thickness must be further reduced 0.003 inch. If the tool-slide is set at an angle of 30 degrees, how much inward adjustment of the tool-slide is required to move tool 0.003 inch in direction D?

    Solution: Since inward movement of tool is to be 0.003 inch, tool-slide must be adjusted inward double this amount or 0.006 inch as shown by graduated dial.

Area and Altitude of Acute Angle Triangle

    Area: To find area, multiply altitude A by length B and divide the product by 2.

    Altitude A: To find altitude A, divide length of base B by cotangent of angle C plus cotangent of angle D.

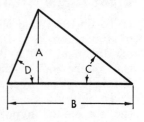

$$\text{Altitude } A = \frac{\text{Length Base } B}{\text{Cot } C + \text{Cot } D}$$

Area and Altitude of Obtuse Angle Triangle

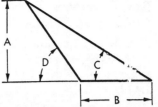

Area: To find area, multiply length of base B by altitude A measured perpendicular to base, and divide the product by 2.

Altitude: To find altitude A, divide the length of base B by the difference between the cotangents of angles C and D.

Diameter, Circumference, and Area of Circle

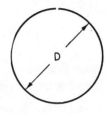

Rule for Circumference: Circumference = diameter $\times$ 3.1416 (accurate enough for practically all requirements). The value 3.1416 is commonly denoted by the Greek letter pi (π).

Note: Exact ratio of circumference to diameter is not known although it has been calculated to 707 decimal places. The first 25 decimals are as follows:

$$3.1415926535897932384626434$$

Rule for Diameter: Multiply circumference by 0.3183.
Rule for Area: Square diameter and multiply by 0.7854.

$$\text{Area} = D^2 \times 0.7854$$

Circle and Square of Equal Area

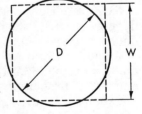

Rule 1: To find width W of square having same area as circle, multiply 0.8862 by diameter D of circle

$$W = 0.8862 \times D$$

Rule 2: To find diameter D of circle having area equal to square, multiply 1.1284 by width W of square

$$D = 1.1284 \times W$$

Note: The reciprocal of 0.8862 or 1.1284 is used in Rule 2 in order to obtain diameter D by multiplication instead of division.

Bar Diameter D to Form Square of Width W

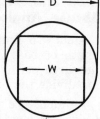

Rule 1: To find smallest diameter D of bar for forming a sharp-cornered square of width W, multiply W by 1.4142

$$D = W \times 1.4142$$

Rule 2: To find largest square W which can be formed on bar of given diameter, multiply D by 0.7071.

$$W = D \times 0.7071$$

Bar Diameter D to Form Hexagon of Width W

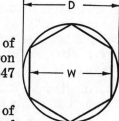

Rule 1: To find smallest diameter D of bar required to form complete hexagon having width W, multiply W by 1.1547

$$D = W \times 1.1547$$

Rule 2: To find maximum width W of hexagon which can be formed on bar of diameter D, multiply diameter of bar by 0.866

$$W = D \times 0.866$$

Length L of Arc for Given Angle and Diameter

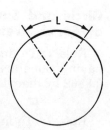

Rule: Multiply 0.008727 by number of degrees in arc L, then multiply product by double the arc radius to find length L.

Angle for Given Arc and Radius: To find angle, multiply 57.296 by length L of arc, and divide product by radius of arc.

Example: An arc L, having a radius of 2 inches, includes an angle of 10 degrees 18 minutes. How long is the arc?

As there are 60 minutes in one degree, the angle equals 10 18/60 or 10.3 degrees; hence,

$$L = 0.008727 \times 10.3 \times 4 = 0.3595 \text{ inch}$$

Chordal Lengths for Dividing Circles

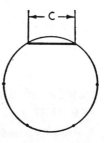

Note: In dividing the circumference of a circle into a given number of equal spaces or divisions, the length of the chord C or the straight-line distance between the dividing points is obtained as follows:

For Six Divisions: Length of chord $C =$ radius of circle.

For any other Number of Divisions: Divide 180 degrees by required number of divisions (N) and find sine of angle thus obtained. Multiply this sine by diameter of circle to obtain chordal length C.

$$C = \sin\frac{180}{N} \times \text{diameter of circle}$$

Example: A circle 4 inches in diameter is to have nine equal divisions. Find chordal length C or distance to which dividers would be set.

$$\text{Sin}\frac{180}{9} \text{ or } 20° \text{ is } 0.34202$$

$$0.34202 \times 4 = 1.36808 \text{ inches}$$

Radius of Arc when Chordal Length and Height H of the Arc are Known

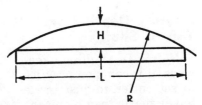

Note: The rule which follows may be useful, especially when the radius of the arc is large and the center is not accessible for making a direct measurement. A straightedge of any convenient length L may be placed against the curved section, thus forming a chord from which height H may be measured.

Rule: Add the square of height H to the square of one-half length L, and divide the sum by twice the height H to obtain radius R of arc.

$$R = \frac{H^2 + (L \div 2)^2}{2 \times H}$$

Example: Assume that straightedge is 30 inches long and height H measures 2 29/32 or, say, 2.9 inches; find radius R.

$$\text{Radius } R = \frac{2.9^2 + 15^2}{2 \times 2.9} = 40.24 \text{ inches}$$

Height of Circular Segment

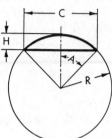

Rule 1: Subtract from the square of radius R the square of one-half chordal length C; then find the square root of the difference and subtract it from radius R to obtain height H of segment.

$$H = R - \sqrt{R^2 - (C \div 2)^2}$$

Rule 2: Divide chordal length C by twice the radius R to obtain the sine of angle A. Next find angle A in table of trigonometric functions and multiply the tangent of one-half angle A by one-half chordal length C.

Example: A shaft 1½ inches in diameter is to have a "flat" 1 inch wide milled on one side. Find depth H of cut from top of shaft, by applying Rule 1.

$$H = 0.75 - \sqrt{0.75^2 - (1 \div 2)^2} = 0.191 \text{ inch}$$

Keyway Depth from Top of Shaft

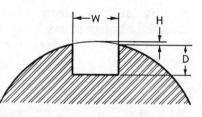

Note: In milling keyways, it is common practice to set cutter to just graze top of shaft; then, by means of graduated dial on elevating screw, the work is adjusted upward an amount equal to height of arc H plus depth D at side of keyway.

Rule: To find H for keyway milling, divide square of width W by four times shaft diameter.

Example: Shaft diameter is 2 inches and keyway width ½ inch; find height H to add to side depth D.

$$H = \frac{0.5^2}{4 \times 2} \quad \frac{0.25}{8} = 0.0313$$

Note: The rule just given is approximate, especially when width W is large in proportion to the shaft diameter; but it is sufficiently accurate for ordinary keyways, which, as a rule, are not wider than one-fourth the shaft diameter. If the more accurate rules found under "Height of Circular Segment" are applied to the preceding example, the resulting value of H will be 0.0317 inch or 0.0004 inch higher than obtained by the approximate rule.

Flats of Equal Length on Intersecting Cylindrical Punches

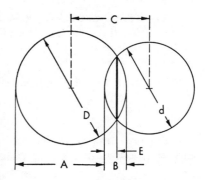

Note: When punches on blanking dies are arranged as shown by diagram, the problem is to determine how much to remove from the punches in order to obtain a given center distance C and the same chordal length on each punch.

Rule: First find dimension B which equals the sum of the radii of the two punches minus the center distance C. To find E, subtract B from D (to find A), multiply the remainder by B and divide the product by double the center distance C. Distance across larger punch equals $A + E$, and across smaller punch $d - E$.

$$B = \frac{D}{2} + \frac{d}{2} - C; \; E = \frac{(D - B) \times B}{2 \times C}$$

Example: Punch diameter $D = 2$ inches, $d = 1.375$ inches, and $C = 1.25$ inches; hence,

$$B = \frac{2}{2} + \frac{1.375}{2} - 1.25 = 0.4375$$

$$E = \frac{(2 - 0.4375) \times 0.4375}{2 \times 1.25} = 0.2734$$

Measurement across larger shaft $= D - B + E = 2 - 0.4375 + 0.2734 = 1.8359$ inches.

Measurement across smaller shaft $= 1.375 - 0.2734 = 1.1016$ inches.

Volume and Area of Cylindrical Tank

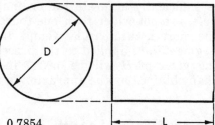

Rule for Volume: To find volume, multiply square of diameter D by length L, and multiply product by 0.7854.

$$\text{Volume} = D^2 \times L \times 0.7854$$

Note: If diameter and length are in inches, volume will be in cubic inches. If dimensions are in feet, volume will be in cubic feet.

Rule for Area of Cylindrical Surface: Multiply circumference of tank by its length.

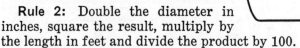

$$\text{Cylindrical area} = \text{circumference} \times L$$

Rule for Total Area: To find area of both cylindrical and end surfaces, multiply circumference by length plus radius.

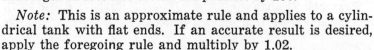

$$\text{Total area} = \text{circumference} \times (\text{radius} + L)$$

Capacity of Tank in Gallons

Rule 1: Find the volume in cubic inches and divide by 231 which is the number of cubic inches per gallon.

Rule 2: Double the diameter in inches, square the result, multiply by the length in feet and divide the product by 100.

Note: This is an approximate rule and applies to a cylindrical tank with flat ends. If an accurate result is desired, apply the foregoing rule and multiply by 1.02.

Example: A tank is 60 inches in diameter and 18 feet long. Determine its capacity in gallons.

Solutions: $60 \times 2 = 120$ and the square of 120 equals 14400. Multiplying by the length in feet, we have $14400 \times 18 = 259200$. Next, divide by 100 merely by dropping the last two ciphers, thus obtaining the approximate capacity of 2592 gallons. If a more precise result is desired, $2592 \times 1.02 = 2643.84$ gallons.

Area and Volume of Spherical Surface

Rule for Area: To find area of surface in square inches, multiply square of diameter D in inches by 3.1416

$$\text{Area} = D^2 \times 3.1416$$

Rule for Volume: To find volume in cubic inches, multiply cube of diameter D in inches by 0.5236

$$\text{Volume} = D^3 \times 0.5236$$

End Diameters of Tapering Part when Taper per Foot is Given

Rule for Large End Diameter **D:** Divide taper per foot in inches, by 12, multiply quotient by length L of taper in inches, measured parallel to axis, and *add* product to smaller diameter d.

$$D = d + \left(\frac{\text{Taper per ft.}}{12} \times L \right)$$

Rule for Small End Diameter **d:** Divide taper per foot, in inches, by 12, multiply quotient by length L of taper in inches, measured parallel to axis, and *subtract* product from larger diameter D.

$$d = D - \left(\frac{\text{Taper per ft.}}{12} \times L \right)$$

End Diameters of Tapering Part when Angle of Taper is Given

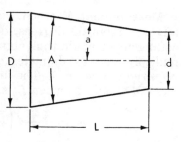

Note: If amount of taper is expressed in degrees, the *included* angle A usually is given. The angle in the rules and formulas which follow, is one-half the included angle or the angle a measured from the center line.

Rule for Large End Diameter D: Multiply tangent of angle *a* by twice the length *L* of taper in inches, and *add* product to small end diameter *d*.

$$D = d + (\tan a \times 2 \times L)$$

Rule for Small End Diameter d: Multiply tangent of angle *a* by twice the length *L* of taper in inches, and *subtract* product from large end diameter *D*.

$$d = D - (\tan a \times 2 \times L)$$

To Find Diam. D of Tapering Part from Measurement M

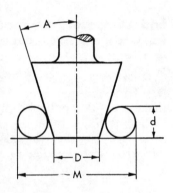

Note: It is impracticable to check diameter *D* at the extreme end of a tapering part by direct measurement when great accuracy is required. The formulas below provide accurate means of checking diameter *D*, assuming that the actual roll diameter *d* and angle *A* on the work are the same as inserted in the formula.

Diameter D for Given Measurement M: Subtract angle *A* from 90 degrees, divide remainder by 2 and find cotangent of angle thus obtained. Add 1 to this cotangent, multiply sum by diameter *d* of rolls, and *subtract* product from measurement *M* over the rolls to find diameter *D*.

$$D = M - d \left(1 + \cot \frac{90 - A}{2} \right)$$

Measurement M when Diameter D is Correct: Subtract angle *A* from 90 degrees, divide remainder by 2 and find cotangent of angle thus obtained. Add 1 to this cotangent, multiply sum by diameter *d* of rolls, and *add* product to required diameter *D*. The final result shows what measurement *M* should be when *D* is correct.

$$M = D + d \left(1 + \cot \frac{90 - A}{2} \right)$$

Example: A taper plug gage is to have included angle of 33° 20′ and a small end diameter *D* of 3.750 inches. If rolls have diameter d of 1 inch, what will measurement M be when end diameter D is correct?

Angle A equals one-half the included angle or 16° 40′

$$M = 3.750 + 1 \times \left(1 + \cot \frac{90 - 16° \, 40'}{2} \right) = 6.093 \text{ inches}$$

Ball Method of Checking Diameter D

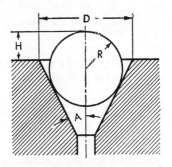

Note: The object is to check accurately the diameter D of a conical hole by measuring height H to top of ball. This method may also be applied to a V-shaped groove by using either a cylindrical rod or ball. In either case, the required dimension D is inserted in the formula which follows. If the actual dimension D on the work is correct, the measured height H will equal the calculated height, assuming that the actual radius R of the ball or rod and angle A, are precisely the same as the values used in the formula.

$$H = R + \frac{R}{\sin A} - \left(\frac{D}{2} \times \cot A \right)$$

Example: Assume that angle A is 30° or ½ of included angle of conical hole; diameter D is 0.827; ball radius $R = 0.3125$. Then,

$$H = 0.3125 + \frac{0.3125}{0.5} - \left(\frac{0.827}{2} \times 1.732 \right) = 0.2213 \text{ inch}$$

Note: This method is accurate provided the *actual* angle of the hole or groove and the *actual* diameter of the ball or rod, are known within very small limits and are used in calculating height H. In the foregoing example, assume that the actual angle A is 29° 50″ and the actual ball radius is 0.3122 inch. Then, if these true values are inserted in the formula, height H will be 0.2187; hence, the error in the calculated height $H = 0.2213 - 0.2187 = 0.0026$ inch. This illustrates how even slight errors between the assumed and actual values might affect the calculation and the accuracy of the work.

Gear or Pulley Speeds or Sizes

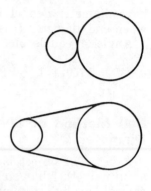

Speed of Driven Gear: To find the speed of driven gear, multiply the number of teeth on the driving gear by its speed in R.P.M. (revolutions per minute) and divide the product by the number of teeth on the driven gear. (Note: Pitch diameters may be used instead of number of teeth and the same result will be obtained.)

Speed of Driven Pulley: To obtain the speed of the driven pulley, multiply the diameter of the driving pulley by its speed in R.P.M. and divide the product by the diameter of the driven pulley.

Size of Driven Gear or Pulley: Multiply size of driver (number of teeth or pitch diameter in case of gear) by its R.P.M. and divide product by required R.P.M. of driven gear or pulley to find its size.

Size of Driving Gear or Pulley: Multiply size of driven gear or pulley by its speed in R.P.M. and divide product by speed of driving gear or pulley to find its size.

Speed of Last Driven Gear or Pulley in Compound Drive

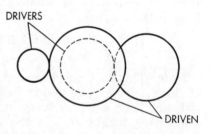

Rule for Gears: Divide product of driving gear sizes (pitch diameters or numbers of teeth) by product of driven gear sizes and multiply quotient by R.P.M. of first driving gear. The final result equals speed of last driven gear.

Rule for Pulleys: Divide product of driving pulley diameters by product of driven pulley diameters and multiply quotient by R.P.M. of first driving pulley. The final result equals speed of last driven pulley.

Ratios of Gear Drives

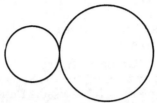

Note: A gear ratio indicates the speed relationship between driving and driven gears. If a driving pinion, for example, has 15 teeth and its driven gear 45 teeth, then the ratio of the *driving* gear speed to the *driven* gear speed $= 45 \div 15 = 3$ or 3 revolutions of the driving gear per revolution of the driven gear. This order, however, might be reversed, in which case the ratio of the *driven* gear speed to that of the *driver* would equal $15 \div 45 = 1/3$. The first method is customary; hence, in the example referred to the ratio, according to common practice, is said to be 3, or "3 to 1," and not one-third.

Ratio for Two-gear Drive: The ratio equals speed of *driving gear* divided by speed of *driven gear;* ratio also equals size of *driven gear* divided by size of *driving gear.* Thus

$$\text{Gear ratio} = \frac{\text{R.P.M. of driving gear}}{\text{R.P.M. of driven gear}} = \frac{\text{Size of driven gear}}{\text{Size of driving gear}}$$

Note: The gear size may be indicated either by number of teeth or by pitch diameter.

Ratio for Compound Drive: (The formula below is applied when there are two or more driving gears and driven gears.)

$$\text{Gear ratio} = \frac{\text{R.P.M. of first driver}}{\text{R.P.M. of last driven}} = \frac{\text{Product of driven gear sizes}}{\text{Product of driving gear sizes}}$$

Gear Sizes for Obtaining a Given Ratio

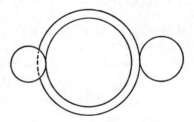

Note: If gearing requires some precise ratio, it may not be possible to obtain the *exact* value desired, and, at the same time, have gear sizes or tooth numbers that are within practical limits. In such cases, the problem is to determine gear sizes which are so close to the theoretically correct sizes that the ratio error is negligible. There are different methods of doing this, but the following is believed to be one of the simplest and most direct. An example will be used to illustrate the procedure.

Example: A driving shaft is to make 4.15957 revolutions per turn of the driven shaft and a compound train of four gears is to be used. Determine practical gear sizes.

Step 1: First, convert the ratio 4.15957 into a common fraction by multiplying and dividing it by some trial number. Suppose the trial number is 1000; then,

$$4.15957 = 4.15957 \times \frac{1000}{1000} = \frac{4159.57}{1000}$$

Note: For decimal ratios between 0.1 and 10, use one of the following trial numbers: 1000, 2000, 2500, 3000, 4000, 5000, 6000, 7500, 8000, 9000, 10000. Determining which of these trial numbers is the most suitable may require several trials of the kind shown by Step 2. The purpose of this next step is to find a common fraction that is so close to the required ratio that the error is negligible.

If the numerator 4159.57 (obtained by Step 1) is rounded off to 4160, the fraction 4160 ÷ 1000 = 4.160. This happens to be within 0.00043 of the required ratio, but assume that a more accurate result is necessary. The procedure then is as follows:

Step 2: Subtract from the numerator one-hundredth of its value and also subtract from the denominator one-hundredth of its value, thus obtaining a new numerator and denominator, and repeat as often as may be necessary to obtain a numerator which can be factored and be rounded off without introducing an excessive error. (The trial numbers 1000, 2000, etc., insure that the denominators will be factorable.)   One-hundredth of numerator = 4159.57 × 0.01 = 41.59 approximately; one-hundredth of denominator = 1000 × 0.01 = 10; hence, we have in this case

$$\frac{4159.57 - 41.59}{1000 - 10} = \frac{4117.98}{990} = \text{new numerator}$$
$$= \text{new denominator}$$

If the numerator is changed to 4118, the value of the fraction will be changed very little and, fortunately, the number can be factored into practical gear sizes.   Thus

$$\frac{4118}{990} = \frac{58 \times 71}{22 \times 45} = \frac{\text{Driven gears}}{\text{Driving gears}} = 4.15959$$

This combination of gearing is within 0.00002 of the ratio. However, as a general rule, the successive changing of the numerator and denominator must be repeated a number of times to obtain a numerator which can be rounded off without introducing excessive error and, at the same time, leave a number which is factorable into suitable gear sizes. In this particular example, gearing having a ratio of 4.15957 + may be obtained by continuing with the successive changes as shown below:

$$\frac{4117.98 - 41.59 = 4076.39}{990 - 10 = \quad 980}$$

Continue because 4076.39 is not close enough to a whole number.

$$\frac{4076.39 - 41.59 = 4034.80}{980 - 10 = \quad 970}$$

Continue because 4034.80 is not close enough to a whole number.

$$\frac{4034.80 - 41.59 = 3993.21}{970 - 10 = \quad 960}$$

Continue because 3993.21 is not close enough to a whole number.

$$\frac{3993.21 - 41.59 = 3951.62}{960 - 10 = \quad 950}$$

Continue because 3951.62 is not close enough to a whole number.

$$\frac{3951.62 - 41.59 = 3910.03}{950 - 10 = \quad 940}$$

The number 3910.03 is very close to 3910 and latter number may also be factored into practical gear sizes. Thus,

$$\frac{3910}{940} = \frac{46 \times 85}{40 \times 47} = \frac{34 \times 115}{40 \times 47} = 4.15957 +$$

Note: When repeated trials with a trial denominator (such as 1000) do not result in a satisfactory solution, try one of the other factors listed, such as 2000, 2500, 3000, etc.

The foregoing example was solved by *subtracting* one-hundredth of the numerator and denominator. In some cases, *addition* is preferable, but this can only be determined by trial.

Tables of numbers and their factors facilitate the solution of gear ratio problems.

Cutting Speeds and Equivalent R.P.M.

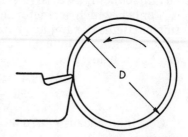

Note: The rules and formulas which follow may be applied to such operations as turning, boring, drilling, and milling. In turning, the cutting speed usually is based upon the diameter of the unturned part. In using rotating cutting tools such as drills and milling cutters, the diameter of the drill or cutter is used. (R.P.M. is the common abbreviation for revolutions per minute.)

R.P.M. for a Given Cutting Speed in Feet Per Minute: Multiply required cutting speed, in feet per minute, by 3.82 and divide product by diameter of rotating work or cutter.

$$\text{R.P.M.} = \frac{3.82 \times \text{cutting speed, ft. per min.}}{\text{Diameter, inches}}$$

Cutting Speed in Feet per Minute for Given R.P.M.: Multiply R.P.M. of rotating work or cutter by its diameter in inches, and divide product by 3.82.

$$\text{Cutting speed, ft. per min.} = \frac{\text{R.P.M.} \times \text{Diameter, inches}}{3.82}$$

Example 1: A steel bar 4 inches in diameter is to be turned at a cutting speed of about 200 feet per minute; find equivalent number of R.P.M.

$$\text{R.P.M.} = \frac{3.82 \times 200}{4} = 191$$

Example 2: A plain milling cutter having a diameter of $3\frac{1}{2}$ inches is rotating at 150 R.P.M.; what is the cutting speed?

$$\text{Cutting speed} = \frac{150 \times 3\frac{1}{2}}{3.82} = 137 \text{ ft. per min.}$$

Milling Cutter Feed Rates

Note: Feed rates in inches per minute are based upon the permissible feed per tooth and vary considerably for different materials and types of cutters. In milling with high-speed steel cutters, the feed rates per tooth as a general rule are approximately as follows:

For cast iron: 0.013 to 0.018 inch per tooth for face mills, 0.010 to 0.014 inch for helical or spiral mills, 0.006 to 0.009 inch for end mills, depending upon the hardness of the iron.

For carbon steel: 0.009 to 0.013 inch per tooth for face mills, 0.007 to 0.010 inch for helical or spiral mills, and 0.005 to 0.006 inch for end mills, depending upon the carbon content.

Feed in Inches per Minute: Multiply feed per tooth by number of teeth and then multiply by R.P.M. of cutter.

Feed Rate per Tooth: Divide feed in inches per minute by number of teeth and multiply quotient by R.P.M. of cutter.

Time Required for Turning, Drilling and Milling

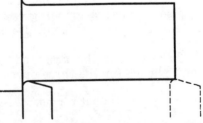

Note: The formulas which follow give the time in minutes for either turning, drilling or milling operations.

Time for Turning: Divide the length, in inches, of the surface to be turned, by the product of the work speed in R.P.M. and the tool feed per work revolution, to obtain the time in minutes.

Time for Drilling: Divide the depth, in inches, of the hole to be drilled, by the product of the drill speed in R.P.M. and the drill feed per revolution, to obtain the time in minutes.

Time for Milling: Divide the length, in inches, of the surface to be milled, by the product of the cutter speed in

R.P.M. and the cutter feed per revolution, to obtain the time in minutes.

Rate of Production for Two or More Machining Operations

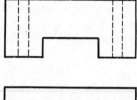

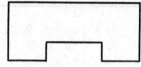

Note: The problem is to determine the rate of production when a given piece requires two or more operations.

Rule: The *product* of the two rates per hour divided by the *sum* of the two rates per hour, is the complete output per hour. (If there are more than two production rates on a given piece, apply the same rule but deal with the operations in pairs by coupling the rate for the first pair with the rate for the third operation, and the resulting rate for these three operations with the rate of the fourth operation, and so on.

Example 1: A piece is being milled at the rate of 60 pieces per hour and then is drilled at the rate of 30 pieces per hour. What is the output per hour of the finished product?

$$\text{Output per hour} = \frac{60 \times 30}{60 + 30} = 20$$

Example 2: Assume that the piece referred to in Example 1, also requires a grinding operation which is done at the rate of 12 pieces per hour. Determine hourly output for the three operations.

The rate for the first and second operations is 20 per hour; hence for the three operations.

$$\text{Output per hour} = \frac{20 \times 12}{20 + 12} = 7\frac{1}{2}$$

To Find Square Root of a Number

Note: In practical work, a table containing powers and roots of numbers may be employed to save time and insure accuracy. However, if the table at hand does not contain a number for which a root is required, the following reverse method of using the table is easily applied and sufficiently accurate for most purposes.

Example 1: Find the square root of 9253 using a table of powers and roots which contains numbers up to 2000 only. The table shows that 9216 is the square of 96; hence, it is evident that the square root of 9253 is a little over 96. In the column of squares of numbers, find a number the first four figures of which are nearest to 9253 and at the same time note if this is the square of a number beginning with the figures 9 and 6. Thus, the square of 962 is 925444 and the first four figures of this higher number are within one of the given number; therefore, the square root of 9253 is 96.2 nearly. The square root of 9253 is 96.192, accurate to three decimal places.

Example 2: Find the square root of 157.5. First determine the approximate value of the square root. The square root of 157 equals 12.53 and 158, 12.5698; therefore, it is evident that the square root of 157.5 is between these values. Since the square of 1255 is 1,575,025, it is evident that the square of 12.55 is 157.5025; hence, the square root of 157.5 is 12.55.

To Find Cube Root of a Number

Note: The cube root of a number may be found by utilizing a table containing cubes of numbers. The method is the same in principle as previously described in connection with square roots.

Example: Find the cube root of 676836 by using the table of cubes.

The column of cubes shows that the cube root is somewhere between 87 and 88. The cube of 878 is found to be 676836152. The first six figures coincide exactly with those of the given number; hence, it is evident that the cube root is almost exactly 87.8.

Example 2: Find the cube root of 0.29539 by using the table of cubes.

Since the number is less than 1, it is evident that the cube root must be less than 1. The cube of the whole number 666 is found to be 295408296. The first five figures of this number coincide very nearly with those of the given number; hence, the cube root is 0.666 very nearly. The cube root, accurate to five decimal places, is 0.66599.

To Find Lead Angle A of Screw Thread

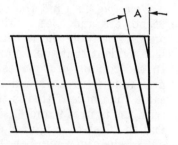

Note: The lead angle A of screw threads is always measured from a plane perpendicular to the screw thread axis. This rule applies also to worm threads. (In the case of helical gears, the helix angle is always measured from the axis.) The lead angle A is greater at the bottom of the thread than at the top. The angle at the pitch diameter usually is required.

Rule for Single Thread: To obtain cotangent of lead angle A, divide the pitch circumference by the pitch; then find the angle equivalent to this cotangent in a table of trigonometric functions.

Rule for Multiple Thread: Multiply the pitch by the number of separate threads or "starts" to obtain the lead. The cotangent of angle A equals the pitch circumference divided by the lead.

Example: The pitch diameter of a double-threaded worm is $3\frac{1}{2}$ inches and the pitch measured in the plane of the axis is 1 inch; find the lead angle.

Solution: Lead $= 1 \times 2 = 2$ inches. Cot $A = \dfrac{3.5 \times 3.1416}{2} =$

5.4978; hence, table of trigonometric functions shows that A is 10° 19′ (to the nearest minute).

To Find Normal Pitch P_n of Screw Thread

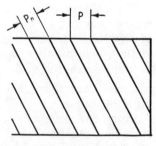

Note: The normal pitch P_n is the pitch measured squarely across or perpendicular to adjacent threads. If a worm is to mesh with a rack, the normal pitch of the worm must equal the pitch of the rack; also, the normal pitch of a hob for cutting spur gears must equal the circular pitch of the gear.

Rule: To find the normal pitch P_n, multiply the axial pitch P by the cosine of the lead angle.

Example: A quadruple Acme thread has an axial pitch of 1½ inches and a lead angle of 18° 34′; find the normal pitch P_n.

Solution: A table of trigonometric functions shows that the cosine of 18° 34′ is 0.94795; hence, normal pitch $P_n = 0.94795 \times 1.5 = 1.4219$ inches.

Change-Gear Formula for Multiple Thread Cutting

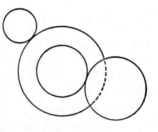

Note: If a lathe does not have a quick-change gear-box but is equipped with ordinary change-gears at the end of the head-stock which are selected and adjusted for each thread-cutting operation, the change-gears for multiple thread cutting may be calculated in the usual manner (as explained on page 226) after converting the lead of the thread into the equivalent number of *single* threads per inch. The general formula which follows contains the lead of the thread. In this formula, the term "constant" means number of threads per inch cut by the lathe when the change-gear ratio is 1 to 1. Ordinarily, this constant equals the number of threads per inch on the lead-screw.

$$\text{Change-gear ratio} = \frac{\text{Constant}}{1} \times \frac{\text{Lead}}{1} = \frac{\text{Drivers}}{\text{Driven}}$$

Example: Lead of thread to be cut equals 1¾ inches and lathe constant is 4. Determine the change-gear ratio.

$$\text{Change-gear ratio} = \frac{4}{1} \times \frac{1\frac{3}{4}}{1} = \frac{4}{1} \times \frac{7}{4}.$$

The values of numerators and denominators are raised to any higher values equivalent to sizes of available change-gears. For example, suppose trial multipliers 20 and 10 are used.

$$\frac{(4 \times 20)}{(1 \times 20)} \times \frac{(7 \times 10)}{(4 \times 10)} = \frac{80 \times 70}{20 \times 40} = \frac{\text{Drivers}}{\text{Driven}}$$

Auxiliary Change-Gears for Increasing Range of Quick-Change Gear-Box

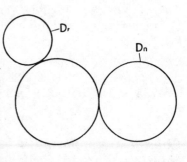

Note: If the lathe is equipped with a quick-change box and is so arranged that auxiliary change-gears may be used at the end of the headstock, the ratio for a given setting of the regular gearbox may be modified by the auxiliary gears in order to cut leads or numbers of threads per inch not included in the regular range. For example, the required ratio for cutting 1¼ threads per inch might be obtained by setting the gearbox for 1½ threads per inch, provided auxiliary changegears of the right size are used. Certain terms will first be defined.

Total or Over-all Ratio: This is the ratio of all gears between the spindle and lead-screw. Total ratio equals number of threads per inch on lead-screw divided by number of threads per inch to be cut.

Component Ratio: This term is used to indicate part of the total ratio. To illustrate, if the total ratio equals $\frac{8}{27}$ and the ratio of the auxiliary change-gears is $\frac{2}{3}$, then the component ratio equals $\frac{4}{9}$ because $\frac{4}{9} \times \frac{2}{3} = \frac{8}{27}$. The practical application for these ratios will be shown by an example of change-gear calculation.

Change-gear Formulas: In the formulas which follow

D_r = number of teeth on *driving* auxiliary change-gear;

D_n = number of teeth on *driven* auxiliary change-gear;

n = numerator of component ratio;

d = denominator of component ratio = threads per inch indicated by one of the gear-box settings;

L = number of threads per inch on lead-screw;

T = number of threads per inch to be cut.

If we assume that the gear-box could be set to cut one thread per inch, then

$$\frac{L}{1} = \frac{D_r}{D_n} \times \frac{n}{d}; \text{ hence } \frac{n}{d} = \frac{L}{1} \times \frac{D_n}{D_r}$$

These two formulas will be designated as formulas **(1)** and **(2)**.

Example 1: Find the auxiliary change-gear sizes and the gear-box setting for cutting 1¼ threads per inch, assuming that the regular range of the gear-box is 1½, 1¾, 2, 2¼, 2½, etc. The lead-screw has 4 threads per inch; available auxiliary change-gears have 35, 40, 48, 50, 60, 70, 72, 90 and 122 teeth.

Solution: Assume that we select for trial the 48 and 72 change-gear sizes ($D_r = 48$; $D_n = 72$). The first step is to find the component ratio. By using the formula **(2)** previously given, we find that

$$\frac{n}{d} = \frac{4}{1} \times \frac{72}{48} = \frac{288}{48} = \frac{6}{1}$$

We now have the component ratio, provided the lathe could be set to cut one thread per inch. For 1¼ threads per inch, which is the required number in this case,

$$\text{Total ratio} = \frac{L}{T} = \frac{4}{1\frac{1}{4}} = \frac{16}{5}$$

From this point on, L is given the value of 16 instead of 4. The next step is to determine what auxiliary change-gears and gear-box setting, are required to obtain a total ratio of $\frac{16}{5}$. Formula **(1)** may also be written

$$\frac{L}{T} = \frac{D_r}{D_n} \times \frac{n}{d}; \text{ hence } \frac{16}{5} = \frac{48}{72} \times \frac{6}{d}$$

Now see if we can retain the gear D_r with 48 teeth and merely replace gear D_n so that $D_n \times d$ balances the equation.

First, multiply 16 by some factor *(F)* to raise $\frac{16}{5}$ to higher terms so that the numerator equals 48×6.

$$F = \frac{Dr \times n}{L} = \frac{48 \times 6}{16} = 18$$

If F does not equal a whole number, then D_r must be changed. Continuing with the calculation, we have:

$$\frac{16 \times 18}{5 \times 18} = \frac{288}{90} = \frac{48}{D_n} \times \frac{6}{d}$$

It is evident now that $D_n \times d$ must equal 90. To find the value of D_n or the number of teeth in the driven gear, merely divide 90 by any value of d that will give a quotient equal to the size of any available change-gear. In this case, $90 \div 1\frac{1}{2} = 60$ which is the number of teeth in one of the change-gears; also, $90 \div 2\frac{1}{4} = 40$. Hence,

$$\text{Total ratio} = \frac{288}{90} = \frac{48}{60} \times \frac{6}{1\frac{1}{2}} = \frac{48}{40} \times \frac{6}{2\frac{1}{4}}$$

If gear D_n with 60 teeth were used, the gear-box would be set for $1\frac{1}{2}$ threads per inch, whereas, if the gear with 40 teeth were used, the gear-box would be set for $2\frac{1}{4}$ threads per inch. This illustrates how the gear-box setting might be varied in order to use an available change-gear.

Example 2: All conditions are the same as in Example 1, except that the lead of the thread to be cut equals $1\frac{3}{4}$ inches, making threads per inch $= 1 \div 1\frac{3}{4} = 4/7$. In this case,

$$\text{Total ratio} = \frac{L}{T} = \frac{4}{4/7} = \frac{28}{4}$$

Hence, L now is given the value of 28. If lathe could be geared for one thread per inch, the component ratio would be:

$$\frac{n}{d} = \frac{4}{1} \times \frac{72}{48} = \frac{6}{1} \text{ and total ratio or } \frac{28}{4} = \frac{D_r}{D_n} \times \frac{6}{d}$$

In this case, if $D_r = 48$, then F will not equal a whole number; hence, try other values of D_r (equivalent to gears on hand). For example, if $D_r = 70$,

$$F = \frac{D_r \times n}{L} = \frac{70 \times 6}{28} = 15$$

Raising the total ratio to higher terms,

$$\frac{28 \times 15}{4 \times 15} = \frac{420}{60} = \frac{70}{D_n} \times \frac{6}{d}$$

One of the settings of the change-gear box is 1½ threads per inch, and this happens to be the setting required, because 60 ÷ 1½ = 40, which represents one of the change-gear sizes. We have then:

$$\frac{420}{60} = \frac{70}{40} \times \frac{6}{1\frac{1}{2}}$$

Therefore, in order to cut 4/7 thread per inch, the driving change-gear has 70 teeth, the driven change-gear 40 teeth, and the quick-change gear-box is set for cutting 1½ threads per inch.

Lead Required for Multiple Thread of Given Normal Pitch

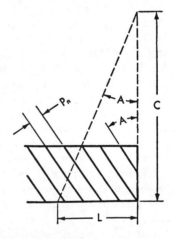

Note: Standard pitches are measured parallel to the axis of the screw thread; hence lathes or other machines for cutting or milling screw threads are equipped with change-gears for cutting a series of pitches or leads as measured parallel to the axis. If the machine must be geared to obtain a given normal pitch P_n, the following formulas may be used for determining the required axial lead.

Formulas: If C = pitch circumference of worm or other screw thread, P_n = normal pitch, N = number of separate threads or "starts" on worm, A = lead angle, L = lead.

$$\text{Tan } A = \frac{N \times P_n}{\sqrt{C^2 - (N \times P_n)^2}} ; \text{Lead } L = \frac{N \times P_n}{\text{Cos } A}$$

Example: A quadruple worm having a pitch diameter of 6 inches is to mesh with, and transmit motion to, a rack having a linear pitch of 1½ inches. Find the lead required to make the normal pitch P_n of the worm also equal 1½ inches.

$$\text{Tan } A = \frac{4 \times 1.5}{\sqrt{18.8496^2 - (4 \times 1.5)^2}} = 0.33576$$

Angle $A = 18° \, 34'$ nearly. Cos $A = 0.94795$.

$$\text{Lead} = \frac{4 \times 1.5}{0.94795} = 6.329 \text{ inches}$$

With this lead, the *axial* pitch $= 6.329 \div 4 = 1.5825$ inches and the *normal* pitch $=$ axial pitch $\times$ cosine lead angle $= 1.5825 \times 0.94795 = 1.50$ inch.

Angle A for Grinding Precision Thread Tool

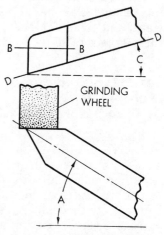

Note: Tool is ground to an angle in plane *B-B* which makes the angle in plane *D-D* of top face equal to the angle of thread to be cut. Angle in plane *B-B*, or perpendicular to front face, is one-half angle A and is somewhat greater than angle in plane *D-D*. In precision thread cutting, the tool may be ground on a surface grinder while held at angle A relative to the machine table, and at angle C measured from a line at right angles to the table travel. Angle C is the required clearance angle, and angle A is determined by calculation. (Note: A special tool-holding block mounted upon a magnetic chuck may be used for this operation.)

Rule: To find tangent of angle A, divide tangent of one-half the standard thread angle, by the cosine of front clearance angle C.

Example: An American standard thread tool is to be ground while held as illustrated by the diagram. The clearance angle is 15 degrees. Determine what angle A is required to make the angle of the tool in plane *D-D* equal to the standard screw thread angle.

$$\text{Tan } A = \frac{\tan 30°}{\cos 15°} = \frac{0.57735}{0.96592} = 0.5977$$

By referring to table of trigonometric functions, it will be found that 0.5977 is the tangent of 30° 52′. This angle A is one-half the included angle of the tool in plane B-B; hence the angle in plane B-B equals 61° 44′ or 1° 44′ larger than the standard angle.

Angle of Forming Tool in Plane B-B

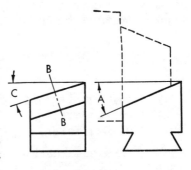

Note: The tool is to be ground at whatever angle in plane B-B is required to obtain angle A on the part to be turned, assuming that top face of tool is in line with axis of work. Plane B-B is perpendicular to the front end of the tool.

Rule: Tangent of angle in plane B-B = cosine of clearance angle C multiplied by the tangent of angle A.

Example: Angle A is to be 30 degrees and clearance angle C on the tool is 10 degrees. The front face of tool is to be ground on a surface grinder. Determine the angle in plane B-B.

Solution: Tangent of angle in plane B-B = cos C × tan A = 0.98481 × 0.57735 = 0.56858; hence, required angle = 29° 37′ nearly.

Angular Depth of Screw Thread

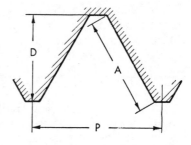

Note: Formulas which are particularly useful in cutting screw threads will be found on page 192. In cutting threads such as the American standard, it is common practice to set the compound rest at an angle of 30 degrees and feed the tool in parallel to the angular side of the thread to obtain better cutting action.

When this is done, the angular depth A may be determined as follows:

Rule for American Standard Thread: The angular depth $A = \frac{3}{4}$ of the pitch P.

Rule for any Thread: The angular depth $A =$ the actual depth D divided by the cosine of $\frac{1}{2}$ the thread angle.

Example: An American standard screw thread is to be cut having a diameter of $1\frac{1}{8}$ inches and seven threads per inch. Determine the angular depth A.

Solution: The table on page 172 shows that the pitch $= 0.1428$ inch; hence, angular depth $A = 0.1428 \times 0.75 = 0.1071$ inch.

Percentage of Thread Depth for Given Tap Drill Diameter

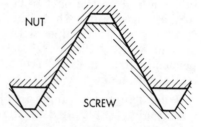

Note: It is customary to use a tap drill size that will leave about three-fourths of the standard thread depth, in order to reduce the strain on the tap and minimize tap breakage without sacrificing screw thread strength to any important degree.

Rule: To find percentage of thread engagement, subtract from the outside diameter of the stud or bolt, the tap drill diameter, and divide the remainder by two times the full depth of engagement; then multiply the quotient by 100 to obtain the percentage. Thus

$$\text{Percentage} = \frac{\text{Major diam. of bolt—Tap drill diam.}}{2 \times \text{Full depth engagement}} \times 100$$

Example: A tap drill 21/32 inch in diameter is to be used in conjunction with a $\frac{3}{4}$ — 10 American standard screw thread. Find the percentage of thread depth. (For full-thread depth, see table, page 172).

$$\text{Percentage} = \frac{0.75 - 0.65625}{2 \times 0.0649} \times 100 = 72\%$$

Note: To find the tap drill diameter, subtract from the outside diameter of the tap an amount equal to 1 divided by the number of threads per inch; then select the nearest commercial drill size. Tap drill sizes based upon this rule leave approximately 72 to 77 per cent of thread depth.

Spline Milling Cutter Angle B and Width C

Note: The rules which follow apply to cutters for milling straight-sided splines. Most splines, however, are formed by the more efficient method of hobbing, and the involute form is often used in preference to the straight-sided spline shown by the diagram.

Cutter Angle for Straight-sided Spline: Included angle B of cutter $=$ 360 $\div$ number of splines N.

Chordal Width C: Divide spline width W by root diameter d of shaft, thus obtaining sine of an angle. Find angle equivalent to this sine and insert it at A in formula below:

$$\text{Chordal width } C = \sin\left(\frac{180}{N} - A\right) \times d$$

Example: A shaft is to have ten splines with a width W of 0.5 inch and root diameter d of 3 inches.

$$\text{Sin } A = \frac{0.5}{3} = 0.16666; \text{ hence, angle } A \text{ is } 9° \ 36' \text{ nearly.}$$

$$C = \sin\left(\frac{180}{10} - 9° \ 36'\right) \times 3 = 0.438 \text{ inch.}$$

Steel Gage Expansion Resulting from Temperature Changes

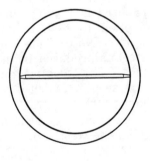

Rule: To find the amount of expansion in inches, multiply length of rod or gage before expansion, by coefficient of linear expansion, and then multiply product by number of degrees F. of temperature change.

Note: The coefficient of linear expansion for steel is 0.00000636; for cast iron, 0.00000556; for brass, 0.00000957.

Example: If a steel end-measuring gage 18.020 inches long is left near a furnace so that its temperature increases from 70 to 90 degrees, how much will the length be increased?

Solution: Increase in temperature is 20 degrees; hence, Amount of expansion $= 18.020 \times 0.00000636 \times 20 = 0.0023''$.

Estimating Weights of Steel Bars and Sheets

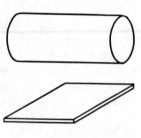

Rule for Round Stock: To find the weight of a round steel bar per foot of length, multiply the diameter of the bar by 4, square the product and then divide by 6. If $D =$ diameter of bar in inches, then this rule, expressed as a formula, is as follows:

$$\text{Weight per foot} = \frac{(4 \times D)^2}{6}$$

This rule and formula is based upon a weight for steel at 489 pounds per cubic foot.

Rule for Hexagon Stock: Determine weight for round bar having diameter equal to width across flats and multiply by 1.10.

Rule for Square Stock: Multiply area of cross-section in inches by 10.2 to obtain the weight per yard of length. (Based upon 489 pounds to the cubic foot.)

Weight of Sheet Steel: Consider the thickness in thousandths as a whole number and divide by 25; then multiply quotient by 1.045 to obtain the weight in pounds per square foot. (Note: This rule conforms to the weight of sheet steel as produced in the modern continuous type of rolling mill. The basic weight, as determined over a long period, has been established at 41.82 pounds per square foot per inch thick.)

Example: A steel sheet has a thickness of 0.0420 inch. Find the weight in pounds per square foot.

If the thickness in thousandths is written as a whole number, we have 42 thousandths; hence $(42 \div 25) \times 1.045 = 1.75$ pounds per square foot.

Per Cent of Gain or Loss

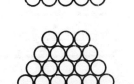

Per Cent of Gain: Divide amount of *gain* by original number to which the per cent of gain applies, and multiply the quotient by 100.

Example: An original production of 50 pieces per hour is increased to 64 pieces per hour by an improved method.

Amount of gain $= 64 - 50 = 14$ pieces.

$$\text{Per cent gain} = \frac{\text{Amount of gain}}{\text{Original number}} \times 100 = \frac{14}{50} \times 100 = 28\%$$

Per Cent of Loss: Divide amount of *loss* by original number to which per cent of loss applies, and multiply the quotient by 100.

Example: Assume that the inspector in a plant rejects 15 machined parts out of a total of 130. Find the percentage of loss.

$$\text{Per cent loss} = \frac{\text{Amount of loss}}{\text{Original number}} \times 100 = \frac{15}{130} \times 100 =$$

11.54 per cent

Shop Safety

by Raymond A. Kelly*

The first step in preventing personal injury or machine damage in the shop is to make sure that you are familiar with and know how to operate correctly the equipment you will be using. Familiarity and know-how may be obtained by: (1) a formal course of instruction, (2) personal instruction by an experienced qualified machinist or (3) a careful reading of the manufacturer's operating instructions that accompany the machine. For the novice or apprentice formal instruction or instruction by an experienced qualified machinist is almost mandatory as a written set of operating instructions may presuppose previous knowledge of or skill in some operating procedure or setup which the student does not have.

How do accidents happen?

Accidents are caused by inattention, taking chances, bad judgement, fatigue, uncooperativeness and horseplay. They are also caused by poor supervision or instruction, improperly guarded machines, improper clothing, defective tools or equipment, insufficient working area and poor lighting.

In becoming familiar with and obtaining know-how about various machines how can we help to avoid accidents?

By strictly following safety rules pertaining to these various machines.

What safety rules apply to the drill press?

1. Run drill at the correct cutting speed
2. Hold work in vise or clamp to table
3. Use correctly ground drill for material being drilled
4. Use a cutting oil if necessary
5. Remove chips with a brush and never by hand

* Machine Shop Instructor, Brooklyn Technical High School.

6. Ease up on pressure as drill breaks through
7. Don't use a dull or cracked drill
8. Don't drill with too much pressure
9. Always try to support job on parallels when drilling
10. Use a drill chuck to hold straight shank drills but *never* tapered shank drills
11. Always clean drill shank and drill sleeve before mounting in clean spindle hole
12. Remove taper shank drill from spindle or sleeve with a drill drift only
13. Guard all driving pulleys, belts and exposed gears
14. Never try to loosen the drill chuck or tapered shank drill while the power is on
15. Lower the drill spindle close to table when releasing drill chuck or tapered shank drill to reduce chance of damage in the event that they fall onto the table
16. *Never* clean the machine while it is in *motion*
17. If drill binds in hole, stop machine and turn drill chuck backwards by hand to release drill
18. When drilling deep holes withdraw drill and clear out chips frequently
19. Remove the drill chuck key from chuck or drill drift from spindle immediately after using
20. Wear safety goggles while drilling.

What safety rules apply to the engine and bench lathes?

1. Make sure that drive plate, face plate or chuck is firmly tightened on lathe spindle
2. In removing drive plate, face plate or chuck do not use machine power
3. Do not use power to install drive plate, face plate or chuck on spindle
4. Move the tool bit a safe distance from collet or chuck when inserting or removing work
5. Don't run machine above the correct cutting speed
6. In setting up the tool holder place it to left side of compound rest to prevent compound rest from running into chuck or lathe dog
7. Hold tool bit short in tool holder to prevent it from breaking or chattering
8. Always make sure that tool bit is ground sharp and with correct clearance
9. If any filing is done on work revolving in lathe, file left handed to prevent slipping into chuck
10. If work is turned between centers make sure that proper adjustment is made between centers and that tail stock is locked in place
11. If work is being turned between centers and expands due to heat generated from cutting tool, readjust centers to avoid excessive friction
12. Don't touch turnings with fingers but get rid of them by using a blunt instrument
13. Set the tool bit on center line of work to prevent work from climbing over tool and cutting above center
14. Don't part work completely through when turning between centers

15. Always wear safety goggles
16. Remove chuck key from chuck immediately after using.

What safety rules apply to the milling machine?

1. Work must be set up securely and correctly in the vise and the vise fastened tightly to table
2. Cutters should be keyed to arbor and run in the correct direction to give the proper either "up" or "down" milling desired
3. In loosening or tightening the arbor nut, the over arm should be in place
4. To remove the arbor nut the machine preferably should be locked; otherwise it should be set for the lowest rpm
5. Before running machine it should be manually tried to make sure that it is clear for cutting
6. If machine is provided with stops make sure they are adjusted properly for job
7. Make sure the power is off when changing arbors, cutters or making any adjustments or changes in setup
8. Always use a cutting oil when necessary
9. Never run the machine above its correct cutting speed
10. Make sure that the machine is stopped before taking any measurements
11. Always use cutters which are sharp and in good condition
12. Don't place anything on the milling machine table such as wrenches, hammers or tools
13. Always stay at the machine while it is running
14. Make sure that the cutter is protected by a guard when it is feasible
15. Always wear safety goggles
16. Apply cutting oil to the cutter as it leaves the work and make sure that the spout does not come in contact with the revolving cutter
17. Don't take too heavy a cut or use too rapid a feed
18. If a machine does not have a lost motion adjustment, use "up" milling only.

What safety rules apply to the bench grinder?

1. Always use safety goggles when grinding
2. Look through the glass guard and not around it. If glass guard cannot be cleaned, change the glass to correct the situation
3. The tool rest should be set to about 1/16 inch clearance between it and wheel
4. Never mount a grinding wheel until you check the rpm of the motor to make sure that the wheel will not be run over its correct cutting speed
5. As work is being ground it should be moved back and forth across the cutting surface to keep the wheel from being grooved or worn in one location
6. Always check a grinding wheel for cracks or defects before using and discard it if it is not in good condition
7. Never grind on the side of a grinding wheel
8. Keep work cool when hand held by placing it frequently in water to prevent burns to fingers. Remember, grinding generates heat
9. Keep grinding wheel dressed
10. Hold work securely in hand while grinding

11. Don't use too much pressure while grinding
12. Use the right type of wheel while grinding because different wheels are designed and made for grinding different metals
13. It is good practice to stand to one side when starting a grinder
14. Never use a grinder if its guard is off
15. Make sure that the grinder has a true, balanced and dressed wheel.

What safety rules apply to the surface grinder?

1. Wear safety goggles
2. Use correct wheel for the job
3. Don't take too heavy cuts
4. Keep wheel dressed
5. Keep all guards in place
6. Don't touch revolving wheel
7. Have work secured well to table by clamping on, or holding in vise
8. Set stops for job
9. Wait until the machine stops before taking measurements
10. Don't run over the safe cutting speed of grinding wheel
11. Inspect wheel thoroughly before starting. Never use a defective wheel. If the wheel is defective, replace it.
12. If an exhaust is not provided, then a respirator must be worn.

What safety rules apply to the shaper?

1. Wear safety goggles
2. Make sure that the work is fastened securely before starting the machine
3. Turn the machine slowly at first by hand if possible, to make sure that the tool and head clear the housing and the work
4. Stop the machine before you attempt making any adjustments to the tool or to the length of stroke
5. Use a "chip guard" to catch the chips that are coming off the job
6. Stop the machine when taking any measurements
7. Run the machine at the speed at which it is safe to use (Don't run the machine above its correct theoretical cutting speed.)
8. Do not allow less than an 18-inch clearance to remain between the wall and the ram when setting the shaper's maximum stroke
9. Don't place anything between the wall and the rear of the shaper which will leave a clearance of less than 18 inches at maximum stroke of shaper.

What safety rules apply to the cylindrical grinder?

1. Always wear safety goggles
2. Never stand in front of wheel when starting machine
3. Start wheels slowly and gradually increase speed. Wet wheels can be out of balance due to water draining to lower half
4. Wheels should be checked for cracks with hammer *handle*. Listen for ring. Dull dead sound would indicate crack
5. New wheels require balancing of center by means of counter weights (Center is spindle adapter that the wheels are mounted on.)
6. Coolant must be directed to point of contact between wheel and work to prevent burning and distortion
7. Dog must be tightened very securely to prevent job from becoming loose and spinning with wheel

8. Wheels must slip easily on center. Holes that are too small cause binding and possible cracks
9. Gaskets and flanges of center must be clean and in good condition
10. Tighten center bolts evenly — bolts should be tightened in sets of opposites
11. Centers of machine (headstock and tailstock) must be tight in spindles, well lubricated and carefully adjusted
12. Steadyrests unless self adjusting, must be readjusted to the reduced diameter as soon as wheel has passed by them
13. Machine stops must be set with wheel outside of work when grinding shoulders
14. When grinding duplicate pieces with shoulders, center holes must be accurately drilled to equal depth
15. Length dimensions must be accurately held when grinding duplicate shoulder pieces
16. Wheels must never be run faster than speed recommended by manufacturer.

What safety rules apply to bench work?

1. Always wear safety goggles
2. In chipping with chisel always chip away from yourself and others
3. Hold work securely in bench vise
4. Hack saw work close to the ends of the vise jaws and do not apply too much pressure or make too many strokes per minute
5. Never use a chisel with a mushroomed head
6. Only use hand pressure to tighten a vise; use handle, and never use added leverage
7. Never strike two hardened surfaces together
8. Never use a file without a handle
9. If job is hot, mark it in some way to make the fact known to others who may come in contact with it
10. Place oil can so that no one will jab himself with the spout
11. Place sharp or pointed tools in such a way that their points or cutting edges will not cause injury to anyone
12. Report all accidents to your superior at once
13. Use a brush to remove chips or filings
14. Remove all burrs from job before handling
15. Refrain from any sort of horseplay
16. Never use a hammer with a loose head.

What safety rules are to be observed to prevent accidents in general?

1. Never operate a machine unless you have been properly instructed in its use
2. Before starting a job know the entire procedure for finishing it
3. Don't rush or take chances. Observe all safety rules
4. Work only with properly guarded and safe equipment, proper ventilation and an ample and properly lighted working area
5. Do not work in the shop if too tired or fatigued
6. Always be properly dressed for the job
7. Never indulge in horseplay
8. Request help if needed
9. Before starting, always check machine for correct setup and always check to see if machine is clear by manually operating it, if possible
10. Practice cleanliness and orderliness in the shop.

INDEX

565